D1250816

DESCRIPTIVE GEOMETRY

Essential Principles and Applications
for
Students of Engineering and Architecture

BY

FLOYD A. SMUTZ

Professor of Engineering Drawing and Descriptive Geometry,
Kansas State College of Agriculture and Applied Science

AND

RANDOLPH F. GINGRICH

Associate Professor of Engineering Drawing and Descriptive Geometry,
Kansas State College of Agriculture and Applied Science

THIRD EDITION

1950

D. VAN NOSTRAND COMPANY, INC.

TORONTO NEW YORK LONDON

NEW YORK
D. Van Nostrand Company, Inc., 250 Fourth Avenue, New York 3
TORONTO
D. Van Nostrand Company (Canada), Ltd., 228 Bloor Street, Toronto
LONDON
Macmillan & Company, Ltd., St. Martin's Street, London, W.C. 2

Published simultaneously in Canada by
D. VAN NOSTRAND COMPANY (Canada), LTD.

First Edition, January 1931
One Reprinting

Second Edition, June 1938
Five Reprintings

Third Edition, May 1950

PRINTED IN THE UNITED STATES OF AMERICA

PREFACE TO THE THIRD EDITION

The value of descriptive geometry in developing the power of visualization and abstract reasoning has never been questioned. In many instances, however, the drafting room application of the methods devised by Monge and followed by many authors, is often very difficult and inefficient. The present trend is to treat the subject as a part of the student's training in graphics, and to adopt the methods that have been found effective in solving problems in the drafting room. This approach is more direct in its application and loses little of its rigor in mental training.

In this third edition the authors have made no fundamental change of their previous work. The chapter "Planes Determined by Traces" and some problems having little application have been omitted. Other problems of greater interest to the engineering student have been added. The application problems have been revised and rewritten in the terms used in industry, and without the aid of illustrations.

The major change from the previous editions is in the use of the nomenclature, methods, and notation recommended by the Engineering Drawing and Descriptive Geometry section of the American Society of Engineering Education. Fortunately this change required little except new words to express the thought and new letters placed on similar illustrations.

The authors wish to express their appreciation to their colleagues and to all those who have expressed criticisms of the previous edition or offered suggestions for this revision.

F. A. S.
R. F. G.

Kansas State College of Agriculture and Applied Science
Manhattan, Kansas, 1950

PREFACE

The authors of this text do not claim to have added any new material to the abstract subject of Descriptive Geometry. In fact, they have omitted many standard problems in their attempt to make the subject one in which the students of the applied sciences will find something of interest as well as practical value. They have deleted much of the purely abstract material and methods, preferring to concentrate attention on the essential principles of the subject.

The sense of satisfaction that is felt in the accomplishment of a definite assignment of work is a great encouragement to the student and is his greatest incentive for additional effort. The amount of abstract material that can be mastered by a class in a two- or three-credit-hour course is necessarily limited. The amount of such material in this text is sufficient to give considerable choice in arranging courses to fit differing requirements. An attempt has been made to include the methods and theories that are required of a draftsman and to exclude much of the material that is purely mental gymnastics. In so doing, nothing has been detracted from the subject, since more material is retained than can be mastered by the best of students in their allotted time. When attention is centered on fundamentals and the amount and character of the work are kept within the ability of the student, the spirit of discouragement and futility that is so prevalent in Descriptive Geometry classes is soon changed to a feeling of self-confidence.

At the risk of becoming monotonous through repetition, all the problems of the text are stated, analyzed, and solved in accordance with the same outline of procedure. This method, when adhered to in class, forces upon the student a mental solution that finds expression through drawings. It is through the mental solution that the ability to visualize is developed, and through the graphic language that visualization finds expression.

A sufficient number of exercises for class assignment have been included to make it possible to carry several similar courses without duplication of assignments. Problem sheets have been devised on which the data of the exercises may be plotted in a negligible length of time.

A sufficient number of application problems are included to make a rigorous drafting course and to illustrate the applications of the subject matter to engineering and architectural work. Through these problems much of the interest and enthusiasm of the student is directed to the mastery of the course.

The material of this text has been used for several years at this institution. In the preparation of their manuscript the authors have had in mind its use in their classes. It is their hope that it may prove of value to other institutions of a similar nature.

F. A. Smutz
R. F. Gingrich

Kansas State Agricultural College
Manhattan, Kansas, 1930

CONTENTS

CHAPTER I

CHAPTER II

CHAPTER III

CHAPTER IV

CHAPTER V

CHAPTER IX

CHAPTER X

CHAPTER XI

CHAPTER I

INTRODUCTION

1.1. Engineering Drawing. The design and construction of a complex mechanism or structure would be very difficult, if not impossible, without the use of engineering drawings. The engineer uses graphics in making the design of a machine in order to determine the stresses in parts of its structure; the clearances, accelerations, and velocities of moving parts, and many other factors that enter into a design. The architect in designing a building could not be sure of its appearance, utility, or the proper functioning of its many elements without drawings. Endless trial and error would be necessary to correlate the many parts of an automobile, airplane, building, or other complex machine or structure without graphics, and modern production methods would be impossible.

The engineer or architect must also describe his design by means of drawings in such detail that workmen can construct it. Such a description attempted by words on a printed page or by oral expression could not be accurate or definite enough for its construction.

The only method of description that has been found satisfactory is to make two or more views of the design that show its shape, its size, and all other pertinent information needed by workmen for its construction. This graphical description is called engineering drawing.

1.2. Descriptive Geometry. Descriptive geometry is the scientific foundation of the art of drawing. It has the same relation to graphics as grammar has to a spoken or written language. Descriptive geometry had its beginning when man first devised a systematic way of making the pictorial representations of objects. Its principles were first compiled in a treatise by Gaspard Monge, a French mathematician of the eighteenth century.

For many years the point of view of the mathematician was assumed in the presentation of the subject to the student. Many of the more recent authors are treating the subject as a part of graphics and are emphasizing its relation to the processes of the drafting room. This is a natural development since it is in the drafting room that descriptive geometry has its greatest application. It is the intent of the authors of this text to present the fundamental concepts of descriptive geometry, and to show their application in the solution of problems that must be solved by the engineer or draftsman.

1.3. Purpose of the Course. The so-called "practical" purpose of a course in descriptive geometry is to develop the ability to "read" and "write" the graphic language. To read a drawing it is necessary to be familiar with the laws of projection and to be able to visualize a three-dimension object from a two-dimension drawing. To make a drawing it is necessary to know the laws of projection and to visualize a two-dimension drawing of a three-dimension object. The laws of projection are simple and easily acquired by most students. Whether it is easy or difficult to acquire, visualization is essential to any engineer. He must visualize before he can make a design or construct a mechanism or structure from the design of another. Perhaps no course of study is so well adapted to the development of the ability to visualize as is descriptive geometry.

Descriptive geometry is also a useful tool in the solution of many problems which the engineer must solve. The size and form of the elements of a structure are often found by graphics rather than analytics. The intersections of surfaces and solids are found by graphics. A large number of the problems of mining and civil engineering are more readily solved by descriptive geometry than by other means. Consciously or unconsciously it is used whenever a design is attempted or a drawing is made.

1.4. Prerequisites. The student should be familiar with the concepts of plane and solid geometry if his work is to be effective. Of greatest importance to him are the orderly mental habits usually associated with those subjects. Geometry is, therefore, prerequisite by reason of its development of rational thinking, and because a knowledge of the nomenclature and fundamental concepts of geometry are a great assistance to effective study.

Many drawings are required to describe the principles of descriptive geometry and to illustrate the application of their principles in the solution of problems. It is essential that the student, through experience in the drafting room or in the study of other subjects, be capable of reading and making simple orthographic drawings. Without such ability he will find it difficult to acquire information from the text or to express himself in the solution of problems.

The application problems that are stated at the end of this chapter are intended as a review of orthographic drawing. They will also serve to correlate the fundamental principles of drawing with the space location concepts that are required in descriptive geometry.

1.5. Space Location. The location of points, lines, planes, or other geometric magnitudes in space is determined by means of linear or angular measurements from three mutually perpendicular reference planes. (See Figure 1.1.) One plane is horizontal and is called the *H* plane. A second plane assumed perpendicular to the horizontal plane and to the line of sight of the observer is called the frontal or *F* plane. The third plane is perpendicular to both the *H* and *F* planes and is called the profile or *P* plane. The *H* and *F* planes divide all of space into four quadrants, and the three planes divide it into octants.

A point in space is located exactly if its linear distance from each of the three reference planes is stated. A line may be located by specifying the location of two points of the line, or by one point and the angles the line makes with the reference planes. Planes are determined by three points, by intersecting lines, or by points and angles.

In this text a "shorthand" method is used to specify the location of a point. When this method is used, the specification of the location of a point A is: $A(2, 1, 3)$. The first number in the parenthesis is the distance to the left of P, the second is the distance to the rear of F, and the third the distance below H. If a minus sign is used before any number in parenthesis, it specifies a distance on the opposite side of the projection plane to which that number refers.

An engineer or draftsman assumes any convenient location for the reference lines and planes. A point on the earth's surface is east or west of a prime meridian, north or south of the equator, and above or below sea level. A machine is to the right or left of a side wall, in front or to the rear of a front wall, and above or below a floor or ceiling. A part of a wing assembly of an aircraft is behind the nose of the ship, to the right or left of a central plane, and above or below a horizontal plane. The choice of location is in some cases more or less standardized but is limited only by the imagination of the draftsman.

1.6. Projections. The draftsman describes the form and size of an object by drawing one or more views of that object as it is seen from some chosen direction. These views are projections of the object on picture planes usually assumed between the observer and the object. If the visual rays (i.e., projectors) from the outlines of the object are assumed to converge toward the eye of the observer, the picture plane will intercept these rays in a perspective of the object. If the visual rays are assumed parallel to each other and perpendicular to the picture plane, that plane will intercept the rays in an orthographic projection of the object. The orthographic projection shows the exact form and size of a surface if it is parallel to the picture plane, and the perspective shows the form and size as it appears rather than as it exists.

Since the purpose of the drawings made by the engineer is to describe the size and form of some object, he has chosen orthographic projection as the best method of expression. The artist, having a different purpose, has chosen perspective as his method of expression. Descriptive geometry is the scientific foundation for either method. It furnishes the rules and accepted methods of graphic expression.

1.7. Projection Planes. Projection planes are the picture planes, sometimes called image planes, upon which the various views of an object, or geometric magnitude, may be assumed to be projected. Such planes may have any desired position relative to an object or to a horizontal or vertical surface.

1.8. Principal Projection Planes. The reference planes as described in Article 1.5 serve also as the principal projection planes. An object projects its top view, or plan, on the horizontal plane; its front view, or front elevation, on the frontal plane; and its side view, or side elevation, on the profile plane. Since these three views are all that are necessary to describe most objects, they are called the principal views and the planes upon which they are projected are called the principal projection planes. The use of additional projection planes, called auxiliary planes, will be discussed in a following chapter.

Figure 1.1 shows in pictorial drawing the location of the principal projection planes as described before. The intersection of the horizontal and frontal planes is called the *HF* axis, the intersection of the frontal and profile planes the *FP* axis, and the intersection of the horizontal and profile planes the *HP* axis.

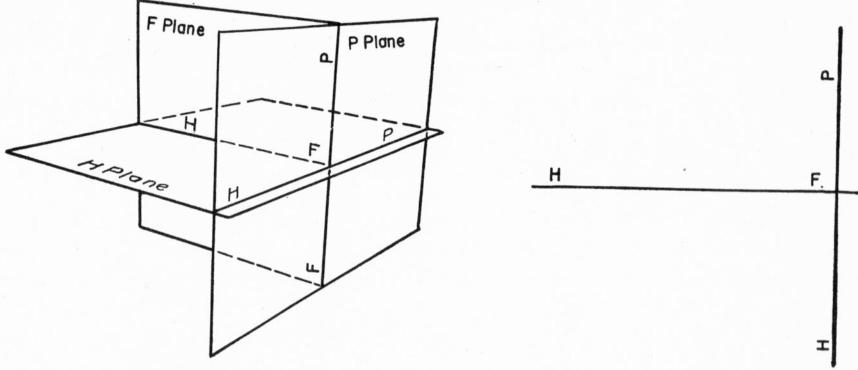

FIG. 1.1. Principal Projection Planes

FIG. 1.2. Top View of Principal Planes

Figure 1.2 is an orthographic top view of the principal planes. The frontal plane and profile plane show as edges, or lines, at right angles with each other. The horizontal plane is in the surface of the paper and being indefinite in extent has no boundaries. The intersections of the planes are indicated by appropriate letters near the ends of the line segments that represent them.

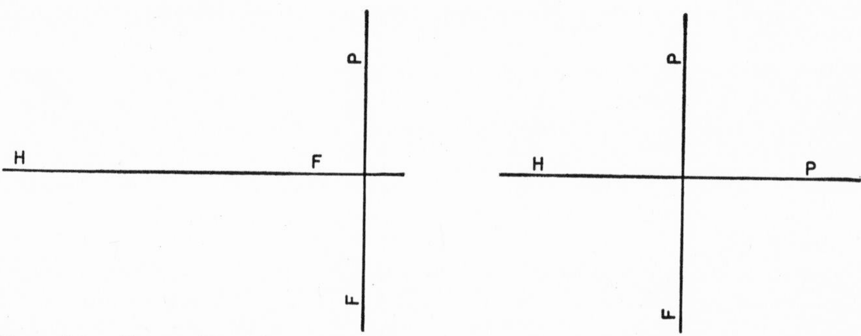

FIG. 1.3. Front View of Principal Planes

FIG. 1.4. Side View of Principal Planes

Figure 1.3 is an orthographic front view and Figure 1.4 an orthographic side view of the principal planes of projection. In front view the *H* plane shows as the *HF* axis and the *P* plane as the *FP* axis. The frontal plane is indefinite and has no boundaries. On the side view the *H* plane and *F* plane show as *HP* and *FP* axes respectively. The *P* plane is indefinite and has no boundaries.

1.9. Definitions and Nomenclature. A treatise on descriptive geometry is like that of any other subject in that it requires a vocabulary peculiar to that subject. Unlike the literature on most subjects the nomenclature used in descriptive geometry is not standardized. This is true to such an extent that one author has difficulty in reading the work contributed by another.

Recognizing the desirability of having a standard, the Drawing and Descriptive Geometry Division of the American Society for Engineering Education appointed a committee to study the problem. The definitions, notations, and nomenclature used in this text are derived in most instances from the report of that committee. A glossary of the nomenclature used in this text is found alphabetically arranged in Chapter XI.

1.10. Drafting Technique. It is assumed that the student will be required to solve several of the drafting problems that are included with each chapter of the text. The drafting technique recommended by the American Standards Association should be used insofar as those recommendations are applicable. These standards are found in the A.S.A. booklet Z14.1-1946 and in many recent engineering drawing texts.

In applying the A.S.A. standards to the solution of a descriptive geometry problem, it must be remembered that a high degree of accuracy is demanded if absurd results are to be avoided. Accuracy cannot be obtained if the construction lines are made heavy. The axis lines and the projections of given and required lines should be clean-cut black lines—not broad and indefinite lines. The construction lines used in the solution of a problem should be fine full lines that contrast in weight with the given and required lines. Construction lines should be left on the finished drawing to show the method of solution. All letters, both capital and lower case, should be of the form recommended for engineering drawing and large enough to be easily read. Small, illegible letters and slovenly inaccurate drawings are the cause of a great many errors and are never acceptable.

1.11. Choice of Problems. The problems that have been selected for the discussions and illustrations of the text are among those that have frequent application in the drafting room. The method of presentation and analysis of these problems has been borrowed from "geometry." This method involves making a definite statement of: first, the problem; second, the given data; third, what is required; fourth, a space solution of the problem; fifth, an analysis of the solution; sixth, a graphical construction and discussion. It should be emphasized that the actual drawing of a problem comes last and is merely an expression on paper of a mental solution.

1.12. Exercises. The problems that are listed at the end of each chapter are exercises in the application of the theories that have been discussed and illustrated in that or a preceding chapter. The drawing space required for the graphical solution of the problems is provided on a standard drawing sheet, 8½″ × 11″ or 9″ × 12″, or some division of that sheet as indicated in the statement of the problem. These divisions are shown in Figure 1.5 and are referred to as layout 1, layout 2, layout 3, and layout 4, as indicated in the figure. The *HF* axis will be located in the center and the *FP* axis in the right margin of the drawing space of each layout unless other locations are specified in a problem. It is recommended that all draw-

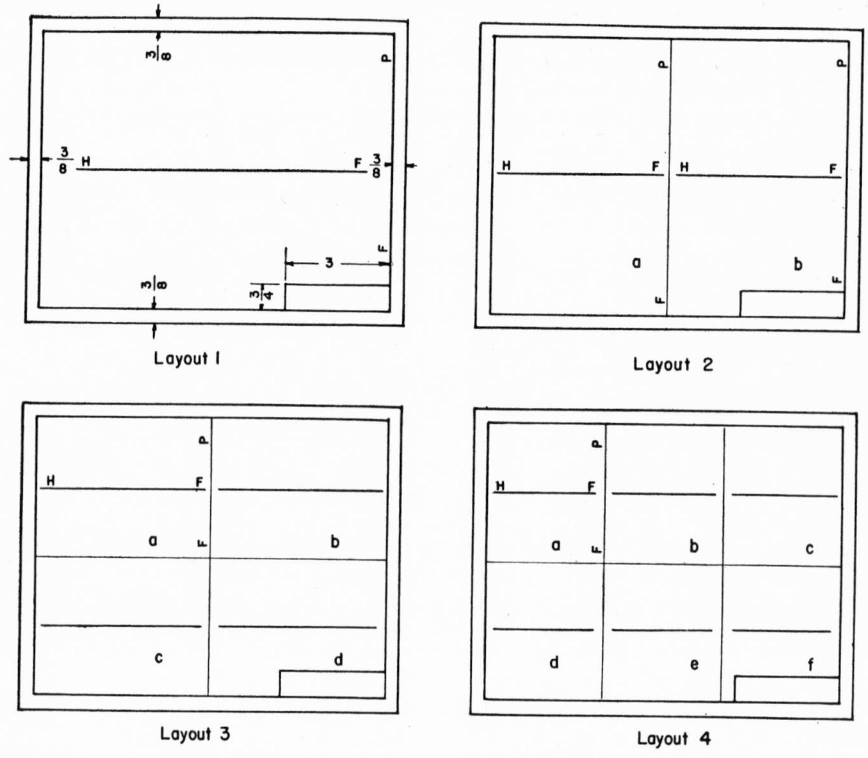

FIG. 1.5. Standard Drawing Sheet

ing should be made accurately and neatly on a good grade of paper using standard drawing instruments, but they may be made freehand on suitable "graph" paper.

1.13. Application Problems.

1.1. *Layout 2.*

(a) In the left half of the sheet make a pictorial (i.e., isometric or oblique) drawing of the three principal projection planes. Indicate by a letter on each which is the *H*, *F*, and *P* plane.
(b) In the right half make a pictorial drawing of a rectangular block 1″ × 2″ × 3″ having a 1″ circular hole in the center of and perpendicular to the 2″ × 3″ faces. Assume that the block rests on one of the 2″ × 3″ faces.

1.2. *Layout 1.* Assume that the rectangular block described in Problem 1.1 (b) is placed in a position such that one of the 2″ × 3″ faces is parallel to and ½″ below *H*, one of the 1″ × 3″ faces is parallel to and 1″ behind *F*, and a 1″ × 2″ face is ½″ to the left of *P*. Draw the *HF* axis line 3″ above the lower margin and the *FP* axis line 5″ from the right margin of the sheet. Project a view of the object on each of the principal projection planes.

1.3. *Layout 1.* Assume the *HF* axis line 3½″ above the lower margin and the *FP* axis line 4½″ from the right margin of the drawing sheet. A rectangular, sheet metal box 2″ × 3″ is ¾″ deep. A lid is hinged to the rear 3″ edge of the box and is opened in an angle of 30 degrees. Assume the box is placed with the bottom 2″ below and parallel to *H*, the front face parallel to and ½″ behind *F*, and the right end parallel to and ½″ to the left of *P*. Project views of the box on the *H*, *F*, and *P* projection planes.

1.4. *Layout 1.* Assume that the *HF* and *FP* axis lines intersect at the center of the sheet. Scale 1″ = 1′ 0″. A rectangular hopper is an inverted truncated pyramid having a base 24″ × 36″ and altitude of 42″. The plane of the lower base slopes upward to the right in an angle of 30 degrees and cuts the center line of the pyramid at a point 18″ below the upper base. The plane of the lower base is parallel to the shorter lines of the upper base. The upper base is 3″ below and parallel to the *H* plane with its longer edges parallel to *F*. The center line of the pyramid is 24″ from *F* and 30″ from *P*. Draw the *H*, *F*, and *P* projections of the hopper.

1.5. *Layout 1.* Same as Problem 1.4 except that the shorter edges of the base are parallel to *F* and that the lower base slopes downward to the rear.

1.6. *Layout 1.* Assume the *HF* axis 4½″ above the lower margin and the *FP* axis 4″ from the right margin. The horizontal base of a concrete foundation is a rectangle 16′ × 8′ with one longer edge parallel to and 2′ behind a frontal reference plane. The upper surface is a rectangle 10′ × 6′ and lies in a floor (*H*). The front surface of the foundation lies in a vertical plane and is symmetric about a vertical center line that is 12′ from a side wall *P*. The foundation is 12′ high. Scale ¼″ = 1′ 0″.

(a) Find the *H*, *F*, and *P* projections of the foundation.
(b) Find the *H*, *F*, and *P* projections of a 3′ square opening through the foundation, the center line of which is perpendicular to *F*, 6′ below the floor, and 9′ from the side wall.
(c) Find the *H*, *F*, and *P* projections of a similar opening that intersects the first and has its center line perpendicular to *P* and 5′ from *F*.

1.7. *Layout 2.* The *HF* axis line is 5″ above the lower margin, and the *FP* axis is 2½″ to the left of the right margin.

(a) The vertical center line of a right hexagonal prism is 1¼″ to the left of *P* and 1¼″ behind *F*. The bases are 1½″ in minimum diameter, parallel to *H*, and have two edges parallel to *F*. The upper base is ½″ below *H* and the prism is 3″ long. The prism is truncated by a plane that is perpendicular to *F* through the mid-point of the center line. The plane slopes upward to the left in an angle of 45 degrees. Draw the *H*, *F*, and *P* projections of the complete prism in fine construction lines. Draw the lower truncated portion in heavy lines.
(b) Same as (a) except that the prism is octagonal.

1.8.

(a) Same as Problem 1.7 (a) except that the truncating plane is perpendicular to *P* and slopes upward to the rear in an angle of 45 degrees.
(b) Same as Problem 1.7 (b) except that the truncating plane is perpendicular to *P* and slopes upward to the rear in an angle of 45 degrees.

1.9. *Layout 2.* The *HF* axis line is 5″ above the lower margin.

(a) A storage tank is made of a cylinder 8′ in diameter and 8′ in height on which rests a hemispherical dome. The center line of the tank is 10′ to the left of *P* and 5′ behind *F*. The base is 14′ below *H*. Draw the *H* and *F* projections. Scale ¼″ = 1′ 0″.
(b) A hexagonal bin is 8′ high and 8′ in smallest diameter. The base is parallel to and 14′ below *H* with two edges parallel to *F*. The roof is a hexagonal pyramid of 4′ altitude. The vertical center line is 10′ to the left of *P* and 5′ behind *F*. Draw the *H* and *F* projections.

1.10. *Layout 2.* The *HF* axis is 5″ above the lower margin and the *FP* axis 2½″ to the left of the right margin.

(a) The vertical center line of a right hexagonal pyramid of 3″ altitude is 1¼″ to the left of *P* and 1¼″ behind *F*. The apex is ½″ below *H*, and two edges of the hexagonal base are parallel to *F*. The base is 1½″ in minimum diameter. The pyramid is truncated by a horizontal plane through the mid-point of the center line. Draw the *H*, *F*, and *P* projections of the complete pyramid using fine lines. Draw the frustum in heavy lines.
(b) Same as (a) except that the pyramid is octagonal.

1.11. *Layout 2.* (See Figure 1.5.)

(a) The apex of an oblique hexagonal pyramid is 1″ to the left of a wall, *P*, 3″ behind a front wall, *F*, and ¼″ below a floor, *H*. The hexagonal base is parallel to and 2¾″ below *H* with its center 3½″ to the left of *P* and 1¼″ behind *F*. The hexagonal base is 1½″ in smallest diameter with two edges parallel to *F*. Draw the *H* and *F* projections of the pyramid.

(b) The apex of an oblique cone is located at a point 1″ to the left of P, 3″ behind F, and ¼″ below H. The center of its 2″ circular base is 3½″ to the left of P, 1¼″ behind F, and 2¾″ below H. The base is parallel to H. Draw the H and F projections of the cone. Show elements of the cone taken at 30-degree intervals on the base.

1.12. *Layout 2.* The HF axis line is 5″ above the lower margin and the FP axis 2½″ from the right margin of the drawing space.

(a) A rectangular jig block is 1″ × 1½″ × 3″ and has a groove ½″ wide by ¼″ deep running lengthwise in the center of one of the 1½″ × 3″ surfaces. Draw the H, F, and P projections of the block. The grooved face is parallel to F with the vertical center line of the block 1″ behind F and 1¼″ to the left of P. The upper surface is ½″ below H.

(b) Same as (a) except that the grooved face is turned toward P so that it lies in a plane that makes an angle of 30 degrees with F.

CHAPTER II

PROJECTIONS OF A POINT

2.1. Notation and Designation. The capital letters A, B, C, etc., are used to specify a point in space. The projection of a point is designated by a lower case letter with a capital letter superscript to indicate the plane upon which the projection is made. For example, the projection of the point A on the frontal plane is a^F, on the horizontal plane a^H, and on the profile plane a^P. If auxiliary planes are used, the projections of A on the first is a^1, on the second a^2, etc.

The projections of a line may be determined by the projections of two points of the line. For example, the line segment AB projects on H as a^Hb^H, on F as a^Fb^F, etc. If a plane be located by three points, its projections are determined by the projections of those points.

2.2. Problem 2.1. To project a point on the horizontal projection plane.

Given: The location of a point relative to the frontal and profile reference planes.

Required: The H projection, or plan view, of the point.

Solution: Find the point in which a projector that is perpendicular to the H plane, and passing through the point, pierces the H plane.

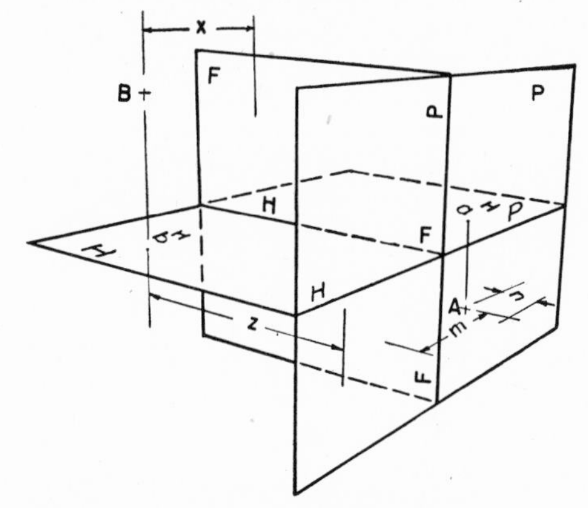

Fig. 2.1. Pictorial of Projection on H

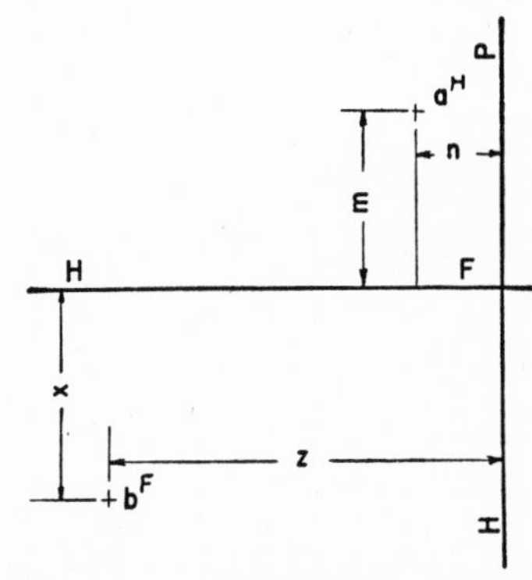

Fig. 2.2. Orthographic of Projection on H

Discussion: In Figure 2.1 it is assumed that the point A is located a distance m behind the frontal plane and a distance n to the left of the profile plane. The perpendicular projector through A pierces the H plane at a^H. This point is, by definition, the projection of A on H.

The point B is located a distance x in front of the frontal plane and a distance z to the left of the profile plane. The perpendicular projector through B pierces the H plane at b^H which is the projection of B on H.

Figure 2.2 shows the H projections of the points A and B as they would be located on an orthographic plan view. The H projection of A is a distance m above (i.e., behind) the frontal plane which shows on the drawing as the axis line FH. The H projection of the point B is located a distance x below (i.e., in front of) the FH axis line. Since point A is a distance n and point B a distance z to the left of the profile plane, their projections will be shown at those distances to the left of the HP axis line, which is the edge view of the profile plane.

2.3. Problem 2.2. To project a point on a frontal plane.

Given: The location of a point relative to the horizontal and profile reference planes.

Required: The F projection, or front view, of the point.

Solution: Find the point in which a projector that is perpendicular to F and passing through the point pierces the F plane.

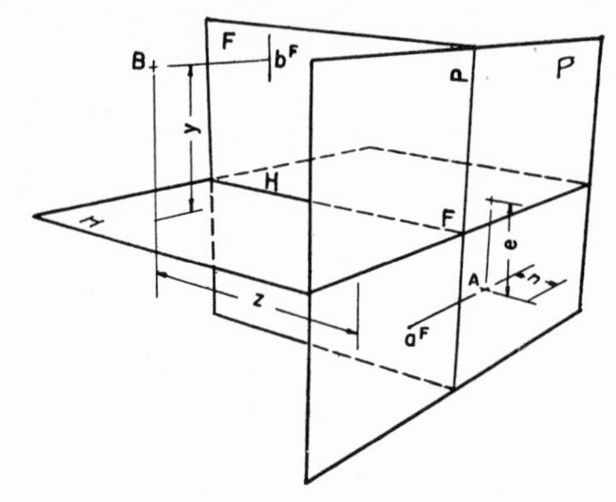

FIG. 2.3. Pictorial of Projection on F

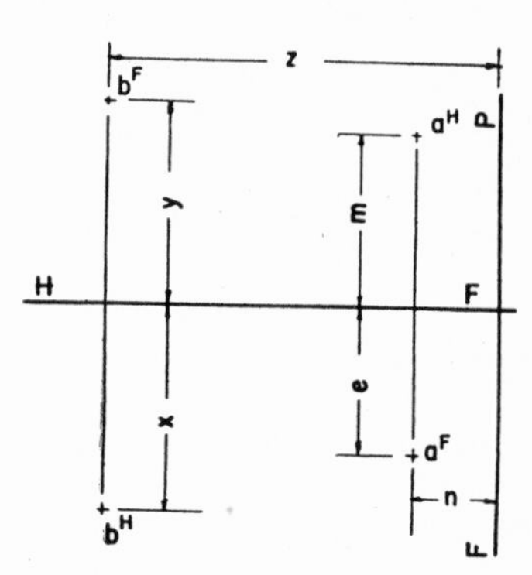

FIG. 2.4. Orthographic of Projection on F

Discussion: It is assumed in Figure 2.3 that the point A is a distance e below the H plane and a distance n to the left of the P plane. The perpendicular projector Aa^F pierces the frontal plane at a^F which is the projection of A on the F plane. This projection is a distance e below the HF axis line and a distance n to the left of the FP axis line.

A projector that is perpendicular to F and through B pierces the frontal plane at b^F a distance y above the HF axis line and a distance z to the left of the FP axis line.

In descriptive geometry problems it is desirable to place all projections on the same drawing. Figure 2.4 shows the frontal projections and the horizontal projections of the points A and B as they would appear in such a drawing. Since the point A is a distance e below H and a distance n to the left of P, the projections of A are so located with respect to the HF and FP axis lines. The point B is above H a distance y, and to the left of P a distance z, and its projections are so located.

2.4. Problem 2.3. To project a point on the profile plane.

Given: The location of a point relative to the frontal and horizontal planes.

Required: To find the projections of the point on the profile plane.

Solution: Erect a perpendicular to the profile plane through the point and find where it pierces P.

Discussion: It is assumed in Figure 2.5 that the point A is a distance m behind F and a distance e below H. A projector through A and perpendicular to P pierces that plane at the point a^P. The projector through B and perpendicular to the P plane pierces it at b^P.

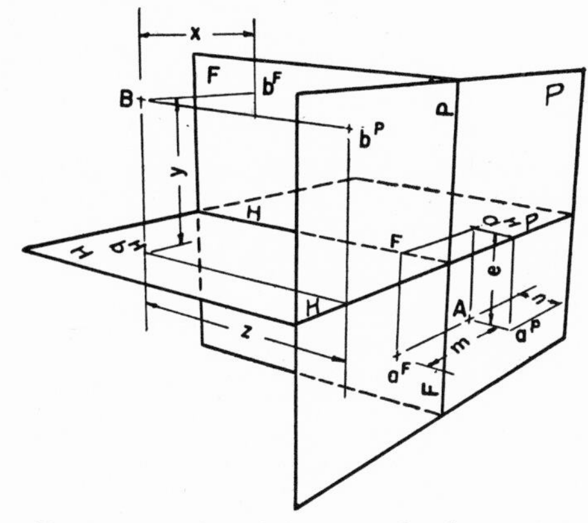

FIG. 2.5. Pictorial of Projection on P

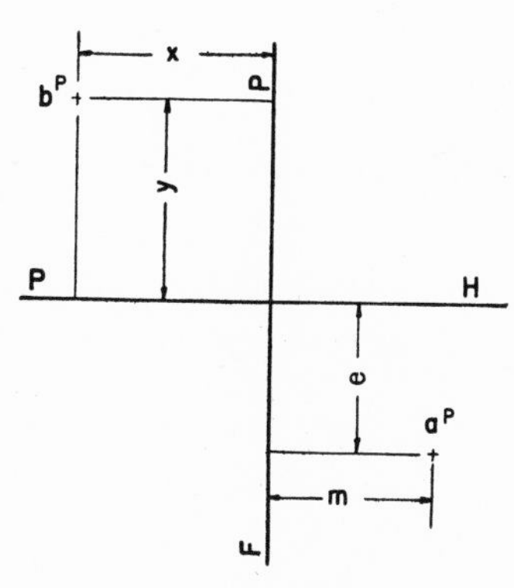

FIG. 2.6. Orthographic Right Side View

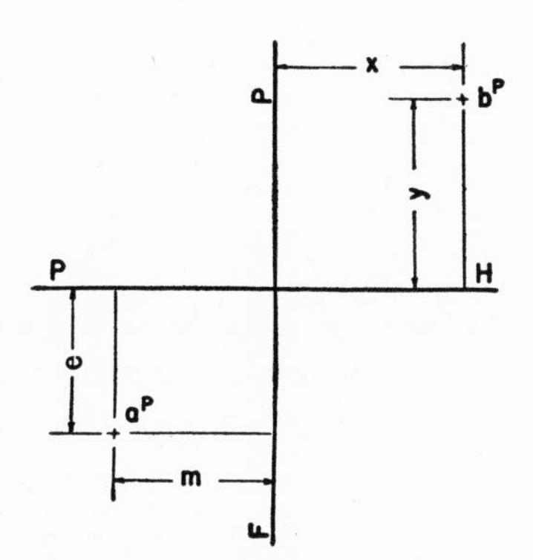

FIG. 2.7. Orthographic Left Side View

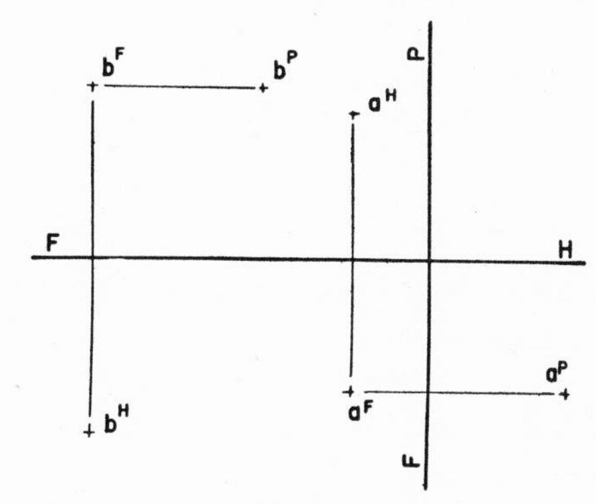

FIG. 2.8. Orthographic H, F, and P Projections

Figure 2.6 shows an orthographic right side view of the points A and B. It should be noted that a^P is to the right (behind) and b^P to the left (in front) of the FP axis line the distances m and x respectively. The point a^P is below and b^P above the HP axis line the distances e and y respectively.

The left side view of the points A and B are shown in Figure 2.7. The point a^P appears on the left and b^P on the right of the FP axis line in this case. Their location relative to H remains the same as in the case of a right side view.

Figure 2.8 shows the H, F, and P projections, or views, of the points A and B as they are located on a single drawing. To read such a drawing it is necessary to visualize it as three separate units: first, a top view showing the location of the points relative to F and P; second, a front view showing the location of the points relative to H and P; third, a right side view showing their location relative to H and F.

2.5. Planes Stationary. In the preceding problems it was assumed that the projection planes remained stationary and that the draftsman changed position. He viewed the points from above to get their top views, from in front to get their front views, and from the side to obtain their side views. These views were then placed with the reference or axis lines coincident so that they made a single drawing composed of three views taken from different directions.

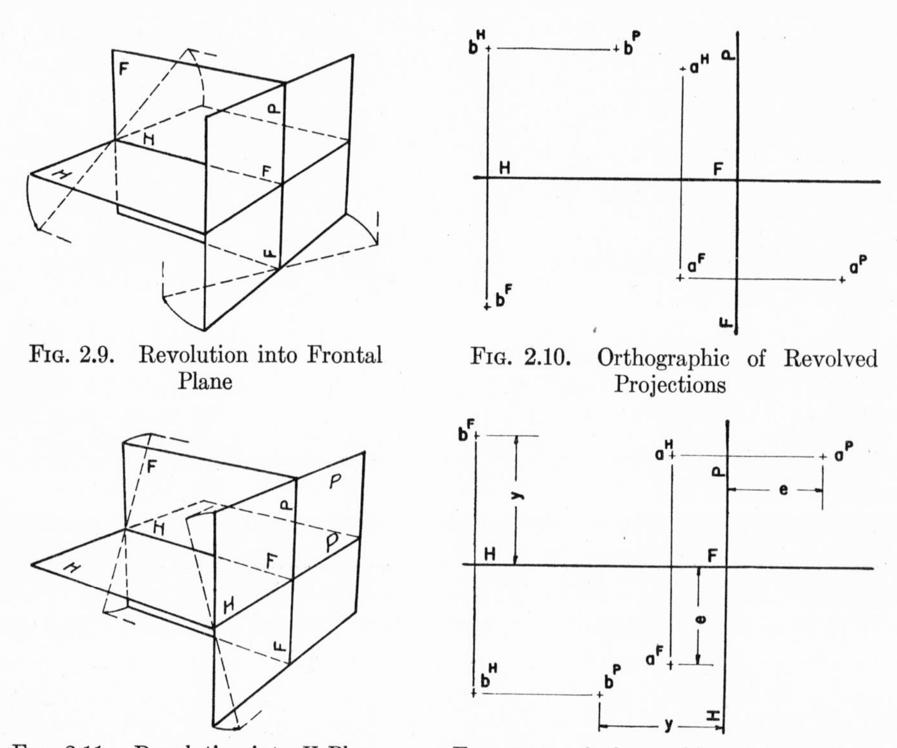

FIG. 2.9. Revolution into Frontal Plane

FIG. 2.10. Orthographic of Revolved Projections

FIG. 2.11. Revolution into H Plane

FIG. 2.12. Orthographic of Projections

2.6. Planes Revolved. The same combination of top, front, and side views shown in Figure 2.8 would result if the projections were made on the three planes and the H and P planes then revolved into the F plane. In making such revolutions the rear portion of H revolves up and the front portion down about the HF axis; the rear portion of the P plane revolves out and the front portion in about the FP axis. In this case the F plane was considered stationary and the H and P planes revolved into it. Figure 2.9 indicates the direction of rotation and Figure 2.10 the location of the projections of points A and B as located in the preceding problems.

The same projections, but in different locations relative to each other, are obtained by assuming that the H plane is stationary and revolving F and P into it about the HF and HP axes. (See Figure 2.12.) The F and H projections retain the position shown in Figure 2.10 but the P projections are revolved through 90 degrees and are at the right of the H projections. It will be seen that the vertical distances e and y now appear on the drawing as horizontals. Since A is a distance e below H, and B a distance y above H, e is measured to the right and y to the left of the HP axis line. This location may be more easily visualized through a study of Figure 2.11.

2.7. Projections on an Adjacent Plane. The revolution of two projections into the plane of a third can be made in any case when the projections are made on a set of adjacent planes. (See glossary.) Let it be assumed that the planes *1*, *2*, and *3*

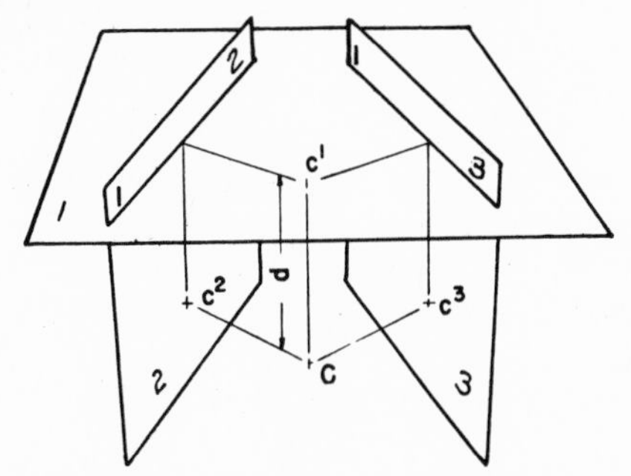

FIG. 2.13. Pictorial of Adjacent Planes

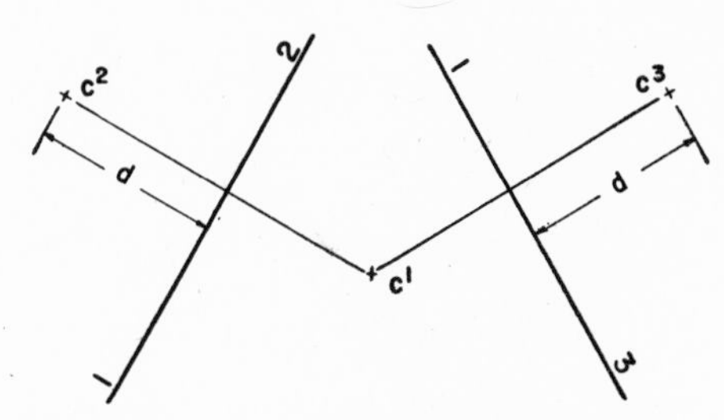

FIG. 2.14. Projections on Adjacent Planes

of Figure 2.13 form a set of adjacent planes having any position in space and that the projections of the point C are c^1, c^2, and c^3 as shown. If the point C is a distance d from the projection plane *1*, the orthographic projections c^2 and c^3 will be the distance d from the *1–2* and *1–3* axes lines.

Revolution of the c^2 and c^3 projections into the plane of c^1 results in the orthographic drawing of Figure 2.14. It will be seen that c^1 and c^2 are located on a projector that is perpendicular to the *1–2* axis line and that c^1 and c^3 are on a projector that is perpendicular to the *1–3* axis line. Since the point C is a distance d away from plane *1* the projections c^2 and c^3 will be located at that distance from the *1–2* and *1–3* axes lines.

2.8. Application Problems.

2.1. *Layout 4.* Assume that the HF and FP axes intersect at the mid-point of each section of the sheet. Draw in each section one of the problems stated below. Fold the profile into F about the FP axis. (Review Article 1.5.)

(a) Draw the H, F, and right profile views of A and B. $A(\frac{1}{2}, 1, \frac{1}{4})$, $B(1, \frac{1}{4}, 1)$.
(b) Draw the H, F, and left profile views of C and D. $C(-\frac{1}{2}, 1, \frac{1}{4})$, $D(-1, \frac{1}{4}, 1)$.
(c) Draw the H, F, and left profile views of E and O. $E(\frac{1}{2}, -1, -\frac{1}{4})$, $O(1, -\frac{1}{4}, -1)$.
(d) Draw the H, F, and right profile views of K and M. $K(-\frac{1}{2}, -1, -\frac{1}{4})$, $M(-1, -\frac{1}{4}, -1)$.
(e) Draw the H, F, and left profile views of O and N. $O(1, -\frac{1}{4}, 1)$, $N(\frac{1}{2}, -1, \frac{1}{4})$.
(f) Draw the H, F, and right profile view of R and S. $R(\frac{1}{2}, 1, -\frac{1}{4})$, $S(1, \frac{1}{4}, -1)$.

2.2. Same as Problem 2.1 except that the profile plane is revolved into H about the HP axis.

2.3. *Layout 4.* The HF and FP axes intersect at the mid-points of each section. Draw in each section the H, F, and right profile projections of a line located below. The profile plane is revolved into F about the FP axis.

(a) Line AB: $A(1\frac{1}{2}, 1\frac{1}{2}, \frac{1}{2})$, $B(\frac{1}{4}, \frac{1}{2}, 1)$.
(b) Line CD: $C(1\frac{1}{2}, -\frac{1}{2}, -1\frac{1}{2})$, $D(\frac{1}{4}, -1, -\frac{1}{4})$.
(c) Line NO: $N(\frac{1}{2}, 1\frac{1}{2}, \frac{1}{2})$, $O(1\frac{1}{2}, -\frac{1}{2}, 1\frac{1}{2})$. Locate the H, F, and P projections of the point F in which the frontal plane is pierced by the line NO (i.e., the F trace of NO).
(d) Line RS: $R(1\frac{1}{2}, \frac{1}{4}, 1)$, $S(\frac{1}{4}, 1\frac{1}{2}, -\frac{1}{2})$. Locate the H, F, and P projections of the point H in which the horizontal plane is pierced by the line RS (i.e., the H trace of RS).
(e) Line KM: $K(1\frac{1}{2}, \frac{1}{2}, 1\frac{1}{2})$, $M(-\frac{1}{2}, 1\frac{1}{2}, \frac{1}{4})$. Locate the H, F, and P projections of the point P in which the profile plane is pierced by the line KM (i.e., the P trace of KM).
(f) Line XY: $X(1\frac{1}{2}, 0, 1)$, $Y(0, 1\frac{1}{2}, 0)$.

2.4. Same as Problem 2.3 except that the profile plane is revolved into the H plane about the HP axis.

2.5. *Layout 4.* The HF and FP axis lines intersect in the center of each section. Find the H, F, and right profile of the plane figures located below. Revolve the P plane into F about the FP axis.

(a) Plane ABC: $A(1\frac{1}{4}, 1, 1\frac{1}{2})$, $B(\frac{1}{4}, 1, 1\frac{1}{2})$, $C(\frac{3}{4}, 1, \frac{1}{4})$.
(b) Plane CDE: $C(1\frac{1}{4}, 1\frac{1}{2}, 1\frac{1}{2})$, $D(\frac{1}{4}, \frac{1}{2}, 1\frac{1}{2})$, $E(\frac{3}{4}, 1, \frac{1}{4})$.
(c) Plane MNO: $M(1\frac{1}{4}, \frac{1}{4}, 1\frac{1}{2})$, $N(\frac{1}{4}, \frac{1}{4}, 1\frac{1}{2})$, $O(\frac{3}{4}, 1\frac{1}{2}, \frac{1}{4})$.
(d) Plane BCD: $B(1\frac{1}{4}, \frac{1}{2}, 1\frac{1}{2})$, $C(\frac{3}{4}, 1\frac{1}{2}, \frac{1}{2})$, $D(\frac{1}{4}, 1, 1)$.
(e) Plane AEO: $A(1\frac{1}{4}, \frac{1}{2}, \frac{1}{2})$, $E(\frac{3}{4}, 1, 1\frac{1}{2})$, $O(\frac{1}{4}, 1, 1)$.
(f) Plane MNO: $M(1\frac{1}{4}, 1\frac{1}{2}, \frac{1}{2})$, $N(\frac{1}{4}, 1\frac{1}{2}, \frac{1}{2})$, $O(\frac{3}{4}, \frac{1}{4}, 1)$.

2.6. Same as Problem 2.5 except that the profile plane is revolved into H about the HP axis line.

2.7. *Layout 4.* Assume that the HF and FP axis lines intersect at the mid-point of each section. Find the H, F, and P projections of the given points. Fold the profile plane into F about the FP axis line.

(a) $A(-\frac{1}{2}, 1, \frac{1}{4})$, $B(-1, \frac{1}{4}, 1)$. Show left profile view.
(b) $C(1, \frac{1}{4}, -1)$, $D(\frac{1}{2}, 1, -\frac{1}{4})$. Show right profile view.
(c) $E(1, -1\frac{1}{4}, -\frac{1}{4})$, $G(\frac{1}{2}, -\frac{1}{4}, -1\frac{1}{4})$. Show left profile view.
(d) $K(1, 1, \frac{1}{2})$, $M(\frac{1}{2}, \frac{1}{4}, 1)$. Show right profile view.
(e) $N(-\frac{1}{2}, -1, -\frac{1}{4})$, $O(-1, -\frac{1}{4}, -1)$. Show right profile view.
(f) $R(1, -\frac{1}{4}, 1)$, $S(\frac{1}{2}, -1, \frac{1}{4})$. Show left profile view.

2.8. Same as Problem 2.7 except that the profile plane is revolved into H about the HP axis line.

2.9. *Layout 4.* Assume that the HF and FP axis lines intersect at the mid-point of each section. Find the H, F, and right profile projections of the given lines. Revolve the profile plane into F about the FP axis line.

(a) $A(1\frac{1}{2}, 1, \frac{1}{4})$, $B(\frac{1}{4}, -\frac{1}{2}, 1\frac{1}{2})$. Show the projections of the F and P traces.
(b) $C(1\frac{1}{2}, 1\frac{1}{2}, \frac{1}{2})$, $D(-\frac{1}{2}, \frac{1}{4}, 1\frac{1}{2})$. Show the projections of the F trace.
(c) $E(1\frac{1}{2}, 1\frac{1}{2}, -\frac{1}{2})$, $G(\frac{1}{2}, \frac{1}{2}, 1\frac{1}{2})$. Show the projections of the H trace.
(d) $K(1\frac{1}{2}, 1, 1\frac{1}{2})$, $M(\frac{1}{2}, \frac{1}{2}, \frac{1}{4})$. Show the projections of the H and F traces.
(e) $N(1\frac{1}{2}, 1\frac{1}{2}, 1)$, $O(\frac{1}{4}, \frac{1}{2}, 1)$. Show the projections of the F and P traces.
(f) $R(1\frac{1}{4}, \frac{1}{4}, \frac{3}{4})$, $S(\frac{1}{2}, \frac{3}{4}, \frac{1}{2})$. Show the projections of the H and P traces.

2.10. Same as Problem 2.9 except that the profile plane is revolved into H about the HP axis line.

2.11. *Layout 4.* Assume that the HF and FP axis lines intersect at the mid-point of each section. Show the right profile revolved into F about FP as an axis.

(a) $A(1\frac{1}{4}, 1\frac{1}{2}, \frac{1}{2})$, $B(\frac{3}{4}, \frac{1}{2}, 1\frac{1}{2})$, $C(\frac{1}{4}, 1, 1)$.
(b) $D(1\frac{1}{4}, \frac{1}{2}, \frac{1}{2})$, $E(\frac{3}{4}, 1\frac{1}{2}, 1)$, $G(\frac{1}{4}, 1, 1)$.
(c) $K(1\frac{1}{4}, 1\frac{1}{2}, 1\frac{1}{2})$, $M(\frac{3}{4}, 1, \frac{1}{4})$, $N(\frac{1}{4}, \frac{1}{2}, 1\frac{1}{2})$.
(d) $O(1\frac{1}{4}, 1\frac{1}{2}, 1)$, $R(\frac{3}{4}, \frac{1}{4}, 1)$, $S(\frac{1}{4}, 1\frac{1}{2}, 1)$.
(e) $B(1\frac{1}{4}, 1\frac{1}{2}, 1\frac{1}{2})$, $C(\frac{1}{4}, 1\frac{1}{2}, \frac{1}{2})$, $D(\frac{3}{4}, \frac{1}{4}, 1)$.
(f) $M(1\frac{1}{4}, 1\frac{1}{2}, \frac{1}{4})$, $N(\frac{1}{4}, 1\frac{1}{2}, \frac{1}{4})$, $O(\frac{3}{4}, \frac{1}{4}, 1)$.

2.12. Same as Problem 2.11 except that the profile plane is revolved into the H plane about the HP axis line.

CHAPTER III

AUXILIARY PROJECTIONS OF LINES

3.1. Principal Projections. A straight line is located in space by two points that lie on the line or by a point and the angles that the line makes with the projection planes. The projection of a line may then be determined by the projections of two points, or the projections of one point and the given angles. The projection of a point on the principal planes has been discussed in Chapter II. The principal projections of a line, therefore, involve no new theories and will not be illustrated or discussed. It is important, however, to visualize the self-evident and obvious truth of the statements regarding special cases of orthographic line projection that follow:

First: *A line will project as a point on any plane that is perpendicular to it.*

Second: *A line will project its true length on any plane that is parallel to it.*

Third: *The angle that a line makes with a projection plane will project its true size on an adjacent plane that is parallel to the line.*

Fourth: *The projection of a line can never be longer than the line itself.*

Fifth: *Parallel lines will have parallel projections on any plane.*

Sixth: *Perpendicular lines will have perpendicular projections on a projection plane that is parallel to one or both of the lines.*

3.2. Drafting Operations. There are five fundamental drafting operations used by the draftsman in applying the theories of descriptive geometry to the problems of the drafting room. The operations are:

Operation I: To project the true length of a line on an auxiliary plane that is parallel to the line.

Operation II: To project a line as a point on an auxiliary plane that is perpendicular to it.

Operation III: To project a plane surface as a line on an auxiliary plane that is perpendicular to that surface.

Operation IV: To project a plane surface in its true size on an auxiliary projection plane that is parallel to that surface.

Operation V: To revolve an oblique line or surface into a position in which it is parallel to, or perpendicular to, a given projection plane.

Since one or more of these operations are required in the solution of almost any problem involving descriptive geometry, it is essential that they be thoroughly understood and the required drafting technique mastered. In this chapter, which is devoted to the projection of lines on auxiliary planes, the use of the first two operations will be illustrated and discussed. A discussion and illustration of the use of the other operations will be included in another chapter.

3.3. Problem 3.1. *Operation I.* To project a line in its true length on an auxiliary plane that is parallel to the line.

Given: The projections of an oblique line on two adjacent planes.

Required: An auxiliary projection of the line that will show the true length of the line.

Solution: Project the line on an auxiliary plane that is perpendicular to one of the given planes and is parallel to the line.

Discussion: It is assumed that the line segment AB is located in space, behind F, and below H as shown in the pictorial drawing of Figure 3.1. The line AB projects on H as a^Hb^H and on F as a^Fb^F. The auxiliary plane *1* is perpendicular to H and parallel to the line AB at any convenient distance z from the line. The projection of AB on plane *1* is a^1b^1. It will be seen in the figure that the line AB and its projection a^1b^1 are opposite sides of a rectangle and therefore equal in length.

It should be emphasized that the auxiliary plane must be parallel to the line and perpendicular to one of the adjacent planes. The fact that the auxiliary plane is also parallel to one of the given projections is indicated in the figure.

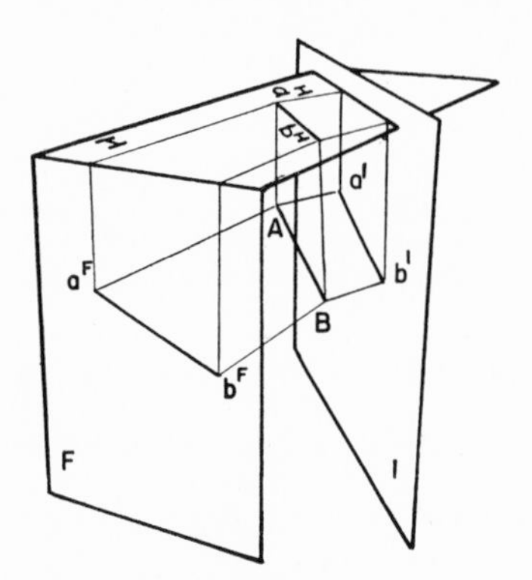

FIG. 3.1. Operation I—Pictorial Drawing

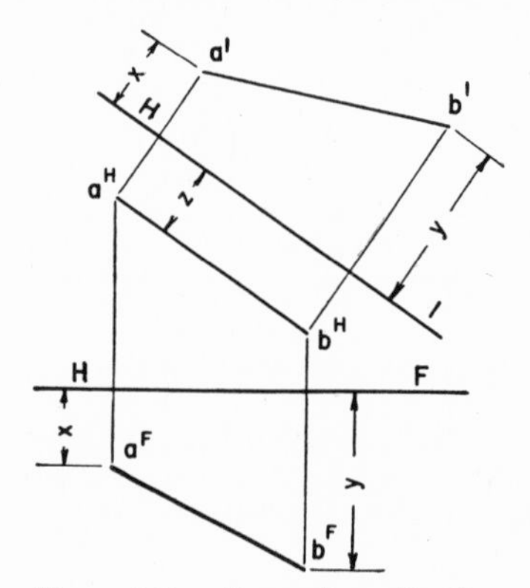

FIG. 3.2. Operation I—Orthographic Drawing

Figure 3.2 shows the H, F, and auxiliary projections of a line segment AB as they would be located on an orthographic drawing. In this case the H plane, being perpendicular to F and the auxiliary plane, was assumed to be stationary in the surface of the drawing and that the F and auxiliary planes were revolved up into it about the HF and $H1$ axes. If the point A is a distance x below H and is projected orthographically onto F and the auxiliary plane *1*, it is evident that a^F is a distance x from the HF axis and that a^1 is an equal distance from the $H1$ axis. The projections of B at b^F and b^1 show in a similar manner that the point B is a distance y below H.

It must not be assumed that the auxiliary plane of Operation I is necessarily perpendicular to H. It may be taken perpendicular to either of two adjacent planes whether they be two of the principal planes, two auxiliary planes, or one principal and one auxiliary plane.

Figure 3.3 shows the projections of a line segment AB on the horizontal and frontal planes, and on an auxiliary plane taken parallel to AB and perpendicular to the frontal plane. Since the frontal plane is perpendicular to both of the other projection planes, it is assumed to be stationary and in the drawing surface, and that the others are revolved into it. The point B shows by its H projection that it is a distance y behind F. The auxiliary projection of B must therefore be located a distance y from the $F1$ axis. The H projection of A at a^H and its auxiliary projection a^1 must be equidistant from the HF and $F1$ axes for the same reason.

In Figure 3.4 it is assumed that the frontal and profile views of the line CD are given. The auxiliary plane is shown perpendicular to the profile plane and parallel to CD. If the profile plane is assumed to be stationary and the frontal and auxiliary planes revolved into it, the distances that C and D are to the left of P will be shown by the location of the frontal and auxiliary projections relative to the FP and $P1$ axes.

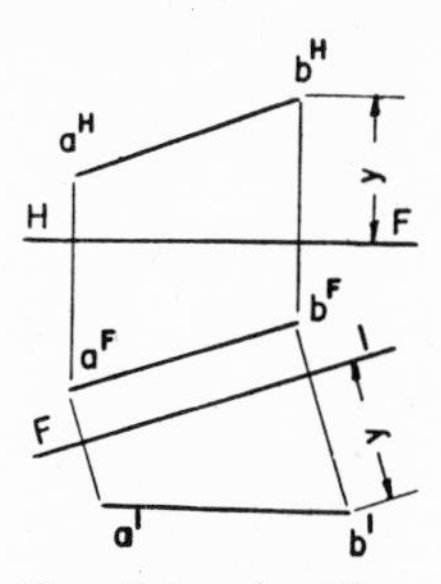

FIG. 3.3. Auxiliary Plane *1* Perpendicular to *F*

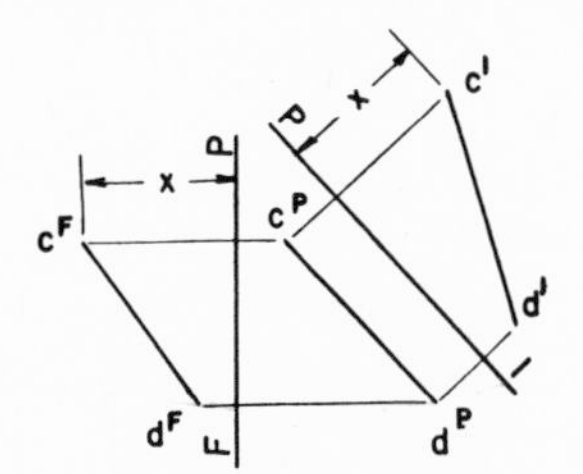

FIG. 3.4. Auxiliary Plane *1* Perpendicular to *P*

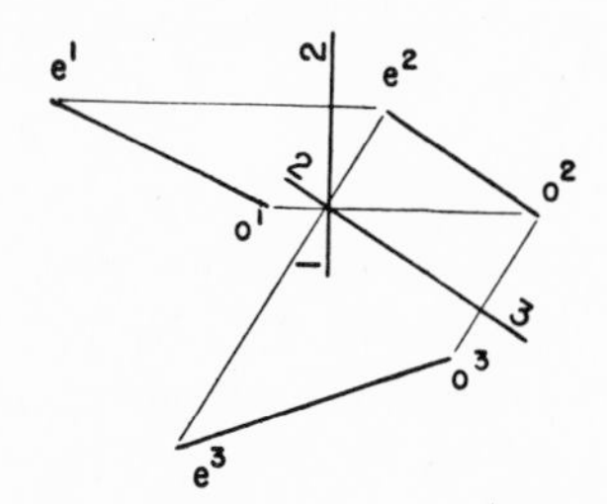

FIG. 3.5. Planes *1* and *3* Perpendicular to Plane *2*

Figure 3.5 shows the projection of the line EO on a set of adjacent planes. The auxiliary planes *1* and *3* are perpendicular to the plane *2*. The plane *2* is, therefore, assumed stationary and the others revolved into it. The distances between e^1 and o^1 and the *1–2* axis are equal to the distances from the *2–3* axis to e^3 and o^3.

3.4. Problem 3.2. *Operation II. General Case.* The line is oblique. To project an oblique line as a point on an auxiliary plane that is perpendicular to the line.

Given: The projections of an oblique line on two adjacent planes.

Required: The projection of the line as a point.

Solution: Project the line on a plane that is perpendicular to it.

Analysis:

1. Project the line on a plane that is parallel to it. (Operation I.)
2. Project the line on a plane that is perpendicular to the line and to the auxiliary plane used in Operation I.

Discussion: It is assumed in Figure 3.6 that the line AB and its projections on F and H are given. Since it is necessary as a preliminary step to project the line in its true length, the auxiliary plane *1* was assumed parallel to AB and perpendicular to H. The line AB projects on plane *1* as a^1b^1 which is equal in length to AB (Operation I). The plane *2* is then assumed perpendicular to the line AB and to the auxiliary plane *1*. Perpendicular projectors from A and B pierce the plane *2* at the point a^2b^2 which is the projection of AB on plane *2*.

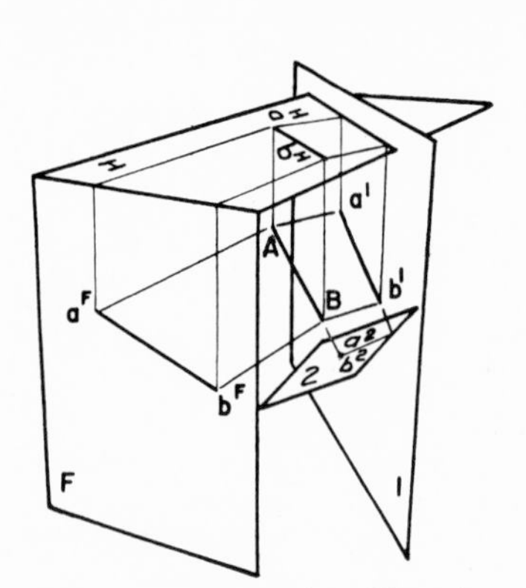

FIG. 3.6. Operation II—Pictorial Drawing

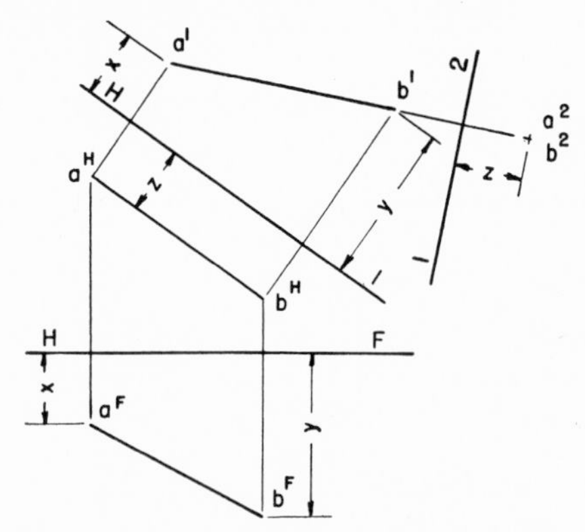

FIG. 3.7. Operation II—Orthographic Drawing

Figure 3.7 shows the orthographic projection of AB on the F, H, *1*, and *2* planes after these planes have been revolved into the surface of the drawing. The F plane and auxiliary plane *1* were first revolved into H about their respective axes. The auxiliary plane *2* was then revolved into the auxiliary plane *1* about the *1–2* axis. Study of the pictorial drawing of Figure 3.6 makes it obvious that a^2b^2 must be located a distance z away from the *1–2* axis if a^Hb^H is that distance from the $H1$ axis.

It should be observed here that the F, H, and *1* planes are a set of adjacent planes in which H is perpendicular to both F and *1*. The H plane is therefore the stationary plane into which F and *1* are revolved. The distances x and y are measured from the HF and $H1$ axes as shown. The H, *1*, and *2* planes are another set of adjacent planes of which plane *1* is perpendicular to both of the others. The plane *1* may then be assumed to be stationary; also it is assumed that H and *2* are revolved into it. Since a^H and b^H are the distance z away from the $H1$ axis, the projection of AB on plane *2* will be located at a^2b^2, a distance z from the *1–2* axis.

In Problem 3.2 and Figures 3.6 and 3.7 the auxiliary plane was assumed perpendicular to H. Operation II is, of course, a general solution and is applicable to any condition in which the projections of a line on two adjacent planes are given. In Figure 3.8 it is assumed that the H and F projections are given and that the plane *1* is parallel to the line and perpendicular to F. The plane *2* is then taken perpendicular to the line AB and the plane *1*. The planes F, *1*, and *2* form a set of adjacent planes. Since plane *1* is perpendicular to both F and *2*, it is assumed to be stationary and the others revolved into it. The distance x that a^2b^2 is located from the *1–2* axis must equal the distance between a^Fb^F and the $F1$ axis.

Figures 3.9 and 3.10 show other applications of Operation II. In Figure 3.9 the *F* and *P* projections were given, and the plane *1* was taken perpendicular to *P* and parallel to the line. The line *CD* projects as the point c^2d^2 on a plane taken perpendicular to it and to the plane *1*. In Figure 3.10 it is assumed that the projections of the line *EO* are given on any two auxiliary planes *1* and *2*. The line *EO* projects as the point e^4o^4 on a plane perpendicular to it and to the plane *3*.

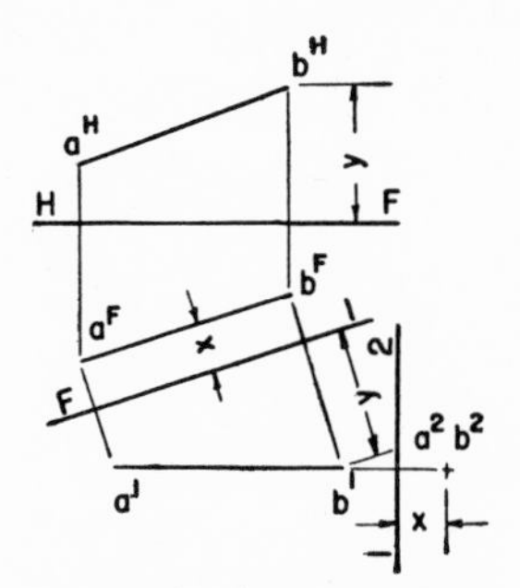

FIG. 3.8. Plane *1*—Perpendicular to *F*

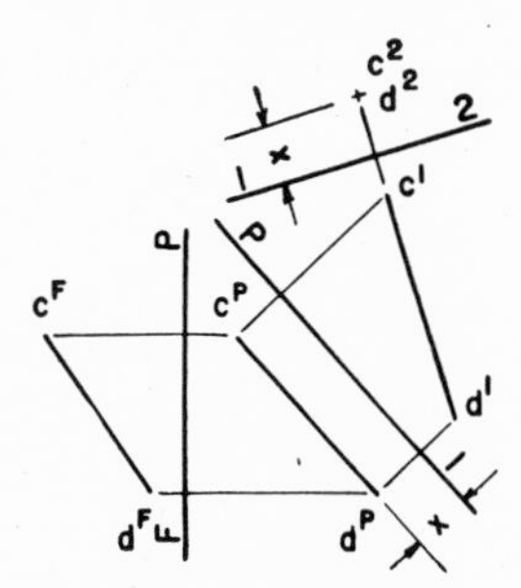

FIG. 3.9. Plane *1*—Perpendicular to *P*

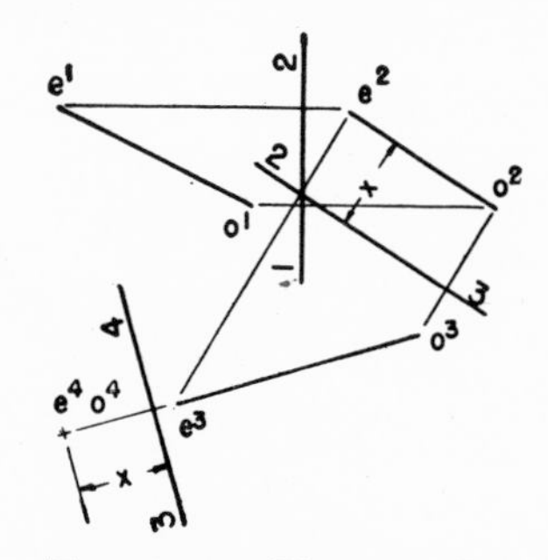

FIG. 3.10. Plane *3*—Perpendicular to *2*

3.5. Problem 3.3. *Operation II. Special Case.* The line is parallel to a projection plane. To project a line as a point on a plane that is perpendicular to it.

Given: The projections of a line on two adjacent planes. The line is parallel to one of the two planes.

Required: A projection of the line that shows it as a point.

Solution: Project the line on a plane that is perpendicular to it.

Discussion: To project a line as a point by use of Operation II, it is necessary to have the projections of the line on two adjacent planes, one of which is parallel to

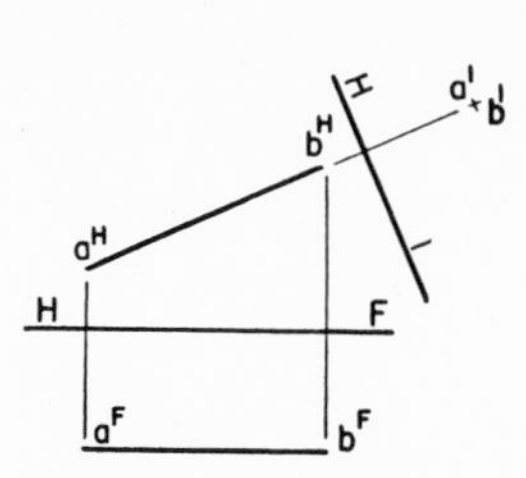

FIG. 3.11. Line Is Parallel to *H*

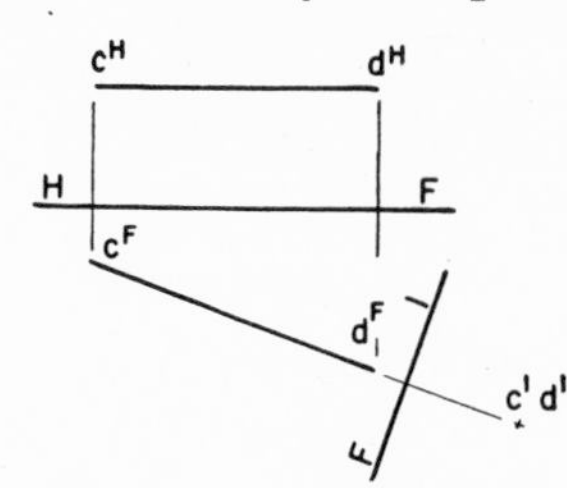

FIG. 3.12. Line Is Parallel to *F*

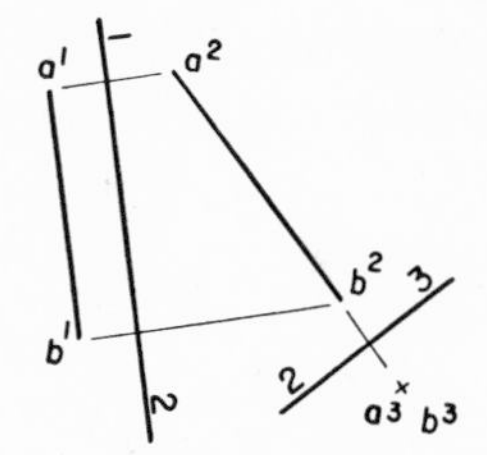

FIG. 3.13. Line Is Parallel to *2*

the line. In the preceding general case problem, Operation I was used to get two such projections. In this special case the line is parallel to one of the given planes and Operation I is not necessary.

In Figure 3.11 the line is parallel to *H* and oblique to *F*. The auxiliary plane *1* is assumed perpendicular to the line and to *H*. The line projects on plane *1* as a^1b^1 and is the required projection.

In Figure 3.12 the line *CD* is parallel to *F* and oblique to *H*. The auxiliary plane *1* is taken perpendicular to *F* and to the line. The projection of *CD* on plane *1* is c^1d^1 and is the required projection of the line.

The line AB of Figure 3.13 is parallel to the auxiliary plane *2*. The plane *3* is assumed perpendicular to AB and the plane *2*. The projection a^3b^3 is the required projection.

3.6. Problem 3.4. To find the true size projection of the angle that an oblique line makes with a projection plane.

Given: The H and F projections of an oblique line.

Required: A true size projection of the angle that the line makes with H.

Solution: Project the angle on a plane that is parallel to the angle.

Discussion: The angle that a line makes with H is measured in a plane that contains the line and is perpendicular to H. The angle will project its true size on any plane that is parallel to this plane. A projection plane that is parallel to the line and perpendicular to H is, therefore, parallel to the angle and will receive the required projection.

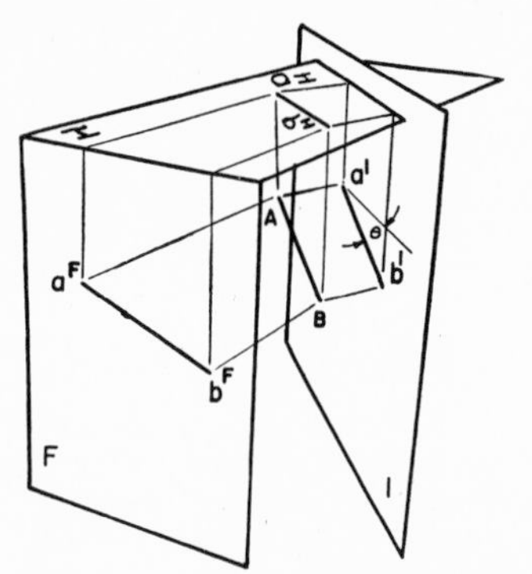

FIG. 3.14. Pictorial Drawing —Projection of Angle with H

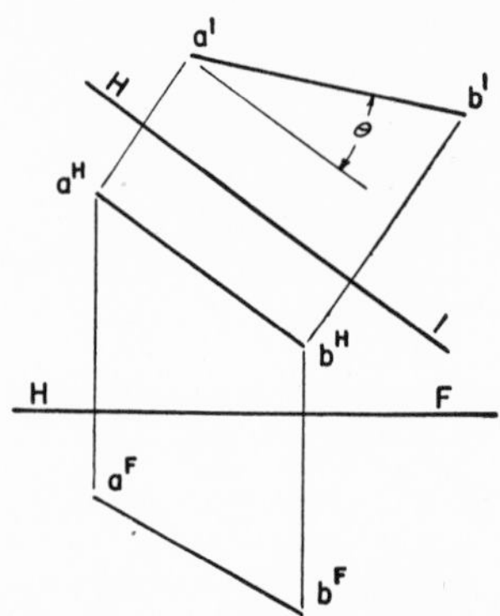

FIG. 3.15. Orthographic Drawing—Projection of Angle with H

In Figure 3.14 the line AB projects as a^Fb^F on F, as a^Hb^H on H, and as a^1b^1 on plane *1*. Since plane *1* is parallel to the line and perpendicular to H, the angle θ that the line makes with H is in true size projection on plane *1*.

Figure 3.15 shows the frontal and auxiliary projections of the line AB revolved into the horizontal plane about the HF and $H1$ axes. The angle θ is the true size projection of the angle with the H plane. This angle is frequently referred to as the slope of the line. The line may be said to be inclined or declined at θ degrees in a given direction. In engineering practice a pipe line may have a grade per foot, a rafter a rise per foot, a road a percent grade, or other technical terms may be used. In any case the angle with a horizontal plane is intended, and the method of projecting its size is not changed.

It was assumed in the discussion and illustration that the angle with H was required. The method is general and may be adapted to the measurement of the angle that a line makes with any projection plane. The solution for any case is, as stated above, to project the angle on a plane that is parallel to it.

3.7. Problem 3.5. To find the projections on two adjacent planes of a right prism whose axis line is parallel to one and inclined to the other of those planes.

Given: The projections on two adjacent planes of the axis line of a prism and a description of the size, shape, and position of the right section.

Required: The projections of the prism on the given adjacent planes.

Solution: Project the prism on two adjacent planes, one of which is parallel, the other perpendicular to the axis.

Analysis:

1. Project the axis line as a point (Operation II).
2. Draw the right section in the required position.
3. Draw the required projections.

Discussion: The projections of a prism are drawn without difficulty on adjacent planes, one of which is parallel and the other perpendicular to the axis of the prism.

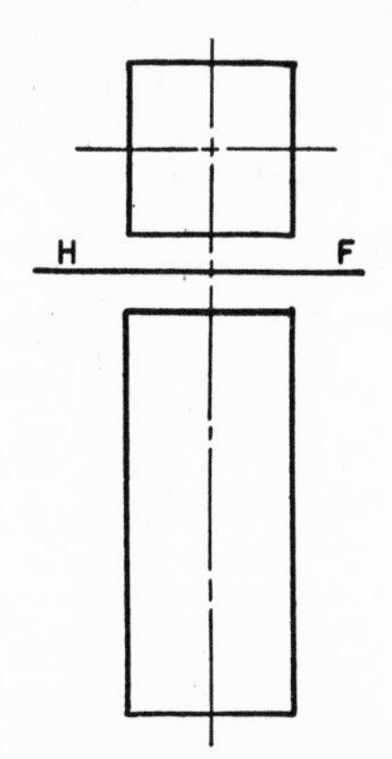

Fig. 3.16. Simplest Views of a Prism

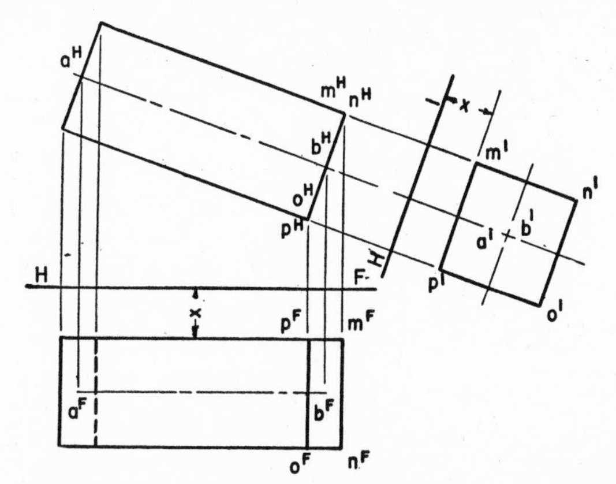

Fig. 3.17. Simple Views Obtained by Operation II

In Figure 3.16 it was assumed that the axis of a square prism was perpendicular to H and that the two faces of the prism were parallel to F. The H projection shows the size, shape, and position of the right section. The F projection shows the length of the prism and the width of one of its faces. These two views are the simplest projections of the prism.

It is the function of the drafting operations that have been discussed to provide a means of making a complex drawing by projecting from others that are easily constructed. In Figure 3.17, Operation II was used to project the axis line AB as a point a^1b^1. The auxiliary projection shows the size and shape of the right section, that the upper and lower faces of the prism are parallel, and that the upper face is a distance x from the H plane. The H and auxiliary projections are similar in form to the views shown in Figure 3.16. They differ in their position but are drawn with no greater difficulty.

The frontal projection may now be found by drawing vertical projectors from the top view and measuring on them the distances that are shown on the auxiliary view. Since the points M and P are a distance x below H, that distance must be shown the same on both the auxiliary plane and F. The projections of the edges of the prism that contain these points may then be drawn parallel to the axis. The points O and N and the edges through them are located in a similar manner. The ends of the prism project on F as rectangles of a form determined by the location of M, N, O, and P.

The visibility of the ends of the prism should be noticed. It is always assumed that the object is viewed from a position in which the observer is looking through a projection plane. The right end is closer to F than is the left end, and it is visible when viewed from the front. The right end is closer to the auxiliary plane than is the left end. The observer must, therefore, see the right end when he looks through the auxiliary plane. The upper surface and not the lower surface is seen when looking through the H plane. It should be remembered that the portion of an object that is closest to a projection plane is always visible in a projection on that plane.

3.8. Problem 3.6. To find the projections on two adjacent planes of a right prism whose center line is inclined to both of those planes.

Given: The projections on two adjacent planes of a center line that is inclined to both projection planes and a description of the size, shape, and location of the right section of a prism of which the given line is a center line.

Required: The projections of the prism on the adjacent planes.

Solution: Project the prism on two auxiliary planes, one of which is parallel and the other perpendicular to the given center line.

Analysis:

1. Project the center line on a plane parallel to it. (Operation I.)
2. Project the center line on a plane perpendicular to it. (Operation II.)
3. Draw the auxiliary projections of the prism in the required position.
4. Draw the required projections.

Discussion: The line AB is assumed to be given by the projections $a^F b^F$ and $a^H b^H$ on the F and H planes as shown in Figure 3.18. It is necessary to have a true length projection of this line before it can be projected as a point. Operation I is used to get the true length view, $a^1 b^1$, and Operation II to project the center line as a point at $a^2 b^2$. The right section is drawn about $a^2 b^2$ as a center and in any desired position (in this case one diagonal of the right section is parallel to H). The projections of the prism on the auxiliary plane *1* and H plane are determined as in the preceding problem. The projection of the prism on plane F is obtained in a similar manner. Projectors perpendicular to the HF axis through the H projections of the various points must contain the F projections of the same points. The distances that the points are below H must show equal on F and plane *1*. Therefore, to locate the F projection of any point of the prism, a vertical projector is drawn through its *H* projection. The *F* projection of the point is located on this projector a distance below the *HF* axis equal to the distance from the *H1* axis to its projection on plane *1*.

In stating Problem 3.6, the line was located with reference to two adjacent planes. The adjacent planes used in Figure 3.18 were the *H* and *F* planes. It

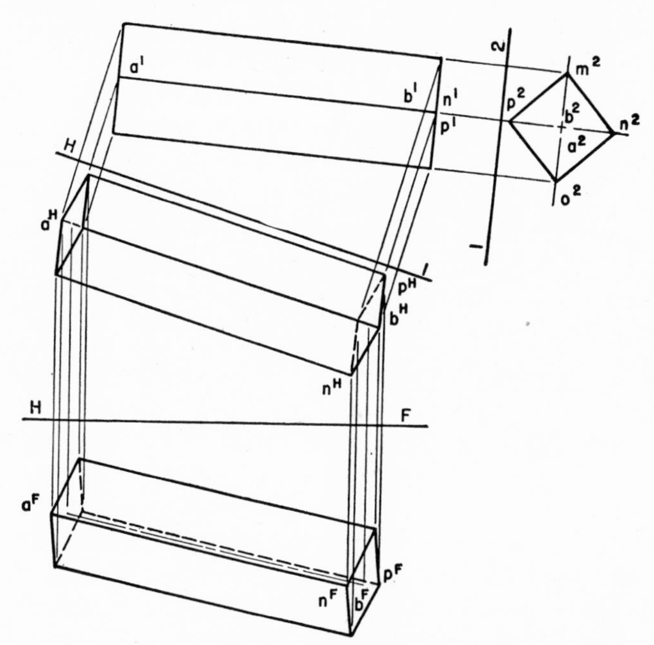

FIG. 3.18. Simple Views Obtained by Operations I and II

should be emphasized that this is a general case problem and that any two planes that are perpendicular to each other could be used. In fact, the same drawing used in Figure 3.18, if relettered might be turned upside down or revolved through any angle and used to illustrate the general case problem. The discussion of such a figure would differ from that given only in the names assigned to the planes.

3.9. Problem 3.7. To find the projections of a line that lies in the right section of a prism when its direction relative to one of a set of adjacent planes is known.

Given: The projections on two adjacent planes of the center line of a prism and the direction relative to one of the adjacent planes of a line that lies in a right section of the prism.

Required: To find the projection of the line on each of the three adjacent planes.

Solution: Assume the projections of a segment of the required line on two lcci of the projections of the line.

Analysis:

1. Assume the projection of a segment of line lying in one projection of a locus of the line.

2. Determine the projection of the segment of line on another locus of its projection.
3. From the two assumed projections of the segment find the third projection.

Discussion: To make the problem definite, let it be assumed that the line CD is the center line of a right square prism that is so located in space that one diagonal of its base at D is parallel to F. In Figure 3.19, c^Hd^H and c^Fd^F are the H and F projections of the center line. A line drawn through d^H and parallel to the HF axis is the locus of the H projection of the required diagonal. The center line CD projects on the auxiliary plane *1* as c^1d^1. The base at D projects on plane *1* as a line drawn through d^1 at right angles to c^1d^1. A projection of the diagonal on plane *1* must be in this line. The points x^H and y^H are assumed on the locus of the H projection and x^1y^1 determined by projecting to the auxiliary plane. These two projections may be used to determine any others that may be required.

The projection of CD on an auxiliary plane *2* that is perpendicular to it is the point c^2d^2. The projection x^2y^2 determines the direction of the projection of the diagonal on plane *2*. The projection of the prism on plane *2* is a square of given size having its diagonal parallel in direction with x^2y^2. The projection of all points of the prism, including the diagonal, may now be found on all other planes on which it is projected.

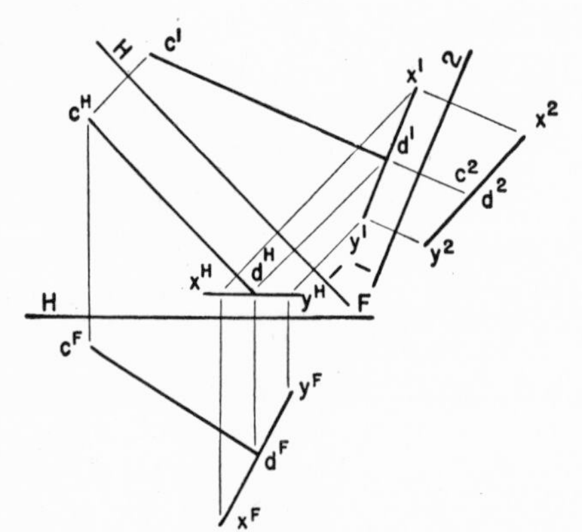

Fig. 3.19. Diagonal Is Parallel to F

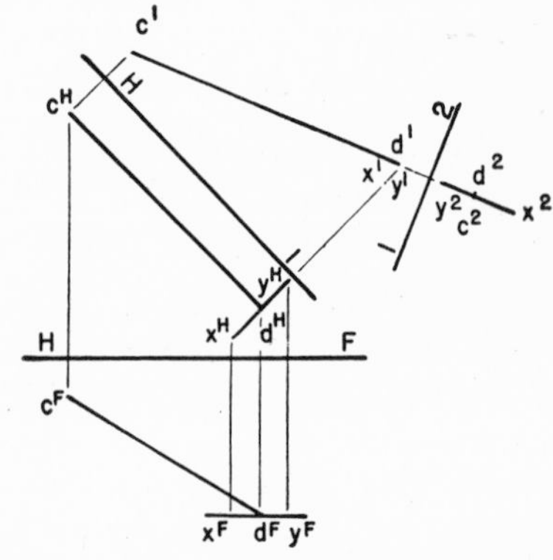

Fig. 3.20. Diagonal Is Parallel to H

In Figure 3.20 the same problem is assumed as in Figure 3.19 except that the diagonal is parallel to H. A line drawn through d^F and parallel to the HF axis is a locus of the F projection of the diagonal. The edge view of the square base on plane *1* must contain the projection of the diagonal in that plane. The points x^F and y^F are assumed on the horizontal line through d^F. Since x^F, y^F, and d^F are the same distance from the HF axis, their projection on plane *1* must be located an equal distance from the $H1$ axis. These points must therefore project as the same point on plane *1* as shown at d^1, x^1, and y^1. These points may now be projected from F and plane *1* to determine their H projections. Their projections on plane *2* and the direction of the projection of the diagonal on that plane can be projected from the *H* and *1* planes.

It is obvious that the projection of the horizontal diagonal on the auxiliary plane *1* must be a point. Since the diagonal is perpendicular to the center line and parallel to *H*, their *H* projections are perpendicular. Plane *1* is therefore perpendicular to a true length projection of line *XY*, and it will project as a point x^1y^1 on that plane.

The statement of Problem 3.7 indicates that the problem is general and that the projections might be made on any set of adjacent planes. In Figures 3.19 and 3.20 the projections were given on the *H* and *F* planes. The theories involved in the construction of the drawing would be unchanged if the projection on any other adjacent planes had been given.

3.10. Problem 3.8. To find the right section of a prism or cylinder.

Given: The projections of a cylinder on two adjacent planes.

Required: A projection of a right section of the prism or cylinder.

Solution: Project the prism or cylinder on an auxiliary plane that is perpendicular to its center line.

Analysis:

1. Project the prism or cylinder on a plane that is parallel to its center line.
2. Project on a plane that is perpendicular to the center line.

Discussion: It will be noticed that this problem is closely related to Problem 3.6. In that problem the right section was given and the projection of the prism was required. In this problem the projections are given and the right section is to be found. The drafting operations required in this problem have been discussed in previous problems and will not be reviewed.

3.11. Application Problems.

3.1. *Layout 4.* Assume that the *HF* and *FP* axis lines intersect at the mid-point of each section. Draw in each section the *H*, *F*, and *P* projections of one of the line segments described and located below. Letter each axis line and draw projectors between views. Designate by letters *T-L* all true length projections.

(a) A line that is 1″ long, perpendicular to *H*, ½″ behind *F*, 1″ to the left of *P* with its upper end in *H*.
(b) A line 1″ long that is perpendicular to *F*, ½″ below *H*, 1″ to the left of *P* with its front end in *F*.
(c) A line 1″ long that is perpendicular to *P*, 1″ below *H* and ½″ behind *F* with its right end in *P*.
(d) Any line that is 1″ long, parallel to and ½″ below *H* and is inclined to *F* in an angle of 30 degrees.
(e) Any line that is 1″ long, parallel to and ½″ behind *F* and is inclined to *H* in an angle of 45 degrees.
(f) Any line that is 1″ long, below *H*, parallel to and 1″ to the left of *P* and inclined in angles of 30 degrees with *H* and 60 degrees with *F*.

3.2. *Layout 4.* Assume that *HF* and *FP* axis lines intersect at the mid-point of each section. Draw in each section the *H*, *F*, and *P* projections of one of the plane figures described below. Letter each axis line and draw projectors between views.

(a) A 1″ square that is parallel to and ½″ behind F with its upper edge ¼″ below and parallel to H.
(b) A 1″ square that is parallel to and ½″ below H with its front edge parallel to and ¼″ behind F.
(c) A 1″ square that is parallel to and 1″ to the left of P, its upper edge parallel to and ½″ below H and its front edge ¼″ behind F.
(d) A 1″ square that is inclined to H in an angle of 30 degrees with its front edge parallel to and ½″ behind F. Two edges are perpendicular to F.
(e) A 1″ square that is inclined to F in an angle of 45 degrees with its upper edge parallel to and ¼″ from H. Two edges are perpendicular to H.
(f) A 1″ square that is parallel to the HF axis line and inclined in an angle of 30 degrees with H.

3.3. *Layout 4.* In each section find the projection of one of the given lines on a plane that is perpendicular to it.

(a) Line AB: A(3, 1, ¼), B(1½, ¼, 1). Take the first auxiliary plane perpendicular to H.
(b) Line CD: C(2, 1, ¼), D(½, ¼, 1). Take the first auxiliary plane perpendicular to F.
(c) Line EO: E(2½, 1, ½), O(2½, ¼, 1½). Take the first auxiliary plane perpendicular to F.
(d) Line NO: N(2½, ¼, 1½), O(2½, 1, ½). Take the first auxiliary plane perpendicular to H.
(e) Line RS: R(3, 1, ¼), S(2, −¼, 1½). Take the first auxiliary plane perpendicular to H.
(f) Line XY: X(3, 1, −¼), Y(2, ¼, 1). Take the first auxiliary plane perpendicular to H.

3.4. *Layout 1.* Assume that the block of Problem 1.2 has been revolved about the axis of the hole from its position in that problem. The revolution is counterclockwise as seen from above and through 30 degrees. The HF axis line is 3″ above the lower margin and the FP axis line 5″ from the right margin. Project a view of the block on each of the three principal planes and on an auxiliary plane *1* that is perpendicular to H and is parallel to and ½″ from one of the 1″ × 2″ faces of the block.

3.5. *Layout 1.* Assume that the box described and located in Problem 1.3 has been revolved through 15 degrees about a vertical axis taken through its center. The revolution is counterclockwise. Project views of the box on H, F, P, and on an auxiliary plane *1* that is perpendicular to H and is parallel to and ½″ from one end of the box. The HF axis is 3½″ above the lower margin, and the FP axis is 4½″ from the right margin.

3.6. *Layout 1.*

(a) Assume the HF axis line 5″ above the lower margin. The center line of a right (i.e., edges are perpendicular to the bases) hexagonal prism is parallel to and 1″ behind F and 9″ to the left of P. The prism is 3″ long with the upper base 1″ below and parallel to H. The bases are 1½″ in maximum diameter with two edges parallel to F. Project a view of the prism on the H and F planes. Assume that the prism is cut by a plane that is perpendicular to F and sloping upward to the left at an angle of 60 degrees through the mid-point of the center line. Project a view of that portion of the prism that is below the cutting plane on a projection plane *1* that is parallel to the cut surface.
(b) The center line of a right circular cylinder of 1½″ diameter is located 4″ to the left of P. All other data are the same as for the prism of part (a) of this problem.

3.7. *Layout 1.*

(a) The axis line of a right hexagonal prism is parallel to F and slopes upward to the right in an angle of 30 degrees from a point located 2½″ below H, 1½″ behind F, and 9½″ to the left of P. The prism is 2½″ long and its base is 1½″ in shortest diameter. Two edges of each base are parallel to H. Project views on H, F, and an auxiliary plane *1* that is parallel to one base of the prism.
(b) The center line of a right hexagonal pyramid is parallel to H and inclined to F in an angle of 30 degrees to the rear from a point X located ½″ to the left of P, ½″ behind F, and 1½″ below H. The point X is the apex of the pyramid. The pyramid is 2½″ in height and its base is 1½″ in smallest diameter with two edges of the base parallel to H. Project views of the pyramid on H, F, and an auxiliary plane *1* that is parallel to the base.

3.8. *Layout 1.* The lower end of the center line of an 8″ × 8″ vertical member of a crane is located at a point E that is 4′ 0″ below an H plane, 2′ 6″ behind an F plane, and 7′ 0″ to the left of a P plane. The center line of a 6″ × 6″ boom intersects, in an angle of 45 degrees, the center line of the vertical member at a point B which is 1′ 0″ above the point E. The center lines of the two members lie in a plane that is perpendicular to H and inclined to F in an angle of 60 degrees. The boom slopes upward, forward, and to the left from the vertical member. Assume that a 3′ 6″ portion of each member (end to end of center line) is cut square at its upper end. Project these two members on the H, F, and auxiliary planes. Scale 1″ = 1′ 0″. The HF axis line is 4½″ above the lower margin.

3.9. *Layout 1.*

(a) The line AB is 3½″ long, parallel to P, and inclined toward F in an angle of 15 degrees, sloping upward and forward from the point B. The point B is 4″ below H, 2″ behind F, and 1¼″ to the left of P. Assume the HF axis line 5½″ above the lower margin and the FP axis line 8″ to the left of the right margin of the sheet. Draw the F, P, and auxiliary projections of the right hexagonal prism of which AB is the center line and which has a minimum diameter of 1¼″. Omit the H projection.

(b) The line CD is 3½″ long, parallel to F, and inclined away from P in an angle of 15 degrees, sloping upward and to the left from the point D. The point D is 4″ below H, 1¼″ behind F, and 1″ to the left of P. Assume the HF axis line 5½″ above the lower margin and the FP axis line 2½″ from the right margin. Draw the F, P, and auxiliary projections of the right octagonal prism of which CD is the center line and having a minimum diameter of 1½″. Omit the H projection.

3.10. *Layout 1.* The line AB is a segment of the center line of a tube ½″ in diameter that is welded to a front wall (F) and to a horizontal plane (H) and passes through a side wall (P). The coordinate location of the points A and B are: A(1, 1½, 1), B(3, ½, 1¾). Assume the HF axis line 3½″ above the lower margin and FP axis line 4″ to the left of the right margin of the sheet.

(a) Find the H, F, and P projections of the line. (Tube not required.)

(b) Locate and letter the H, F, and P projections of the horizontal trace (H), the frontal trace (F), and the profile trace (P) of the line AB. (The point in which one of the principal planes is pierced by a line is called the trace of that line on that plane.)

(c) Find the angle (LH) with the horizontal, the angle (LF) with the frontal, and the angle (LP) with the profile plane (i.e., the angles in which the tube must be cut to fit these planes).

(d) Show by dimension the distance from the F trace to the P trace and the over-all length of the line between H and F.

3.11. *Layout 1.* Assume the same data as Problem 3.10.

(a) Project the right section of the tube on a plane perpendicular to its center line.

(b) Draw the H, F, and P projections of the tube showing the intersections of the tube with the H, F, and P planes.

(c) Find the angle (LH) with the horizontal, the angle (LF) with the frontal, and the angle (LP) with the profile plane (i.e., the angles in which the tube must be cut to fit these planes).

3.12. *Layout 1.* Draw the H and F projections of a 12″ square timber having the line AB as its center line and with its ends at A and B cut at right angles with this line. A diagonal of any right section is parallel to H. The coordinate location of the points are: A(4½, 2, 1), B(8, 1, 2). Assume the HF axis line 3″ above the lower margin. Scale of the drawing of the timber is 1″ = 1′ 0″.

3.13. *Layout 1.* Same as above except that the diagonal of the right section is parallel to F.

3.14. *Layout 1.* Draw the F and P projections of a 9″ square timber having the line CD as its center line and with its ends at C and D cut at right angles with this line. A diagonal of any right section is parallel to P. The coordinate location of the points C and D are: C(2½, 1, 5), D(1, 2½, 1). The HF axis line is 7″ above the lower margin. Scale of the timber is 1″ = 1′ 0″.

3.15. *Layout 1.* Same as above except the diagonal of the right section is parallel to F.

3.16. *Layout 1.* The edges of a sheet metal chute are parallel and are cut by a front wall (F) in the points B, C, D, and E. The edge that is cut by the wall at the point B passes through the point A. Assume the HF axis line 3″ above the lower margin. The coordinate location of the points are: A(4¼, 1¾, ½), B(8½, 0, 2¼), C(8½, 0, 2¾), D(7½, 0, 2¾), E(7½, 0, 2¼).

(a) Find the H and F projections of the chute.

(b) Find the intersection of the chute and ceiling (H).

(c) Find the right section of the chute.
(d) Find the intersection of the chute with the plane of a side wall that is parallel to P and passes through point A.

3.17. *Layout 1.* The line AB is one edge of a sheet metal chute that intersects a side wall (P) in the points B, C, D, and E. The edges of the chute are parallel. The coordinate location of the points are: $A(1\frac{1}{2}, 0, 1)$, $B(0, 4, 2\frac{1}{4})$, $C(0, 4, 3)$, $D(0, 3, 3)$ and $E(0, 3, 2\frac{1}{4})$. Assume the HF axis line 3″ above the lower margin and the HP axis line 6″ from the right margin of the sheet. Show the P projection revolved about an HP axis line. Omit the F projection. Take the first auxiliary plane perpendicular to P.

(a) Find the H and P projections of the chute.
(b) Find the right section of the chute.
(c) Find the intersection of the chute with the F plane.

3.18. *Layout 1.* The line CD is the center line of a tube that intersects the vertical wall (F) in a circle of ½″ diameter with its center at the point C. The coordinates of the points are: $C(1\frac{1}{2}, 0, 1)$, $D(0, 3\frac{1}{2}, 2\frac{1}{4})$. Assume the HF axis 3″ above the lower margin and the HP axis line 6″ from the right margin of the sheet.

(a) Find the H and P projections of the tube.
(b) Find the intersection of the tube with the P plane.
(c) Find the right section of the tube. Take the first auxiliary plane perpendicular to P.

3.19. *Layout 1.* Assume the points $A(7, \frac{1}{2}, 2\frac{1}{4})$, $B(4, 2, \frac{7}{8})$. Scale ¾″ = 1′ 0″. A tank is 36″ long, 24″ wide, and 9″ deep. The longer edges are parallel to F and the bottom is parallel to H with its center at B. The line AB is the center line of a 9″ circular duct. Find the intersection of the duct with the bottom of the tank and with the F plane. Find the length of the center line from the F plane to the bottom of the tank. Find the angle of cut at each end of the duct.

CHAPTER IV

AUXILIARY PROJECTIONS OF PLANES

4.1. Introduction. In the preceding chapter, drafting Operations I and II were discussed, and their use in finding the true length and point projections of a line was illustrated. This chapter is devoted to a discussion and illustration of the application of drafting Operations III and IV and their use in projecting planes and plane figures. Before the use of these operations is attempted, it is necessary that three simple problems be understood.

4.2. Problem 4.1. To find the projections of an assumed point that lies on a given line.

Given: The projections of a line on any two adjacent planes.

Required: The projections of some assumed point of the line.

Solution: A projector drawn at 90 degrees to the axis of the adjacent planes will join the projections of the point.

Analysis:

1. Assume a point on one projection of the given line.
2. Draw a projector at 90 degrees with the axis of the projection planes.
3. The intersection of this projector with the other projection of the line is the required projection of the point.

Discussion: In Figure 4.1 the projections of the line AB on the F and H planes are assumed to be given. The H projection of X, at x^H, may be located at any point on a^Hb^H. A projector drawn at right angles to the HF axis and through x^H intersects a^Fb^F at x^F. The point X is on the line AB and x^H and x^F are the required projections.

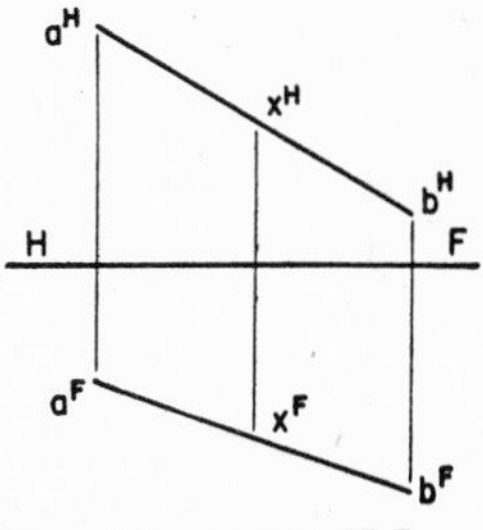

FIG. 4.1. Point X Is on Line AB

4.3. Problem 4.2. To assume a line that is parallel to one of two adjacent planes and on a given plane figure.

Given: The projections of a plane figure.

Required: To find a line that is parallel to one of the projection planes and on the plane figure.

Solution: Find two points of the required line.

Analysis:

1. Assume a projection of a line that intersects two lines of the plane figure and is parallel to one of the projection planes.
2. Locate the other projections of the points of intersection.
3. Draw the second projection of the line.

Discussion: In Figure 4.2 the line XY is parallel to F and on the plane ABC. The H projection of XY is parallel to the HF axis and intersects a^Hc^H at x^H and

a^Hb^H at y^H. Perpendicular projectors through x^H and y^H intersect a^Fc^F at x^F and a^Fb^F at y^F. The F projection of the line may now be drawn through the F projections of X and Y.

In Figure 4.3 the F projection of the required line is drawn parallel to the HF axis through the F projection of C and intersects d^Fe^F at x^F. A perpendicular projector through x^F intersects d^He^H at x^H. The H projection of the line may now be drawn through the H projections of C and X. Since the F projection of CX is parallel to the HF axis, and the points C and X are points of the plane, the line CX is a line of the plane and is parallel to H.

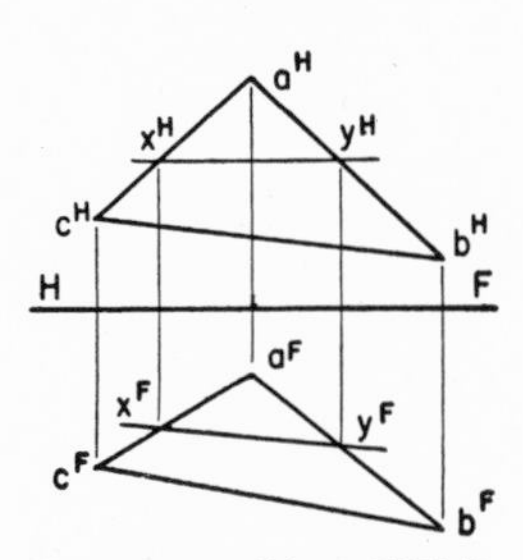

FIG. 4.2. Line XY Is Parallel to F

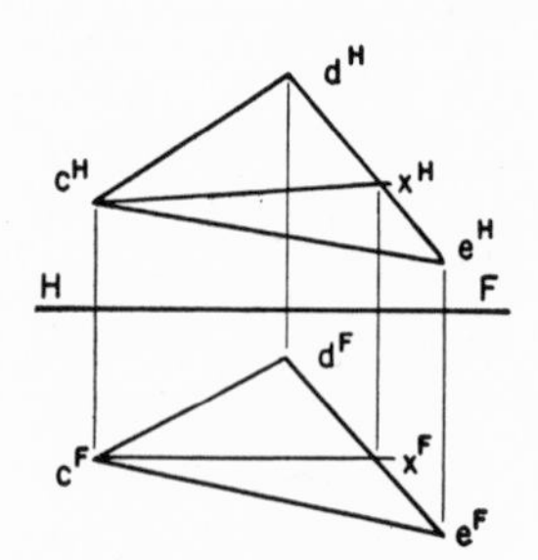

FIG. 4.3. Line CX Is Parallel to H

4.4. Problem 4.3. To find a second projection of a point that lies on a given plane when one projection of the point is known.

Given: Two projections of a plane and one projection of a point on the plane.

Required: A second projection of the point.

Solution: The projections of the point lie on the projections of any line of the plane that is drawn through the point.

Analysis:

1. Draw a projection of a line that lies on the plane through the known projection of the point.
2. Locate the second projection of the line.
3. Locate the second projection of the point.

Discussion: It is obvious that any number of lines of a plane may be drawn through a point that lies on that plane. The method of locating the projections of such a line has been discussed and illustrated in the preceding problems. Since the projections of the point must lie on the projection of the line, the unknown projection may be found as in Problem 4.1.

4.5. Problem 4.4. *Operation III.* To project a plane figure as a line on a projection plane that is perpendicular to it.

Given: Two projections of a plane figure.

Required: To project the plane as a line (i.e., in edge view).

Solution: Project the plane figure on a projection plane that is perpendicular to a line that lies in the plane figure.

Analysis:

1. Assume any line of the plane figure that is parallel to one of the projection planes.
2. Project the plane figure on a plane that is perpendicular to the assumed line.

Discussion: A plane figure will project in edge view on a projection plane that is perpendicular to any line of the plane figure. Two planes of a set of adjacent planes must be perpendicular to the third. The projection plane that is required in this problem is, therefore, one that is perpendicular to a line of the plane figure and to one of the adjacent planes upon which the figure is projected.

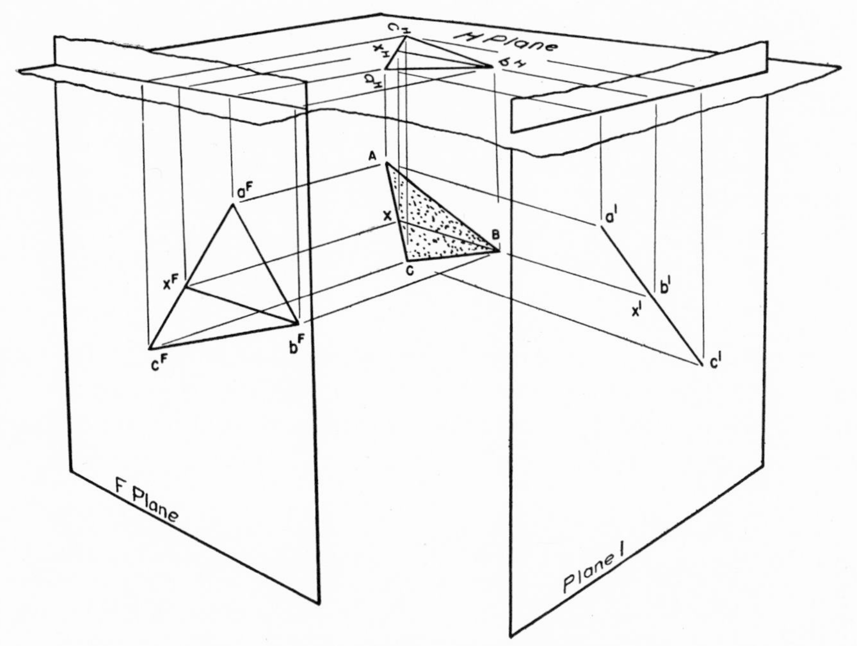

FIG. 4.4. Pictorial Drawing of Operation III

Figure 4.4 shows in pictorial drawing the triangle *ABC* located behind a frontal plane and below a horizontal plane. The line *BX* is a horizontal line of the triangle and projects on *F* and *H* as $b^F x^F$ and $b^H x^H$. Any auxiliary plane that is perpendicular to *BX* is perpendicular to the triangle *ABC* and to the *H* plane. In the figure, plane *1* is perpendicular to *BX* and the triangle projects on it as the line $a^1 b^1 c^1 x^1$.

Figure 4.5 shows in orthographic drawing the use of Operation III in projecting the triangle *ABC* as the line $a^1 b^1 c^1 x^1$. The line *CX* is assumed on the triangle and parallel to *H*. The *H1* axis is the edge view of the auxiliary plane *1*. Since plane *1* is perpendicular to *CX* and to *H*, its edge view will be a line perpendicular to $c^H x^H$. When revolved into the *H* plane, the projections of *A*, *B*, *C*, and *X* fall a distance away from the *H1* axis equal to the distance from their *F* projection to the *HF* axis line.

In Figure 4.6 the line CX is parallel to the F plane. The auxiliary plane *1* is perpendicular to CX and is, therefore, perpendicular to the triangle ABC and to the F plane. The *F1* axis is perpendicular to $c^F x^F$. When the projections on the auxiliary plane are revolved into F, they fall in the line $a^1 b^1 c^1 x^1$ as shown in the figure.

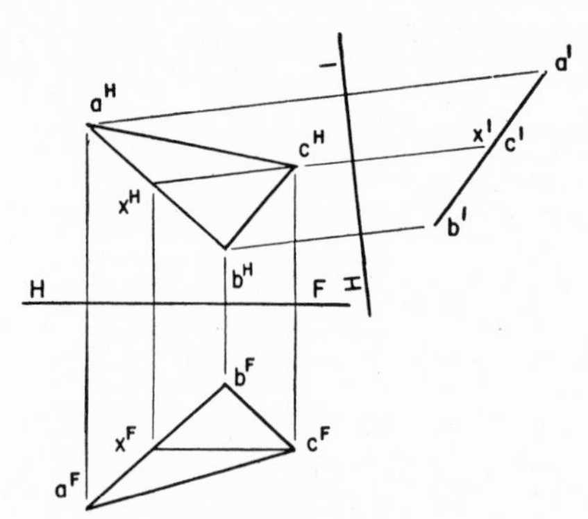

Fig. 4.5. Operation III. The Line Is Assumed Parallel to H

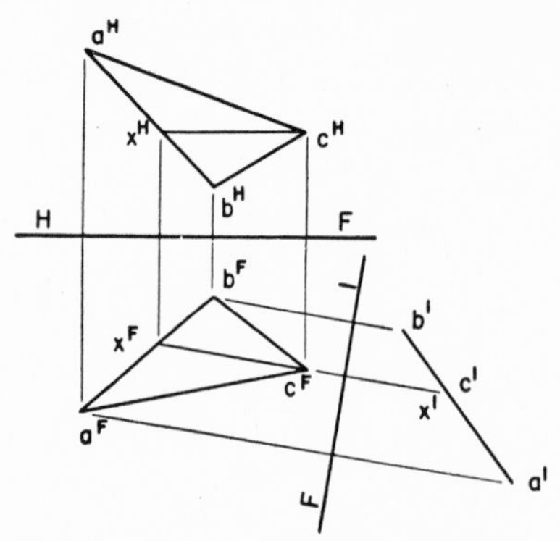

Fig. 4.6. Operation III. The Line Is Assumed Parallel to F

4.6. Problem 4.5. *Operation IV.* To project a plane figure in true size.
Given: The projections of a plane figure on two adjacent planes.
Required: A true size projection of the plane figure.
Solution: Project the plane figure on a projection plane that is parallel to it.
Analysis:

1. Project the given figure on a plane that is perpendicular to it. (Operation III.)
2. Project the figure on a plane that is parallel to it.

Discussion: The orthographic projection of any plane figure will be in true size on any projection plane that is parallel to it. In the application of this principle on a drawing it is necessary to have an edge view of the plane figure before the parallel projection plane is located. Operation III is, therefore, usually the most convenient preliminary step in applying Operation IV in the solution of the problem.

It will be seen that Figure 4.7 is the same as 4.4 except that the plane *2*, together with the projection of the triangle on it, has been added. The plane *2* is parallel to the triangle ABC, and $a^2b^2c^2$ is a true size projection of the triangle.

Figure 4.8 shows in orthographic drawing the construction necessary for the graphical solution of the problem. The triangle ABC is projected as a line on a plane perpendicular to it by the use of Operation III. The axis line *1–2* is the edge view of the projection plane *2* and is parallel to the edge view of ABC. When revolved into plane *1* about the *1–2* axis, the projections of ABC on plane *2* fall at $a^2b^2c^2$. The location of these points relative to the *1–2* axis is necessarily the same as the location of the H projections relative to the *H1* axis.

Figures 4.9 and 4.10 are included to emphasize that the drafting operations are general and may be used whenever the given projections are on adjacent planes.

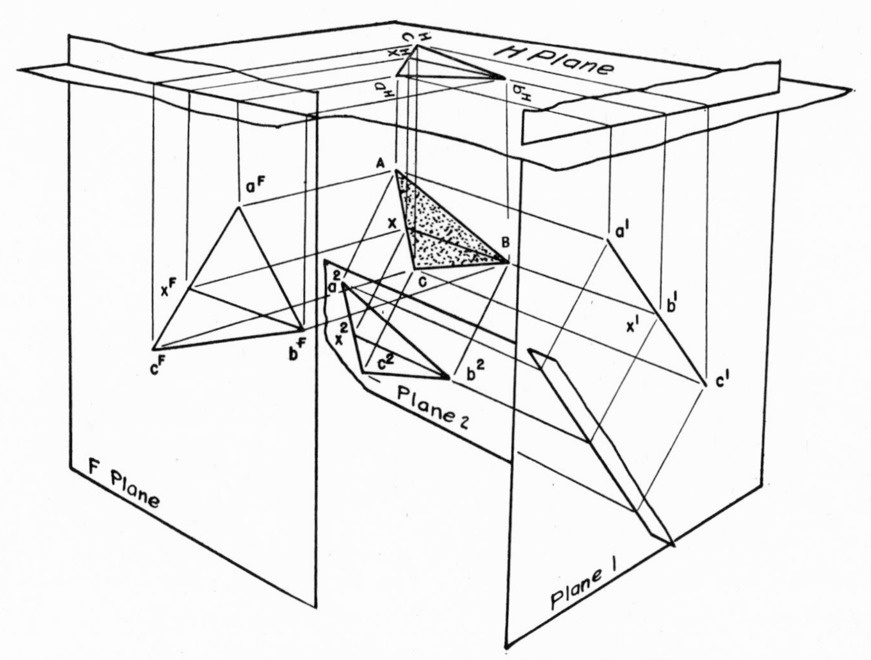

Fig. 4.7. Pictorial Drawing of Operation IV

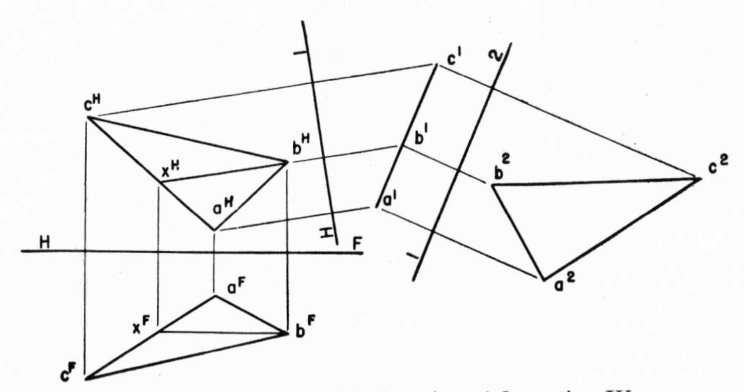

Fig. 4.8. Orthographic Drawing of Operation IV

In Figure 4.8 the projections of the triangle on F and H were given, and plane *1* was perpendicular to H. In that problem, plane *1* might have been taken perpendicular to F. In Figures 4.9 and 4.10 the given projections are on F and P. The first auxiliary plane is perpendicular to F in Figure 4.9 and perpendicular to P in Figure 4.10. If the given projections had been on auxiliary planes, the construction would have been the same in every essential.

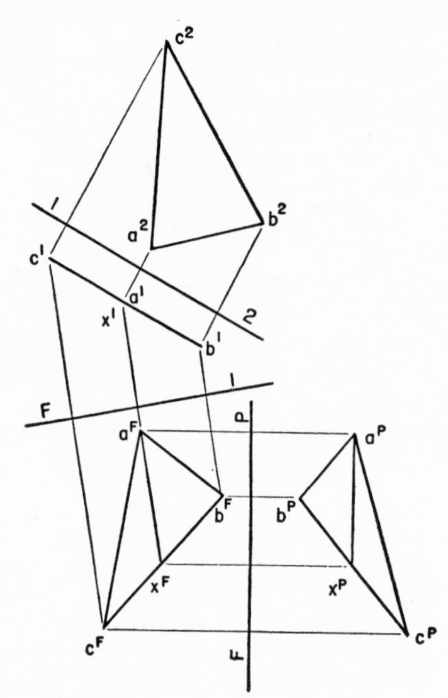

FIG. 4.9. F and P Projections Given—Auxiliary Plane Perpendicular to F

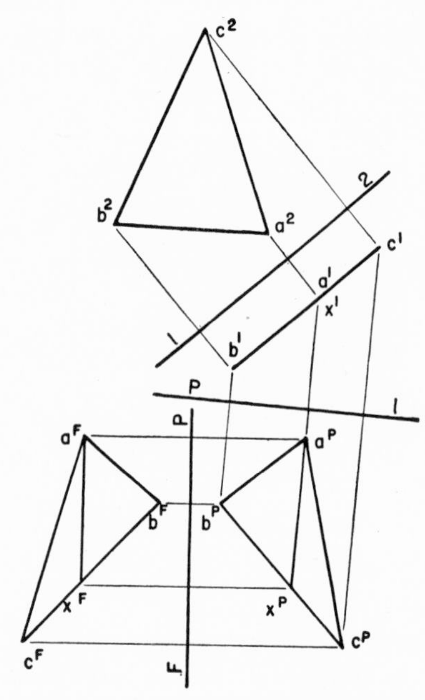

FIG. 4.10. F and P Projections Given—Auxiliary Plane Perpendicular to P

4.7. Problem 4.6. To project a plane figure in true size. (Second Method.)
Given: The projection of a plane figure on two adjacent planes.
Required: A true size projection of the plane figure.
Solution: Project the plane figure on a plane that is parallel to it.
Analysis:

1. Project the figure on a plane that is parallel to one of its lines. (Operation I.)
2. Project the figure on a plane that is perpendicular to that line. (Operation II.)
3. Project the figure on a plane that is parallel to it. (Operation IV.)

Discussion: It has been stated in a previous paragraph that a plane figure will project as a line on any projection plane that is perpendicular to a line of that figure. In Problem 4.4 a special case line that was parallel to one of the adjacent projection planes was used in applying Operation III. In a few problems it will be more convenient to use one of the given lines and Operations I and II to obtain an edge view of the figure.

In Figure 4.11 the *H1* axis line is parallel to $a^H b^H$, and Operation I is used to project the line *AB* in its true length. The *1–2* axis line is perpendicular to $a^1 b^1$, and Operation II is used to project *AB* as a point on plane *2*. The projection of the triangle on plane *1* is $a^1 b^1 c^1$ and on plane *2* it is the line $a^2 b^2 c^2$. The axis line *2–3* is parallel to $a^2 b^2 c^2$, and the true size projection $a^3 b^3 c^3$ is made on plane *3*.

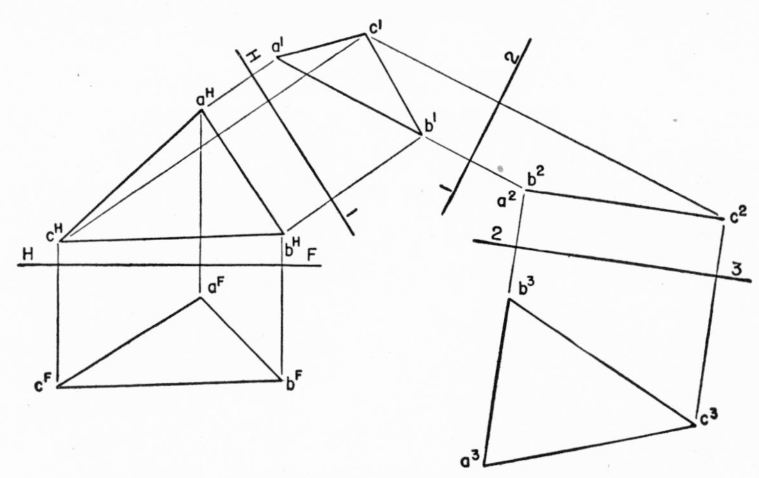

FIG. 4.11. Second Method: Plane Projected in True Size

The solution is, of course, general. The first auxiliary plane might be taken perpendicular to *H* and parallel to either of the given lines or any assumed line of the plane. It might also have been taken perpendicular to *F* and parallel to any line of the plane. If the given projections had been made on auxiliary planes instead of *H* and *F*, the method of solution would have been the same.

4.8. Problem 4.7. To project the true size of the dihedral angle between an oblique plane and a projection plane.

Given: The projection of an oblique plane on two adjacent planes.

Required: The dihedral angle between the given plane and one of the projection planes.

Solution: Project the angle on a plane that is parallel to it.

Analysis:

1. Assume an auxiliary plane that is perpendicular to the oblique plane and to the projection plane.
2. Project the given oblique plane on the auxiliary plane.
3. Measure the angle between the auxiliary axis line and the oblique plane.

Discussion: The dihedral angle between two planes is measured in a plane that is perpendicular to both. This angle will project its true size on a projection plane that is parallel to the angle. In Figure 4.12 it is assumed that the oblique plane *CDE* is given and that its angle with *H*, sometimes called slope or dip of the plane, is required. The auxiliary plane *1* is perpendicular to *H* and to the plane *CDE*.

The H plane projects on plane *1* as the line *H1* and the plane CDE as the line $c^1d^1e^1$. The angle A between these projections is the required angle.

A similar construction is shown in Figure 4.13. In this case it is assumed that the angle between the oblique plane ABC and F is required. Plane *1* is perpendicular to F and ABC. The auxiliary projection of F is the *F1* axis line, and of plane ABC the line $a^1b^1c^1$. The angle L between these projections is the required angle.

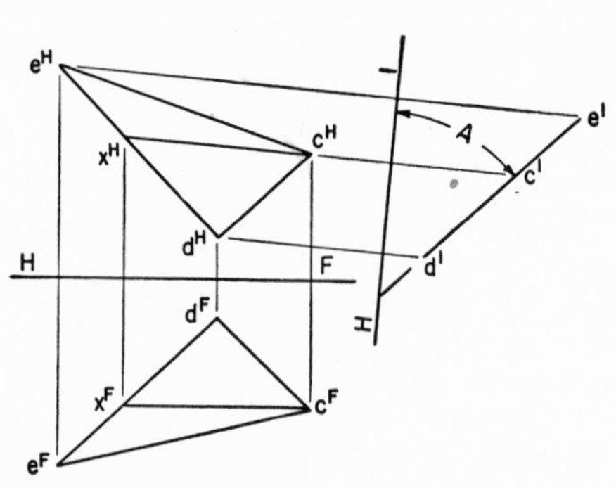

FIG. 4.12. Dihedral Angle between a Plane and H

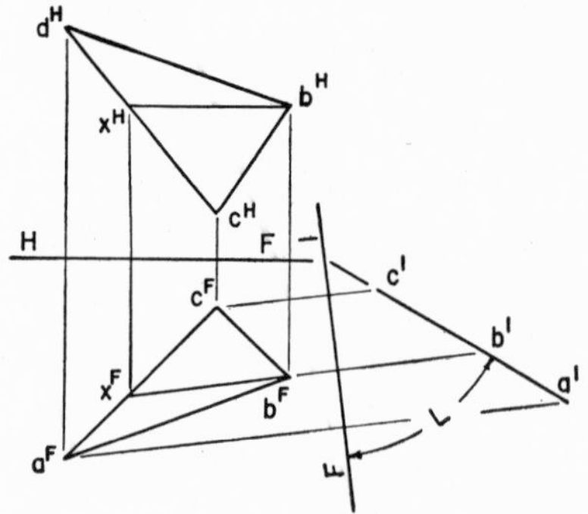

FIG. 4.13. Dihedral Angle between a Plane and F

4.9. Problem 4.8. To find the projections of a line drawn from a given point to a given plane.

Given: The projections of a point and a plane on two adjacent planes.

Required: The projections of a line drawn from the point to the plane.

Solution: Project the line and plane on a projection plane that is perpendicular to the given plane.

Analysis:

1. Assume an auxiliary plane that is perpendicular to the given plane and to one of the adjacent planes.
2. Project the point and plane on the auxiliary plane.
3. Draw the required projections of the line.

Discussion: The problem as stated is not definite in that an infinite number of lines may be drawn from the point to the plane. This discussion is limited to three specific lines. A more general solution will be discussed in a subsequent problem. The lines assumed here are a horizontal line of given direction, a line that is perpendicular to the plane, and a vertical line.

In Figure 4.14 it is assumed that the shortest horizontal line from the point O to the plane is required. The auxiliary plane *1* is perpendicular to H and to the given plane. The oblique plane projects as a line and the point O as o^1 on the auxiliary plane. A line drawn through o^1 parallel to the *H1* axis to the edge view of the oblique plane at x^1 is the projection of the required line on plane *1*. Since the shortest horizontal line is specified, o^Hx^H is parallel to the *H1* axis. The F projection is determined by the auxiliary and H projections.

It should be noticed here that the angle that the line OX makes with F is shown in the H projection. If a given angle with F had been specified, the H projection would have been drawn at that angle with the HF axis instead of parallel to the $H1$ axis.

In Figure 4.15 it is assumed that a line OY that is perpendicular to the oblique plane is required. The oblique plane projects as a line on the auxiliary plane *1*

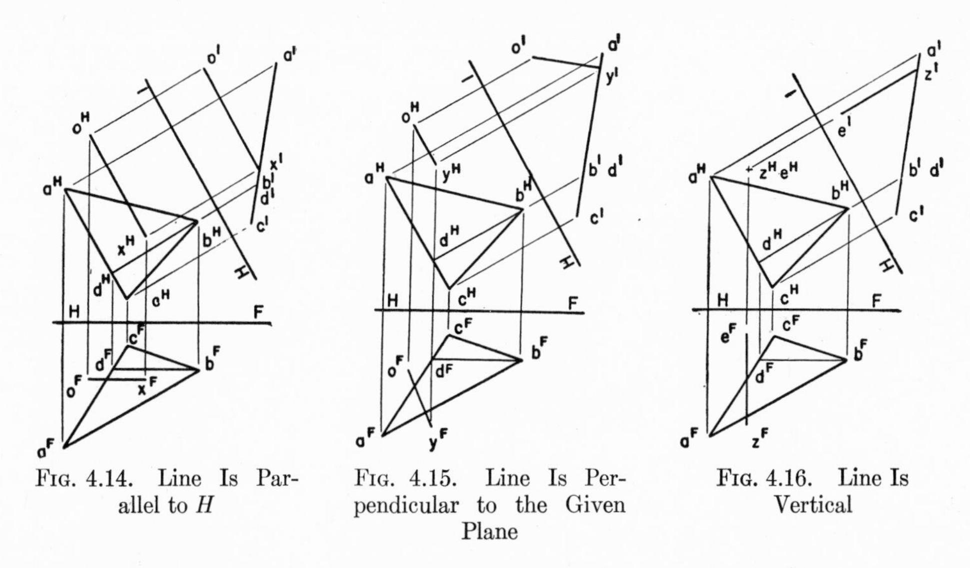

FIG. 4.14. Line Is Parallel to H

FIG. 4.15. Line Is Perpendicular to the Given Plane

FIG. 4.16. Line Is Vertical

taken perpendicular to H. The projection of OY on plane *1* is o^1y^1 and it is perpendicular to the edge view of the oblique plane. It will be seen that the line OY would project as a point o^2y^2 on a second auxiliary plane taken parallel to the oblique plane. Since o^2 and y^2 would be the same distance from the *1–2* axis, their H projections must be equal distances from the $H1$ axis. The F projection is determined by the H and auxiliary projections.

Figure 4.16 shows the projections of a vertical line EZ from the point E to the oblique plane. The H projection of a vertical line is a point. The projection of the line on an auxiliary plane that is perpendicular to H is at right angles to the $H1$ axis of that plane. The F projection is determined by the auxiliary and H projections.

It must not be assumed that the first auxiliary plane should be taken perpendicular to H in every problem. The problems assumed above could be solved as readily if the auxiliary plane had been perpendicular to F. It should also be remembered that H and F are merely two adjacent planes and any theories applicable to them may be applied to any two adjacent planes.

4.10. Problem 4.9. To project the angle between two intersecting lines in its true size.

Given: The projections of two lines that intersect.

Required: A true size projection of the angle at the intersection of the lines.

Solution: Project the lines on a projection plane that is parallel to the plane determined by the lines.

4.11. Problem 4.10. To find the projections of a line that passes through a given point and makes a specified angle with a given line.

Given: The projections of a line and a point not in the line.

Required: The projection of a line that contains the point and that intersects the given line in an angle of specified size.

Solution: Project the line and point on an auxiliary projection plane that is parallel to the plane determined by them. Draw the projection of the required line on the auxiliary plane. Determine the required projections of the line.

4.12. Problem 4.11. To find the projections of a plane figure that lies on a given plane.

Given: The projections of lines, or points, that determine a plane.

Required: The projections of a specified plane figure that lies on the oblique plane.

Solution: Project the oblique plane on an auxiliary projection plane that is parallel to it. Draw the projection of the specified plane figure on the auxiliary plane. Determine the required projections.

4.13. Problem 4.12. To find the point in which a plane is pierced by a line. (First Method.)

Given: The projections on adjacent planes of a line and an oblique plane.

Required: The point in which the plane is pierced by the line.

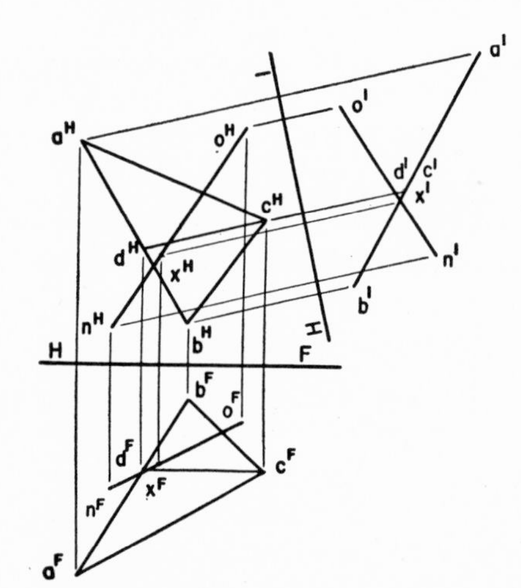

Fig. 4.17. Piercing Point of a Line

Solution: Project the oblique plane and the line on an auxiliary plane that is perpendicular to the oblique plane.

Analysis: *Method I.*

1. Assume an auxiliary plane that is perpendicular to the oblique plane and to one of the adjacent planes.
2. Project the plane and line on the auxiliary plane.
3. Determine the required projections of the piercing point.

Discussion: In Figure 4.17 it is assumed that the H and F projections of the oblique plane and the line ON are given. The auxiliary plane *1* is perpendicular to H and to the given plane. The projection of the oblique plane on plane *1* is an edge view of the oblique plane. The projection of ON pierces the plane at x^1 which is one projection of the required point. Since this point is necessarily a point of the line, the H and F projections of the point are determined by projecting to the H and F projections of the line.

4.14. Problem 4.13. To find the point in which a plane is pierced by a line. (Second Method.)

Given: Two projections of a line and an oblique plane.

Required: The projections of the point in which the plane is pierced by the line.

Solution: The line of intersection of the given plane, with any plane that contains the given line, will cross the given line at its piercing point.

Analysis: *Method II.*

1. Assume a plane through the line and perpendicular to one of the adjacent projection planes.
2. Find the intersection of the assumed plane with the given plane.
3. Locate the point in which this line of intersection crosses the given line.

Discussion: The given elements of the problem are shown in pictorial drawing in Figure 4.18. The line AB pierces the plane $CDEF$ at the point O. In Figure 4.19

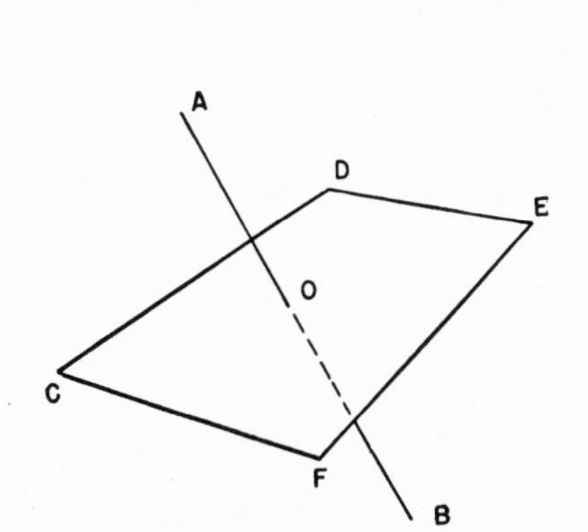

FIG. 4.18. Pictorial Drawing of a Line and Plane

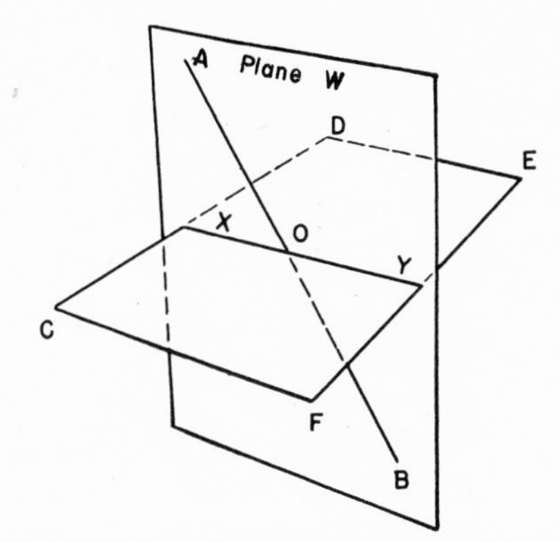

FIG. 4.19. Pictorial Drawing of Intersecting Planes

a plane W that contains the line AB and that is perpendicular to $CDEF$ has been added. The intersection of the plane W with $CDEF$ is the line XY. The line XY intersects the line AB at its piercing point O. Line XY is determined by the point X in which CD pierces W and the point Y in which EF pierces that plane.

It will be noticed that the piercing point of AB was found through use of the line XY and that XY was found through use of piercing points. To that extent, the problem of finding the intersection of two planes and the problem of finding the piercing point of a line constitute one problem and must be discussed as such when this second method is used. The solution of either of the problems is quite obvious in the pictorial illustrations.

Figure 4.20 shows in orthographic drawing the use of the second method of finding the piercing point of a line. The line AB and the oblique plane CDE are assumed to be given. A vertical plane assumed through AB has its H projection coincident with $a^H b^H$. The line CD of the given plane pierces the assumed plane at X, and the line CE at the point Y. The line XY is, therefore, the intersection of the given and assumed planes. The F projection of XY crosses the F projection of AB in the point o^F. The H projection of O at o^H is determined by projecting from o^F.

It must be remembered that, in any descriptive geometry problem, a line or a plane is indefinite in extent. In a drawing, a line segment is used to locate an infinite line. In like manner intersecting lines, or given points, determine a plane of indefinite extent that contains those lines or points.

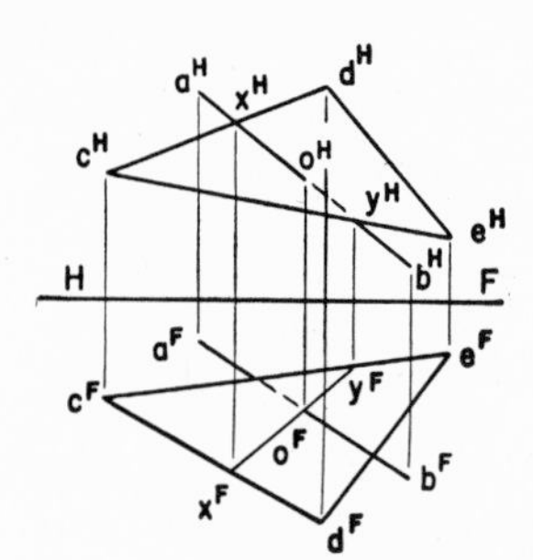

FIG. 4.20. A Line Pierces a Plane

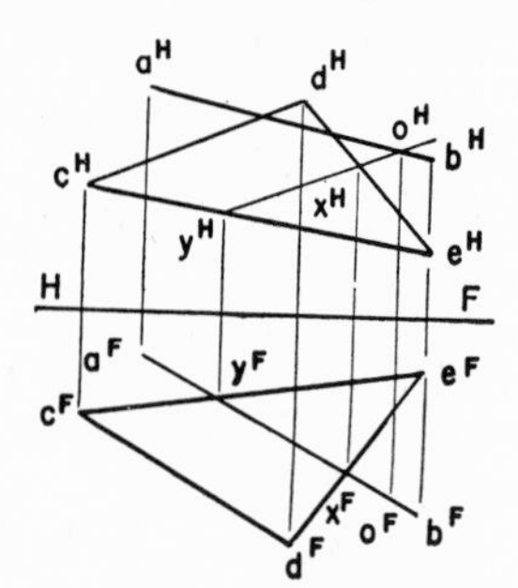

FIG. 4.21. Line Pierces Outside of Triangle

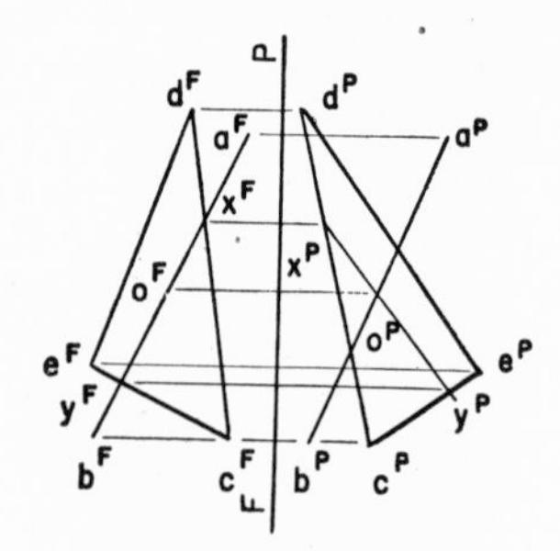

FIG. 4.22. F and P Projections Are Given

Figure 4.21 illustrates the conditions in which a line segment AB pierces the plane of CDE at a point O outside of the triangular plane figure determined by those points. In this illustration a plane containing the line AB and perpendicular to F was assumed. The edge view of this plane is coincident with a^Fb^F. The intersection of the given and assumed plane is the line XY whose F projection is x^Fy^F and H projection is x^Hy^H. The projections of XY are extended beyond the limits of the triangle to determine the projections of the piercing point at o^H and o^F.

In many cases the projections that determine a plane are on adjacent planes other than H and F. In Figure 4.22 the F and P planes were assumed, and the auxiliary plane passed through AB and perpendicular to F. The line of intersection, XY, of the given and auxiliary planes, and the piercing point, O, were found as in the preceding illustrations.

4.15. Problem 4.14. To find the line in which two planes intersect.

Given: The projections of two planes that are not parallel.

Required: The projections of their line of intersection.

Solution: Determine two points that lie in both planes and draw the required line through them.

Analysis: *Method I.*

1. Find the projections of the points in which two lines of one plane pierce the other plane.
2. Draw the projections of the required line through the projections of the piercing points.

Discussion: The intersection of two planes is a line that lies in both planes. Two points determine a line. The points in which two lines of one plane pierce the other are two points that lie in the intersection. See Figure 4.19.

In Figure 4.23 the plane ABC is projected in edge view on an auxiliary plane *1* that is assumed perpendicular to H and to ABC. The line OR of plane NOR pierces ABC at the point X and the line ON at the point Y. On the auxiliary plane these points project as x^1 and y^1. The projections of X and Y on the H and F planes are determined by projecting them to the H and F projections of the lines on which they lie. The H and F projections of the intersections are drawn through the corresponding projections of X and Y.

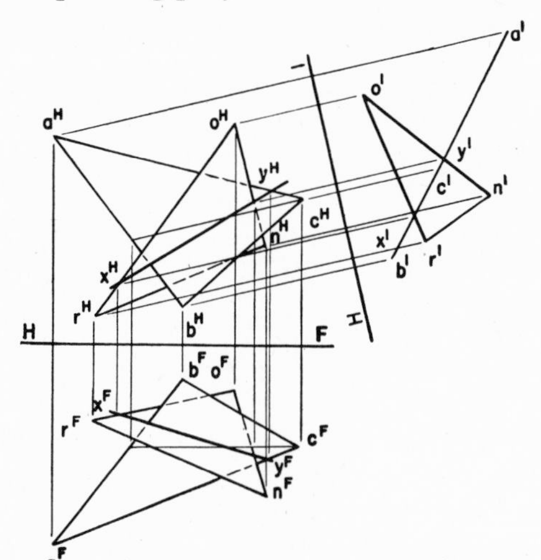

Fig. 4.23. Intersection of Planes

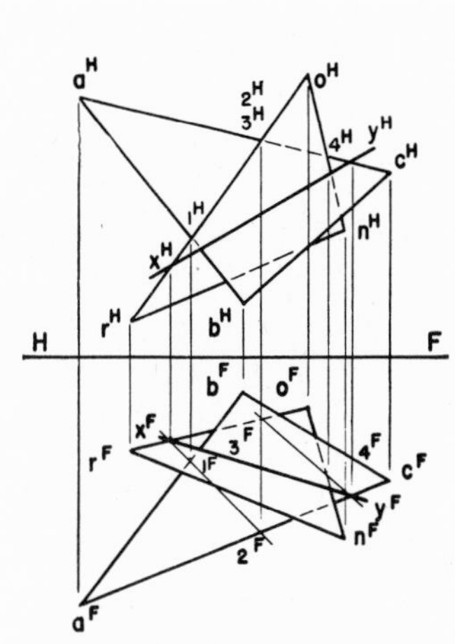

Fig. 4.24. Intersection of Planes

In this illustration it was convenient to find the piercing points of the given lines ON and OR. In many cases the location of the given lines is such that they do not pierce the other plane within the limits of the drawing. In other cases the piercing points are so placed that they cannot be definitely located on any of the given lines. In any case where the given lines are not satisfactory, the draftsman may choose auxiliary lines from the infinite number of lines that lie on the plane.

In Figure 4.24 the piercing points of the two lines are found through use of the second method discussed and illustrated in Problem 4.13. A plane assumed through AC and perpendicular to H projects on that plane as a^Hc^H. Line OR pierces the assumed plane at point *3* and line ON at point *4*. The extension of 3^F4^F crosses a^Fc^F at the point y^F, and y^H is projected from y^F to the H projection of AC. Another auxiliary plane through OR and perpendicular to H is pierced by lines AB and AC at points *1* and *2*. The extension of 1^F2^F crosses o^Fr^F at the point x^F, and x^H is found by projecting from x^F to the H projection of OR. Since X and Y are points common to both planes, the intersection must pass through them.

Analysis: *Method II.*

1. Assume auxiliary planes that intersect the given planes.
2. Find the intersections of the given planes with the auxiliary planes.
3. Locate the points that are common to the intersections.

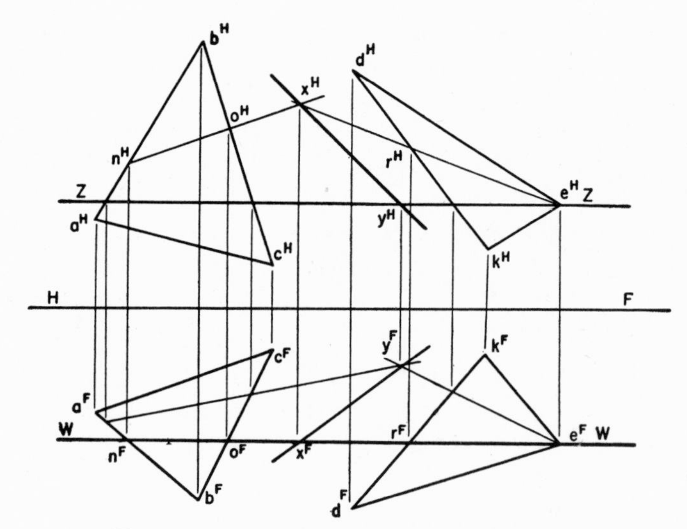

FIG. 4.25. Intersection of Planes—Method II

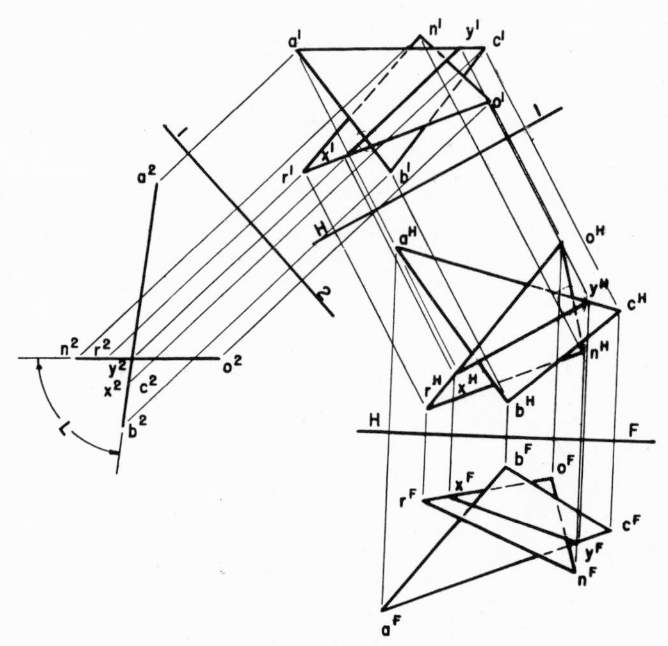

FIG. 4.26. True Size of Dihedral Angle

Discussion: In Figure 4.25 the planes *ABC* and *DEK* are assumed to be given. The auxiliary plane *W* is perpendicular to *F* and intersects *ABC* in the line *NO* and the plane *DEK* in the line *ER*. The lines *NO* and *ER* intersect in the point *X*. Since all points of the line *NO* lie in the plane *ABC*, and all points of the line *ER* lie in the plane *DEK*, the point *X* must lie in both planes.

A plane *Z* perpendicular to *H* intersects the given planes in lines that intersect at the point *Y*. The points *X* and *Y* are two points that are common to the given planes and determine the required intersection.

4.16. Problem 4.15. To project the dihedral angle between two planes in its true size.

Given: The projections of two planes that intersect.

Required: A true size projection of the dihedral angle between the planes.

Solution: Project the angle on a plane that is parallel to it. (Any plane that is perpendicular to the line of intersection of the given planes is parallel to the required angle.)

Analysis:

1. Determine the projections of the line of intersection of the planes.
2. Project the given planes on an auxiliary plane that is parallel to their line of intersection.
3. Project the planes on a plane that is perpendicular to their line of intersection.

Discussion: To illustrate the drafting procedure outlined in the analysis, the planes *ABC* and *ORN* of Figure 4.23 have been assumed as given. Their line of intersection, *XY*, was determined in that problem. In Figure 4.26 the plane 1 is parallel to *XY*, and the plane *2* is perpendicular to that line of intersection. The projections of the planes on the auxiliary plane *2* are the two straight lines intersecting at the point x^2y^2. Since the two given planes are in edge view and their intersection appears as a point on plane *2*, the angle, *L*, is a true size projection of the angle between the planes.

4.17. Problem 4.16. To project the true size of the angle between a line and a plane.

Given: The projections of a line and a plane.

Required: A true size projection of the angle that the line makes with the plane.

Solution: Project the angle on a plane that is parallel to it.

Analysis:

1. Project the line and plane on an auxiliary plane that is perpendicular to the given plane.
2. Project the line and plane on an auxiliary plane that is parallel to the plane.
3. Project the line and plane on a plane that is parallel to the line and perpendicular to the plane.

Discussion: The angle that a line makes with a plane is measured in a plane that contains the line and is perpendicular to the given plane. It is necessary, therefore, to project the angle on a plane that is parallel to the line and perpendicular to the given plane. The analysis given above is an outline of the drafting procedure used in projecting the angle, L, in Figure 4.27. Since plane *3* is parallel to the line and perpendicular to the plane, the required angle, L, is projected in true size.

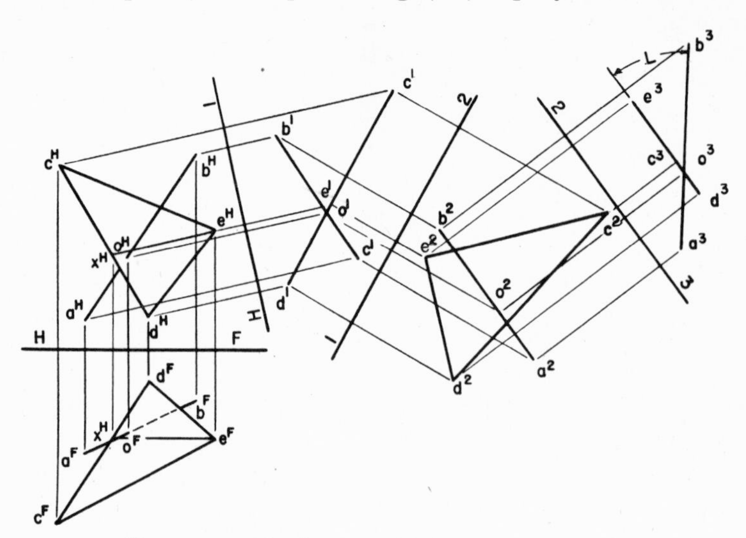

FIG. 4.27. The Angle between a Line and Plane

4.18. Application Problems.

SERIES A. *Layout 3.* Locate in each section the projections of the points A, B, and C and the point or line of plane ABC that is specified in a problem below. The locations of points A, B, and C are: $A(1, \frac{1}{4}, \frac{1}{4})$, $B(3, 1\frac{1}{2}, 1)$, and $C(4, \frac{1}{2}, \frac{1}{2})$.

4.1.

(a) The point X lies on AB and is 2″ from P.
(b) A line of plane ABC is parallel to and 1″ from F.
(c) A line of plane ABC through C that is parallel to H.
(d) A line of plane ABC through B that is parallel to AC.

4.2.

(a) The point Y is on line AB and 1″ from F.
(b) A line of plane ABC is parallel to and ¾″ from H.
(c) A line of plane ABC through C that is parallel to F.
(d) A line of plane ABC through A that is parallel to BC.

4.3.

(a) The point $Z(3, 1, ?)$ is on plane ABC.
(b) A line of plane ABC is parallel to and 2″ from P.
(c) A line of plane ABC through A and parallel to H.
(d) A line of plane ABC through C and parallel to AB.

4.4.

(a) The point $W(2, \frac{1}{2}, ?)$ is on plane ABC.
(b) A line of plane ABC through the center points of AB and AC.
(c) A line of plane ABC through A that is parallel to F.
(d) A line of plane ABC through C and parallel to P.

SERIES B. *Layout 3.* In each section locate the projections of the points $D(3, \frac{1}{4}, \frac{1}{4})$, $E(4, 1\frac{1}{2}, 1)$, and $K(4\frac{1}{2}, \frac{1}{2}, \frac{1}{2})$ of an oblique plane.

4.5.

(a) Assume the first auxiliary plane perpendicular to *H*. Indicate by the letters *LH*, the angle that *DEK* makes with *H*, and by the letter *B* the angle between the lines *DE* and *EK*.
(b) Assume the first auxiliary plane perpendicular to *F*. Indicate by letters *LF* the angle that *DEK* makes with *F*, and by letter *B* the true size of the angle between the lines *DE* and *EK*.
(c) Point $C(4, 1, ?)$ is the center of a ½″ square that lies on plane *DEK* with one diagonal parallel to *F*. Take the first auxiliary plane perpendicular to *F* and find the *H* and *F* projections of the square.
(d) Same as (c) except the first auxiliary plane is perpendicular to *H*.

4.6.

(a) Locate the projections of a line *CX* that is 1″ long and perpendicular to *DEK* at point $C(4, 1, ?)$. Point *C* is on plane *DEK*. Also, draw a line *BZ* from $B(3\frac{1}{2}, \frac{1}{2}, 1)$ and perpendicular to *DEK* and piercing *DEK* at *Z*.
(b) Find the point in which the line $A(4, 1, \frac{1}{4})$, $B(3\frac{1}{2}, \frac{1}{2}, 1)$ pierces the plane *DEK*. Check by use of a second method.
(c) Locate the projections of a horizontal line *CX* through $C(3\frac{1}{2}, \frac{1}{2}, 1)$ that bears north 60 degrees west and pierces the plane *DEK* at *X*. Find the projections of a vertical line *CY* that pierces the plane *DEK* at *Y*.
(d) Locate the projections of the shortest line *CZ* that slopes upward to the rear in an angle of 30 degrees with *H* from the point $C(3\frac{1}{2}, \frac{1}{2}, 1)$ to intersect the plane *DEK* at *Z*.

4.7. *Layout 1.* Find the true size of the dihedral angle between the planes *ABC* and *BCD*. $A(9, 1, 2)$, $B(8, 2, \frac{1}{2})$, $C(7\frac{1}{2}, \frac{1}{2}, 1\frac{1}{2})$, and $D(6\frac{1}{2}, 1, 2)$.

4.8. *Layout 1.* Assume the *HF* axis line 3½″ above the lower margin and the points $A(9\frac{1}{2}, \frac{1}{2}, 1)$, $B(8\frac{1}{2}, 2, 1\frac{1}{2})$, $C(8, \frac{1}{2}, \frac{1}{2})$, $D(7\frac{1}{2}, 2, \frac{1}{2})$, $E(6\frac{1}{2}, 1\frac{1}{2}, 1\frac{1}{2})$, and $K(6, \frac{1}{2}, 1)$.

(a) Find the line of intersection of the planes *ABC* and *DEK*.
(b) Find the dihedral angle between the planes *ABC* and *DEK*.

SERIES C. The coordinate location of the points *A*, *B*, and *C* for the problems of this series are $A(9\frac{1}{2}, 2\frac{1}{2}, \frac{1}{2})$, $B(8\frac{1}{2}, 1, 2\frac{1}{2})$, $C(7\frac{1}{2}, 1\frac{1}{2}, \frac{1}{2})$. The *HF* axis line should be drawn 3½″ above the lower margin. Use Layout 1.

4.9. The line *AB* is the center line of a 6″ × 12″ air-conditioning duct. A line drawn through *C* and intersecting the line *AB* in an angle of 60 degrees at *X* is the center line of a 6″ square duct. Two faces of the smaller duct are flush with the broad faces of the large duct and are parallel to the plane of the points *A*, *B*, and *C*. The intersection of the center lines is closer to point *B* than to point *A*. Scale of duct 1″ = 1′ 0″. Use drafting Operations I, II, and IV.

(a) Show the *H* and *F* projections of the center lines.
(b) Project the air ducts on a plane that is parallel to both.
(c) Project the right section of each duct on a plane that is perpendicular to its center line.
(d) Indicate by dimension the distance from the point *B* to the point *X*.

4.10. The lines *AB* and *CX* are the center lines of two ½″ diameter tubes used as struts in the fuselage of an airplane. The point *X* is on the line *AB* ½″ from point *A*. Assume the tubes to be welded at their intersection. Use drafting Operations I, II, and IV.

(a) Find the *H* and *F* projections of the center lines *AB* and *CX*.
(b) Project both tubes on a plane that is parallel to them and show their intersection.
(c) Project each tube on a plane perpendicular to its center line.
(d) Indicate the angle of intersection of the center lines of the tubes.

4.11. The lines *AB* and *CX* are the center lines of two ½″ tubes used in a fuel supply line of an airplane. The line *CX* is parallel to *F* and intersects *AB* at point *X*. Assume that the tubes are welded at their intersection. Use drafting Operations III and IV.

(a) Find the H and F projections of the lines AB and CX.
(b) Project the tubes on a plane parallel to them and show their intersection.
(c) Project each tube on a plane perpendicular to its center line.
(d) Dimension the distance from B to X.
(e) Indicate the angle between AB and CX.

4.12. The line AB and AC are the center lines of two struts of a bridge portal. The timber AB is 8″ square and the timber AC is 4″ square. Two faces of each timber are parallel to the plane ABC. Use scale 1″ = 1′ 0″. Use drafting Operations III and IV.

(a) Project the timbers on a plane that is parallel to both.
(b) Project each timber on a plane that is perpendicular to its center line.
(c) Indicate the angle of cut for the small strut if it is beveled to fit against the face of the larger timber.

4.13. A 90-degree tee fitting is used to join a piece of tubing, of which AB is the center line, to a similar tube having CX as its center line. The point X is the point in which the center lines intersect. The tubes are ¾″ in diameter. The dimensions of the tee fitting may be assumed.

(a) Find the H and F projections of the center lines.
(b) Project the tubes and fitting on a plane parallel to them.
(c) Project each tube and fitting on a plane perpendicular to its center line.

4.14. The line AB is the center line of a shaft which is intersected at X in an angle of 90 degrees by the center line CX of a second shaft. Power is transmitted from one shaft to the other by means of bevel gears having a maximum diameter of 9″ and a face width of 3″. The gears may be drawn as friction cones, that is, the gear teeth need not be shown. The shafts are 2″ in diameter. Scale 1″ = 1′0″. The face width is the length of the line of contact of the gears.

(a) Find the H and F projections of the center lines.
(b) Project the shafts and gears on a plane parallel to both shafts.
(c) Project the shafts and gears on a plane perpendicular to AB.
(d) Project the gears and shafts on a plane perpendicular to CX.

SERIES D. *Layout 1.* The coordinate location of the points A, B, C, and D for all of the problems of this series are $A(9, 1\frac{1}{2}, 2)$, $B(7, \frac{1}{2}, \frac{1}{2})$, $C(8, 2\frac{1}{2}, 3)$, $D(9\frac{1}{2}, 2\frac{1}{2}, 1)$.

The points A, B, and C are used to determine an oblique plane surface such as a bulkhead of an airplane or ship, a stratum of ore in a mine, a roof plane of a building, or any other surface of interest to the engineer. The point D is a point not in the plane and is used to determine the location, relative to the plane, of some other item.

4.15. The axis of a right square prism is perpendicular to the plane of the points A, B, and C, and passes through point D. The prism is 1¾″ in length and one diagonal of each of its ½″ square bases is parallel to H. The lower base is on the extended plane of A, B, and C.

(a) Find the H and F projections of the prism.
(b) Project the right section of the prism in its true size.

4.16. The point D is the apex of a right square pyramid. The base is a 1″ square on the extended plane of A, B, and C. One diagonal of the base is parallel to F.

(a) Find the H and F projections of the pyramid.
(b) Project the pyramid on a plane perpendicular to its center line.

4.17. Assume that the points A, B, and C are located on a roof plane, and that the point D is the center of a 6″ square that forms the top of a vertical chimney. The front face of the chimney is parallel with F. Scale 1″ = 1′ 0″.

(a) Find the H and F projections of the chimney and its intersection with the roof plane.
(b) Find the true shape of the intersection.
(c) Find the angle between the center line of the chimney and the roof plane.

4.18. Same as Problem 4.17 except that the point D is the center of a 6′ circle that forms the top of a vertical smoke stack.

4.19. Assume that the points A, B, and C are on the upper surface of a stratum of ore and that a 6′ square tunnel is constructed from the point D to the stratum. The tunnel bears due south and its floor is parallel to H. The end at D is perpendicular to the center line of the tunnel. Scale 1″ = 1′ 0″.

(a) Find the H and F projections of the tunnel and its intersection with the stratum.
(b) Find the true shape and size of the intersection with the stratum.
(c) Find the angle between the center line of the tunnel and the stratum.

4.20. Same as Problem 4.19 except that the center line of the horizontal tunnel bears south 45 degrees east.

4.21. Assume that the points A, B, and C determine the plane of a bulkhead and that D is a point on the center line of a ½″ outside diameter tube welded to the bulkhead. The tube is horizontal and perpendicular to the F plane.

(a) Find the H and F projections of the tube and its intersection with the plane of the bulkhead.
(b) Find the true size of the intersection with the bulkhead.
(c) Find the angle in which the tube must be cut to fit against the plane.

4.22. A ⅛″ × ½″ flat bent bar is to be riveted to a plane surface determined by the points A, B, and C. The center line of the bar is the line DX. The point X is located on the plane of ABC, 1 7/16″ below H and 7 11/16″ from P.

(a) Draw the H and F projection of the center line.
(b) Project the plane and bar on a plane that is parallel to the plane ABC.
(c) Project the plane and bar on a plane parallel to the bar and perpendicular to the plane ABC.
(d) Find the angle in which the bar must be bent to be riveted to the plane.

4.23. A plane surface of a wing section passes through the point D and intersects the plane ABC in a horizontal line AX.

(a) Find the H and F projection of the plane DAX.
(b) Find the angle in which a fitting must be formed to attach the planes along the line AX.
(c) Project both planes on a plane parallel to ABC.
(d) Find the true size of the angles at A, B, and C, between the lines of the triangle ABC.

4.24. Same as Problem 4.23 except that the line of intersection of the planes is parallel to F.

4.25. A plane surface through the point D is parallel to H and intersects the plane ABC in a horizontal line XY.

(a) Find the H and F projections of the plane DXY.
(b) Find the angle in which a fitting must be formed to attach the plane ABC and DXY along the line XY.

4.26. A plane surface through D intersects the plane ABC in the line AC. Use Operations *III* and IV taking the first auxiliary plane perpendicular to H.

(a) Find the H and F projections of the planes ABC and DAC.
(b) Find the angle between the planes.

SERIES E. *Layout 1.* The points A, B, and C determine an indefinite plane. The point D is a point not in that plane. The coordinate locations of the points are: A(2, 1, 1), B(1½, 2, 3), C(½, ½, 3¾), and D(½, 1½, 1). The HF axis line is assumed 6″ above the lower margin and the FP axis line 3″ from the right margin of the sheet. The H projection is not required.

4.27. A line drawn from the point D perpendicular to the plane ABC is the axis line of a ½″ square prism having one base at D and the other in the plane. Two edges of each base are parallel to F.

(a) Find the F and P projections of the prism.
(b) Show by dimension the length of the prism.

4.28. A line through point D is parallel to F and makes an angle of 30 degrees with P sloping downward and to the left from D, and piercing the plane ABC at a point X. The line DX is the axis line of a ½″ square prism having one base in the plane and the other at D. The base at D is cut in a right angle with the axis and one diagonal of that base lies in a plane that is perpendicular to the plane *ABC* through *DX*.

(a) Find the *F* and *P* projections of the prism.
(b) Show by dimension the length of *DX*.
(c) Find the angle that *DX* makes with the plane *ABC*.

4.29. Same as Problem 4.28 except that *DB* is the center line of the prism.

4.30. The plane surface of a bulkhead is parallel to *F* and passes through the point *D* and intersects the plane *ABC* in the line *XY*.

(a) Find *F* and *P* projections of the plane *DXY*.
(b) Find the angle to which a fitting must be formed to attach the plane *ABC* to *DXY* at their intersection.
(c) Find the true size of the angles at *A*, *B*, and *C*, between the lines that form the triangle *ABC*.

4.31. The plane surface of a fuel tank is perpendicular to *F* and inclined to *P* in an angle of 30 degrees and passes through the point *D* sloping downward to the left from *D*. The plane *ABC* is intersected by the surface of the tank in the line *EF*.

(a) Find the *F* and *P* projections of the plane *DEF*.
(b) Find the angle to which a fitting must be formed to attach the plane *ABC* to *DEF* at their intersection.

4.32. A plane surface through the point *D* intersects the plane surface *ABC* in the line *AC*.

(a) Find the *F* and *P* projections of the plane *DAC*.
(b) Find the angle between planes *ABC* and *DAC*.

4.33. A plane surface through the point *D* intersects the plane *ABC* in a line *XY* that is parallel to and ⅛″ from *BC*.

(a) Find the *F* and *P* projections of the planes *ABC* and *DXY*.
(b) Find the angle between the planes.

4.34. *Layout 1.* Assume the points *A*(8, 1, 2), *B*(4½, 2, 1), and *C*(6, ¾, ½). The *HF* axis line is 3″ above the lower margin. Draw the plan and elevation of two intersecting timbers whose center lines are *AB* and *CD*. Line *AB* is intersected at *D* by a perpendicular line to *AB* from the point *C*. One diagonal of the 1″ square base at *A*, or *B*, lies in the plane of *ABC*. Two of the plane surfaces of the timber *CD* are parallel to the plane of *ABC*. The timbers are 1″ square with their ends at *A*, *B*, and *C* cut at right angles to their center lines.

4.35. Same as Problem 4.34 except the points are: *A*(4, 1, 2), *B*(7½, 2, 1), and *C*(6, ¾, ½).

4.36. *Layout 1.* A vertical line through the point *A* is the center line of a 2″ shaft on which is mounted a pulley of 24″ diameter and 6″ face and with point *A* in its central plane. A line perpendicular to *F* through the point *B* is the center line of a 2″ shaft on which is mounted an 18″ pulley with the point *B* in its central plane. Place an idler of 12″ diameter near the center of the space between the pulleys at such an angle that a belt drive over the pulleys will be reversible. (A belt must be delivered from the face of one pulley into the center plane of the next pulley over which it runs.) The location of the points are: *A*(2, 1½, ¾), *B*(9, ½, 1½). (Assume the *HF* axis line 3″ above the lower margin.)

(a) Draw the *H* and *F* projections of the pulleys and of a 4″ belt on them.
(b) Indicate the angle of contact of belt with the pulley face on each pulley.
(c) Find the angles that the idler shaft makes with *H* and *F*.
(d) Indicate, by dimensioning, the length of the center line of the shaft between the ceiling and the wall.

4.37. Using the data determined in Problem 4.36, design bearings to be attached to the ceiling and wall to support the idler shaft.

4.38. *Layout 1.* The upper surface of a stratum of rock outcrops on a horizontal plane of 1000′ elevation in a line, the direction of which is north 60 degrees east, through a point *C*(8, ¾, 0). A vertical sounding at the point *B*(7¼, ½, 0) struck the stratum at the point *D* at an elevation of 955′.

A point A is located 70′ east and 10′ south of B and its elevation is 960′. The point E is 100′ due east of the point B and its elevation is 940′. The stratum is 10′ thick measured in a vertical line. Scale 1″ = 40′ 0″.

(a) Find the outcrop of the stratum on H.
(b) Find the outcrop of the stratum on F.
(c) Find the H and F projections of the center line of the shortest tunnel from A to the stratum.
(d) Find the H and F projections of the vertical shaft from E to the stratum.
(e) Find the angle of dip of the stratum.
(f) Find the angle that the tunnel at A makes with the H plane.

4.39. *Layout 1.* Scale 1″ = 20′ 0″. The direction of the outcrop of a stratum of rock on a horizontal plane of 1000′ elevation is north 60 degrees east through point A. The point B is another point in the stratum. The direction of the outcrop of a second stratum with the same horizontal plane is north 45 degrees east through the point C. The point D is a second point of this stratum. The location of the points relative to projection planes are:

A is 100′ west of P, 15′ north of F, and 1000′ elevation.
B is 90′ west of P, 10′ north of F, and 962.5′ elevation.
C is 160′ west of P, 25′ north of F, and 1000′ elevation.
D is 120′ west of P, 15′ north of F, and 975′ elevation.
E is 75′ west of P, 20′ north of F, and in the first stratum.

(a) Find the lines in which the strata outcrop on H and F.
(b) Find the H and F projections of the center line of a horizontal tunnel that bears north 60 degrees west from the point E to a point in the second stratum.
(c) Find H and F projections of a vertical shaft from the point E to the second stratum.
(d) Find the intersection of the strata.

4.40. *Layout 1.* Same as Problem 4.39 except that the tunnel slopes upward in an angle of 15 degrees and that the shaft is perpendicular to the second stratum.

4.41. *Layout 1.* Scale 1″ = 50′ 0″. Assume that the east edge of a proposed extension of an athletic field is in the profile plane and its south edge in the frontal plane. The north edge is 175′ north of F and the west edge 350′ west of P. A sounding at B located 250′ west of P and 37.5′ north of F struck a stratum of rock at an elevation of 962.5′. The stratum dips toward F in an angle of 30 degrees and strikes north 60 degrees west. The elevation of the H plane is 1000′.

(a) Find the outcrop of the stratum on the horizontal and vertical plane.
(b) The point C located 350′ west of P and 125′ north of F is one corner of a foundation of a field house. To what depth must pile be driven at the point C to reach the stratum?

4.42. *Layout 1.* Scale 1″ = 20′ 0″. Assume that the H plane has an elevation of 1000′ and is the proposed level of a basement floor. Soundings at points A and B locate the upper surface of a stratum of rock, the strike of which is north 60 degrees east. The stratum is 10′ thick measured in a vertical line. The point A is 120′ west of P, 20′ north of F, and at 990′ elevation. The point B is 90′ west of P, 20′ north of F and at 975′ elevation.

(a) Find the outcrop of the stratum on the proposed floor level and on a surface of a foundation wall that lies in the F plane.
(b) Show in dashed lines the outcrop on the floor if it is lowered 15′.
(c) Find the outcrop on the surface of a foundation wall that is parallel to P and through the point B.
(d) Indicate the angle of dip of the stratum.

4.43. *Layout 1.* Scale 1″ = 20′ 0″. Assume that the H plane has an elevation of 1000′. The point A is 125′ west of P, 20′ north of F, and 970′ elevation. The point B is 90′ west of P, 15′ north of F, and 985′ elevation. The plane R passes through the point A, strikes north 45 degrees east, and dips downward toward F in an angle of 60 degrees. The plane S passes through the point B, strikes north 60 degrees west, and dips downward toward F in an angle of 45 degrees.

(a) Find the intersection of planes R and S with the H and F planes.
(b) Find the intersection of planes R and S.
(c) Find the dihedral angle between R and S.

CHAPTER V

REVOLUTION METHOD

5.1. Introduction. The four drafting operations that have been discussed in the preceding chapters are sufficient for a graphical solution of almost any descriptive geometry problem. In using those operations, the draftsman assumes that the object remains in some fixed position and that he projects a view of it on auxiliary planes that have any desired position relative to the object. This drafting procedure is known as the auxiliary plane method, or direct method, of solving a problem.

In some special cases a problem may be solved more directly through the use of another operation which is identified as Operation V. When using this operation the draftsman assumes that the object is revolved to some desired position relative to the principal projection planes. This procedure is known as the Revolution Method of solving descriptive geometry problems.

Both methods have their merit and possess certain advantages. Except in specific problems neither can be said to be the best method. Best results are obtained when both methods are understood and either or both can be used in the solution of a problem. When the two methods are integrated in this manner, the Revolution Method becomes a fifth drafting operation for the graphical solution of descriptive geometry problems.

5.2. Revolution. The concept of revolution introduces the idea of rotating some magnitude, such as a point, line, or plane, about some fixed axis. A point revolved about an axis describes a circular path lying in a plane that is perpendicular to the axis. A line revolved about an axis that is parallel to it will generate a cylinder. A line that intersects the axis will generate a cone when revolved about the axis. Many more illustrations might be used, but the problems of this chapter involve the rotation of points and lines and attention will be confined to them.

5.3. Choice of Axis. It is convenient in drafting to assume an axis of revolution so located that it is perpendicular to one, and parallel to the other, of two adjacent projection planes. When so located, the circular path of revolution of a point will project on one plane as a true circle and on the other as a straight line. If the axis is located in an oblique position relative to the projection planes, the circular path projects as an ellipse on each. Since the ellipse cannot be as easily and accurately drawn as the circle, an oblique axis should be projected on auxiliary planes that are parallel and perpendicular to it before the revolution is made.

5.4. Revolution of a Point. In Figure 5.1 the point A and axis CD are assumed to be given. The axis is perpendicular to H and parallel to F. The point A revolves in a circular path that lies in a plane that is perpendicular to CD. Since CD is parallel to F, the plane of the circle projects on F as a straight line drawn through a^F. The plane of the circle is parallel to H, and a circle drawn through a^H with $c^H d^H$ as its center is the H projection of the path of revolution.

In Figure 5.2 the axis AB is parallel to H and oblique to F. The line AB and point C are projected on an auxiliary plane *1* that is perpendicular to AB and to H. The line AB projects on plane *1* as a^1b^1 and the path of revolution as a circle drawn through c^1 with its center at a^1b^1. The H projection of the circle is a line drawn through c^H at right angles with a^Hb^H. If the elliptical F projection is required, it may be constructed by projecting assumed points from the known views.

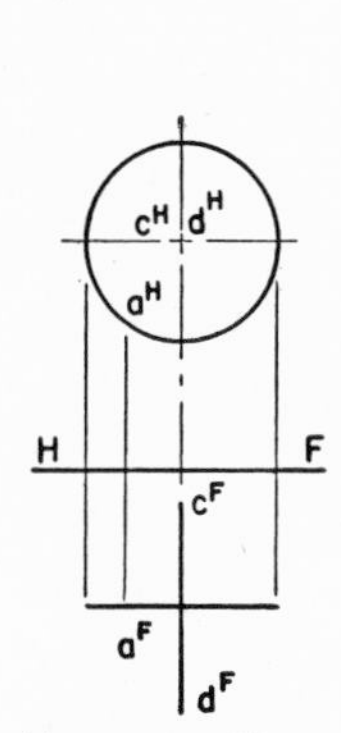

FIG. 5.1. Revolution—Axis Perpendicular to *H*

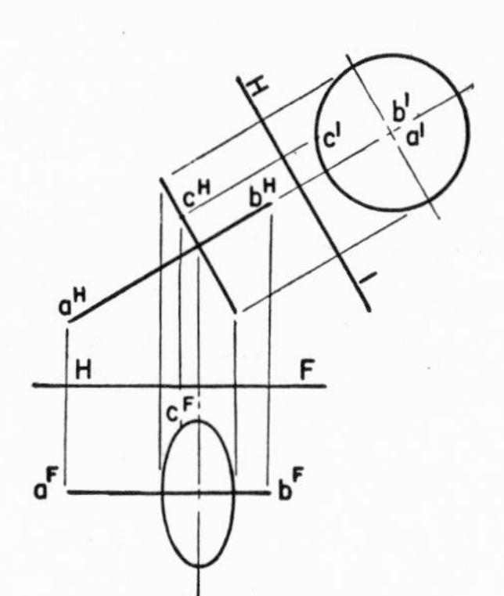

FIG. 5.2. Revolution—Axis Perpendicular to *1*

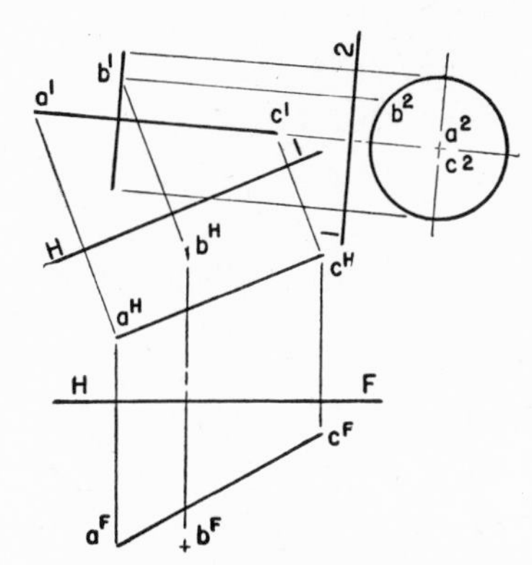

FIG. 5.3. Revolution—Axis Perpendicular to *2*

Figure 5.3 illustrates a method employed to revolve a point about an oblique axis. The line AC is projected on a plane *1* that is parallel to it and on a plane *2* that is perpendicular to it. The projection of the path of revolution of the point B can now be determined as in the preceding illustrations.

5.5. Revolution of a Line. Since a line is determined by two points, the revolution of a line may be made by revolving two points of the line. In Figure 5.4 the line AB is revolved about the vertical axis AC. The point A is on the axis and may be considered to be revolving in a circle of zero radius. The point B describes a circle, and the projection of its path is found as in the preceding illustration. It should be noticed that the line AB generates a cone in its revolution, also, that when AB was in the position indicated by the projections $a^Hb_1{}^H$ and $a^Fb_1{}^F$, it projects its exact length on F, and that the angle LH and LO are in true size projection.

The revolution of a line AC about an axis AB that is perpendicular to F is shown in Figure 5.5. The axis in this case is perpendicular to F and parallel to H. The cone generated by the revolution appears as a circle when projected on F and as a triangular figure when projected on H. The outside elements of the cone as projected on H are in true length, and the base and apex angles are in true size.

The oblique line AC is the axis of revolution for the line CB of Figure 5.6. The axis is parallel to the auxiliary plane *1* and perpendicular to plane *2*. The projections of the cone generated by the revolving line on planes *1* and *2* are found as in the preceding illustrations and differ from them only in the position they occupy on the drawing.

5.6. Problem 5.1. To project an oblique line segment in its true length. (Operation V.)

Given: The projections of an oblique line on two adjacent planes.

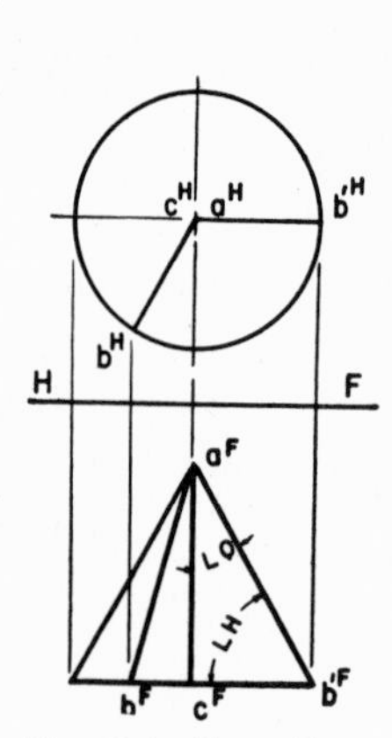

FIG. 5.4. Cone Generated—Axis Perpendicular to *H*

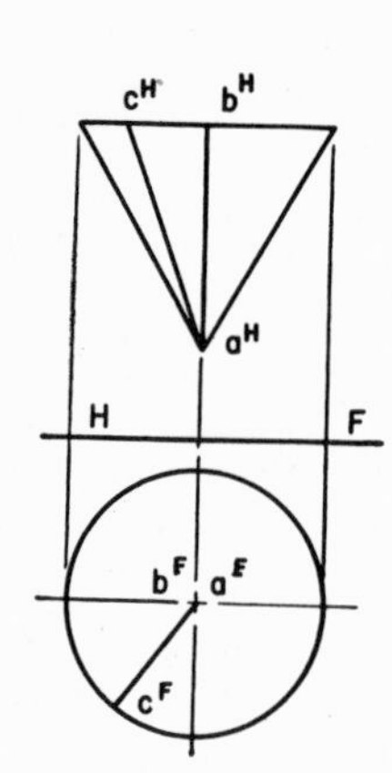

FIG. 5.5. Cone Generated — Axis Perpendicular to *F*

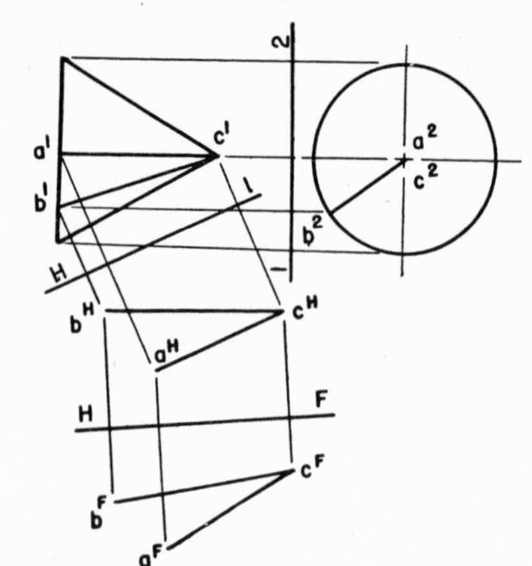

FIG. 5.6. Cone Generated—Axis Perpendicular to *2*

Required: A true length projection of the line.

Solution: Revolve the line to a position in which it is parallel to one of the projection planes.

Analysis:

1. Assume an axis that is parallel to one and perpendicular to the other projection plane.
2. Revolve the line to a position in which it is parallel to a projection plane.

Discussion: It is assumed in Figure 5.7 that the oblique line AC is given by its projections on H and F. The vertical line AX is the axis of revolution. When revolved about this axis, the line AC generates a cone. The projections of a portion of the base of the cone are shown as $c^H c_1{}^H$ and $c^F c_1{}^F$. In the position AC_1 the line is parallel to F and the projection $a^F c_1{}^F$ is equal in length to the line AC.

A similar construction is shown in Figure 5.8. The axis AY is perpendicular to F. The line AC is revolved about the axis to a position in which it is parallel to H. The projection $a^H c_1{}^H$ is equal in length to the line AC.

In Figure 5.9 the projections of a line CE on the H and P planes are assumed to be given. The revolution is made about an axis CZ that is perpendicular to H. The projection $c^P e_1{}^P$ is the true length of CE.

5.7. Problem 5.2. To find the angle between an oblique line and a projection plane.

Given: The projections of an oblique line on two adjacent planes.

Required: A projection that will show the true size of the angle that the line makes with one of the projection planes.

Solution: Revolve the angle to a position in which it is parallel to a projection plane.

Analysis:

1. Assume an axis that is in the plane of the required angle.
2. Revolve the angle about the axis until it is parallel to a projection plane.

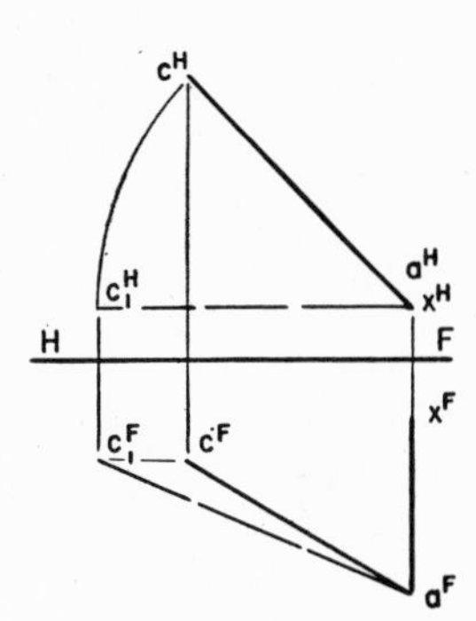

FIG. 5.7. True Length —Projected on F

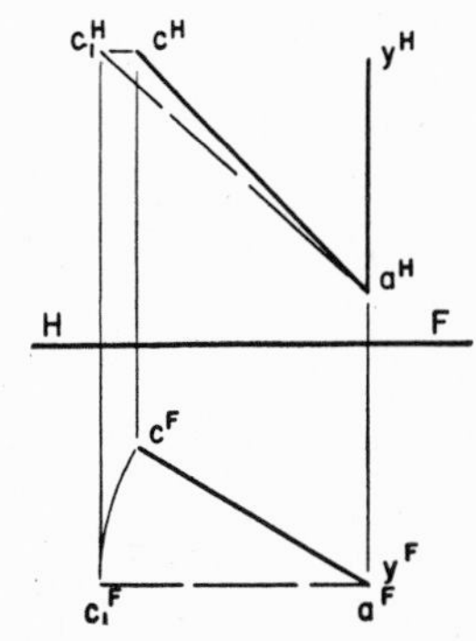

FIG. 5.8. True Length —Projected on H

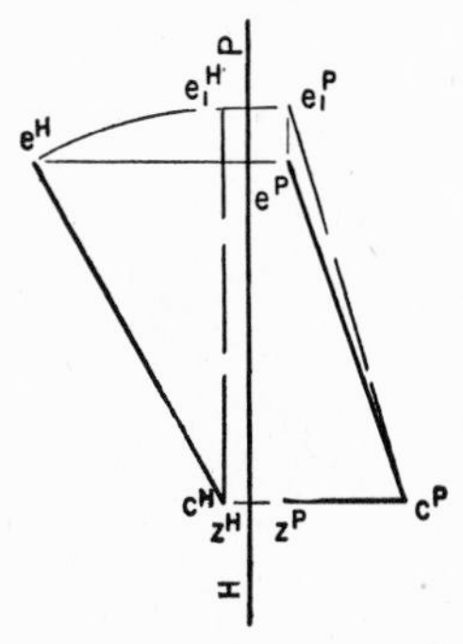

FIG. 5.9. True Length —Projected on P

Discussion: The angle that a line makes with a given plane is measured in a plane that contains the line and is perpendicular to the given plane. A plane that is perpendicular to H and through the line AB of Figure 5.10 is revolved parallel to F about a vertical axis through the point A. In this position the angle that the line makes with H is projected in true size as LH.

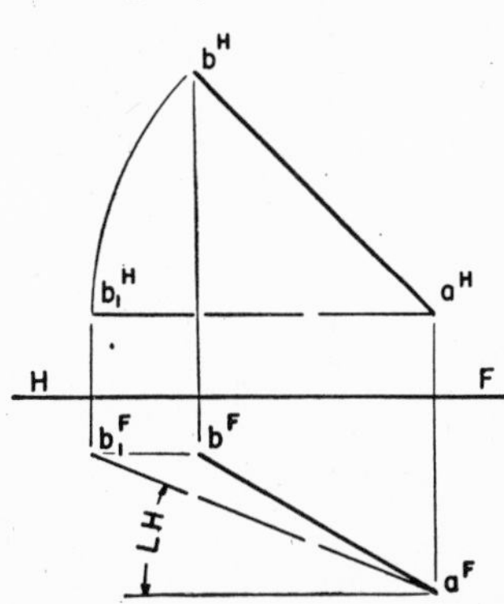

FIG. 5.10. True Size of Angle with H

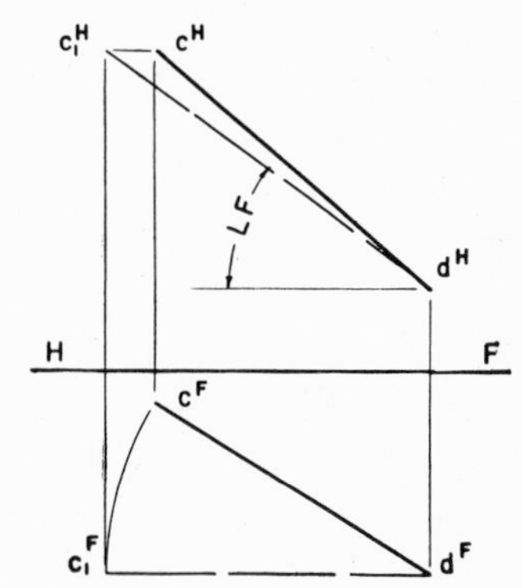

FIG. 5.11. True Size of Angle with F

In Figure 5.11 a plane that contains the line CD and is perpendicular to F is revolved to a position in which it is parallel to H. The angle LF that the line CD makes with F is shown in true size as LF in the H projection.

5.8. Problem 5.3. To measure the angle between two intersecting lines.

Given: The projections of two lines that intersect.

Required: The angle formed by the intersecting lines.

Solution: Revolve the angle to a position in which it is parallel to a projection plane.

Analysis:

1. Assume a plane through the lines and perpendicular to one of two adjacent planes.
2. Revolve the plane to a position in which it is parallel to the other adjacent projection plane.

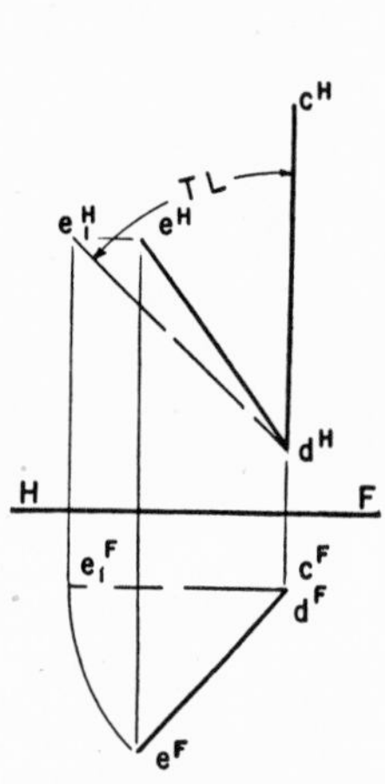

FIG. 5.12. True Size of Angle Projected on *H*

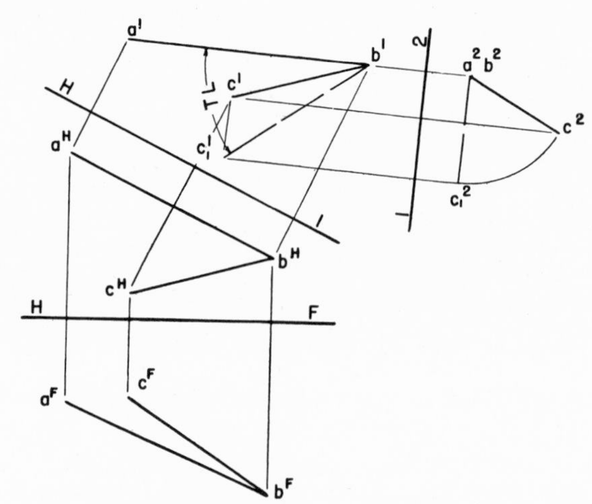

FIG. 5.13. True Size of Angle Projected on Plane *2*

Discussion: In Figure 5.12 the given lines are *CD* and *DE*. The line *CD* is perpendicular to *F*. A plane through the given lines is, therefore, perpendicular to *F*. When revolved about the line *CD* to a position in which the plane is parallel to *H*, the angle between the lines projects on *H* in its true size as *TL*.

In Figure 5.13 the oblique lines *AB* and *BC* form the angle to be measured. The line *AB* is assumed as an axis and it is projected on plane *1* taken parallel to it and on plane *2* perpendicular to it. The axis projects as a point on plane *2* and in true length on plane *1*. In this position the revolution is made as in the preceding figure, and the angle between *AB* and *BC* projects its true size on plane *1* as *TL*.

5.9. Problem 5.4. To draw the projections of a line that passes through a point and makes a required angle with a given line.

Given: The projections of a line and a point.

Required: The projections of a line that passes through the given point and intersects the given line in a specified angle.

Solution: Revolve the plane that is determined by the given line and point to a position in which it is parallel to a projection plane. Draw the projection of the specified line.

5.10. Problem 5.5. To project an oblique plane figure in true size.

Given: The projections of an oblique plane figure.

Required: A projection of the plane figure that will show its true size.

Solution: Find the projections of one line of the plane figure on planes that are parallel and perpendicular to that line. Revolve the plane figure about this line as an axis to a position in which the figure is parallel to a projection plane.

5.11. Problem 5.6. To find the projections of a line that passes through a point and makes given angles with two adjacent projection planes.

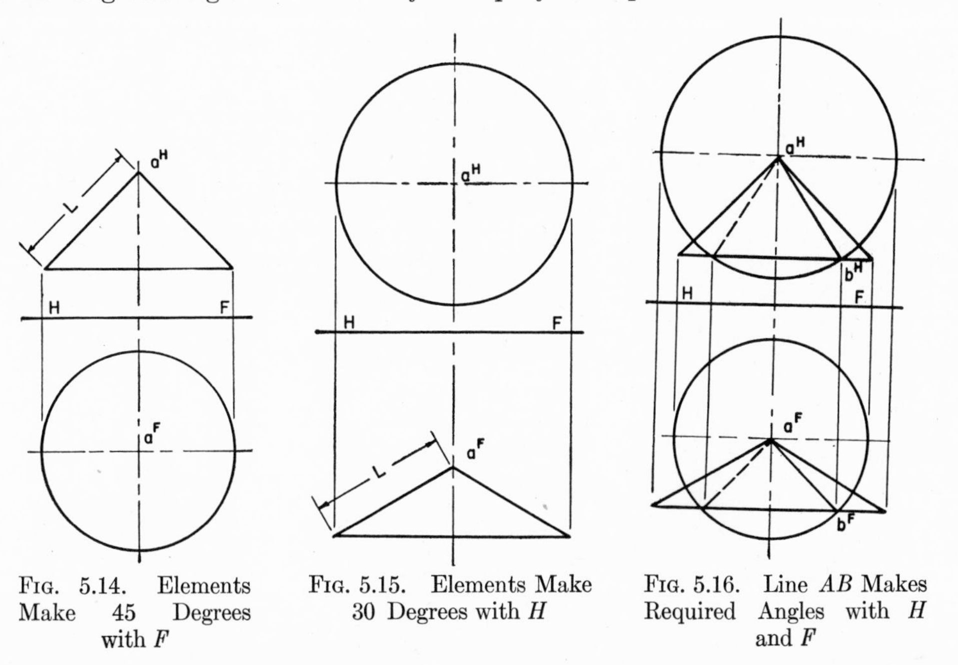

Fig. 5.14. Elements Make 45 Degrees with *F*

Fig. 5.15. Elements Make 30 Degrees with *H*

Fig. 5.16. Line *AB* Makes Required Angles with *H* and *F*

Given: The projections of a point and the angle that a line through the point makes with each of two adjacent projection planes.

Required: The projections of the line.

Solution: Find the intersection of two cones that are loci of the line.

Analysis:

1. Draw the projections of a cone with apex at the given point and with elements that make the required angle with one projection plane.
2. Draw the projections of a second cone with its apex at the given point and whose elements, which must be equal in length to those used in step 1 of this analysis, make the required angle with the other projection plane.
3. Find the intersection of the cones.

Discussion: The three steps of the analysis are shown in the illustrations. In Figure 5.14, the cone has its apex at *A*, and the elements of length *L* make angles of 45 degrees with *F*. In Figure 5.15 the cone has its apex at *A*, and the elements of length *L* make angles of 30 degrees with *H*. Figures 5.14 and 5.15 are superimposed in Figure 5.16. It will be seen in this figure that the point A is common to both cones. The point B in which the bases of the cones intersect is also common to both cones. Since the elements of the cones are equal in length, the cones will intersect in a straight line, AB, that lies on both cones and makes specified angles with H and F.

5.12. Problem 5.7. To find the angle that a line makes with an oblique plane.

Given: The projections of a line and an oblique plane.

Required: A true size projection of the angle that the line makes with the plane.

Solution: Revolve the angle to a position in which it is parallel to a projection plane.

Analysis:

1. Project the line and plane on an auxiliary plane *1* that is perpendicular to the given plane.
2. Project the line on a plane *2* that is parallel to the given plane.
3. Revolve the angle to a position in which it is parallel to plane *1*.
4. Project the revolved angle on plane *1*.

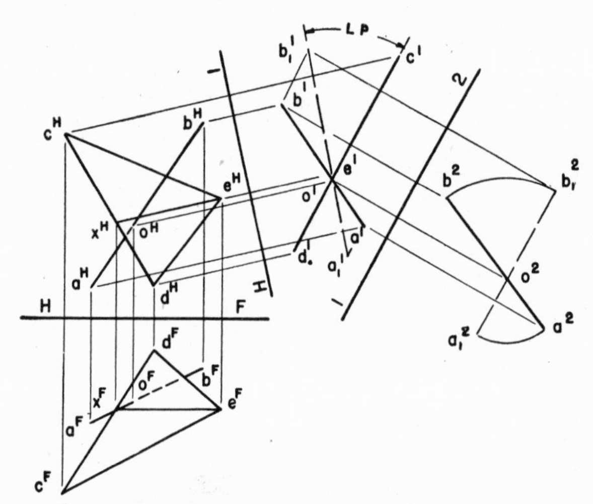

FIG. 5.17. Angle between Given Line and Plane

Discussion: In Figure 5.17 the auxiliary plane 1 is perpendicular to the given oblique plane CDE and to H. The oblique line AB pierces the plane CDE at the point o^1 in this projection. The projection of AB on plane *2* is $a^2b^2o^2$. The axis of revolution is assumed through O and perpendicular to plane *2*. When revolved parallel to plane *1*, the line projects on plane *2* as $a_1{}^2b_1{}^2$ and on plane *1* as $a_1{}^1b_1{}^1$. In this position the angle between the line and plane is parallel to plane *1* and projects its true size as LP.

It will be noticed that the same line and plane were used in this illustration and in Figure 4.27. A comparison of the illustrations indicates that the latter involves less drafting and less drawing space than the former.

5.13. Problem 5.8. To find the projections of a line that passes through a given point and makes given angles with an oblique plane and a projection plane.

Given: The projections of a point and an oblique plane.

Required: The projections of a line through the point and making given angles with the given oblique plane and a projection plane.

Solution: Determine two cones that are loci of the required line.

Discussion: Let it be assumed that the point A and the oblique plane CDE of Figure 5.18 are given and the line is to make angles of 45 degrees with CDE and 30 degrees with H. The plane CDE projects in edge view on the auxiliary plane *1* which is perpendicular to H. The required line must lie on a cone whose apex is at A and whose elements make an angle of 45 degrees with CDE. The projection of such a cone on plane *1* is the triangle $a^1x^1y^1$, and on plane *2* the circle with its center

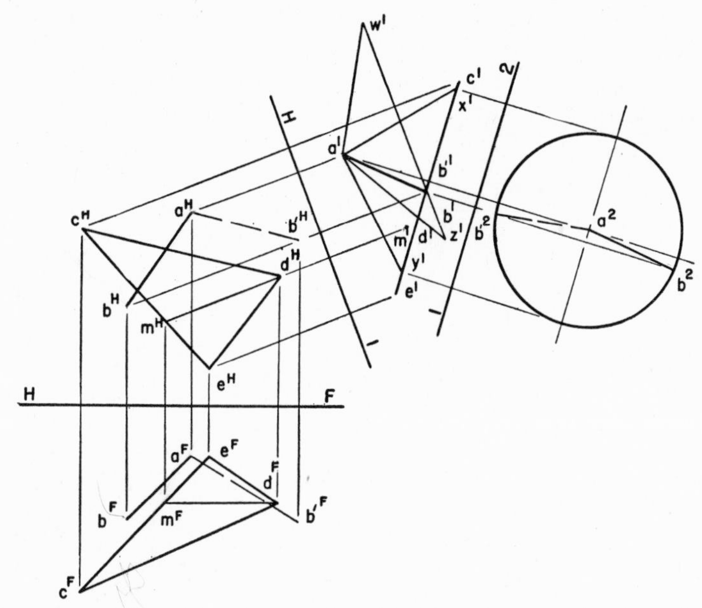

FIG. 5.18. Line Makes Required Angles with Given Plane and a Projection Plane

at a^2. Another locus of the required line is a cone with apex at A and whose elements make an angle of 30 degrees with H. The projection of such a cone on plane *1* is the triangle $a^1w^1z^1$. Since the cones were constructed with elements of equal length, their bases intersect in the points B and B'. The lines AB and AB' lie on both cones, and either of them satisfies the conditions of the problem.

5.14. Problem 5.9. To find the dihedral angle between two planes that intersect.

Given: The projections of two intersecting planes.

Required: A projection of the dihedral angle between the planes that will show its true size.

Solution: Project the angle on a plane parallel to it.

Analysis:

1. Project the planes on a plane that is parallel to their intersection.
2. Assume a plane that is perpendicular to the intersection.
3. Find the intersections of the assumed plane with the given planes.
4. Revolve the angle determined by the intersections to a position in which it is parallel to a projection plane.
5. Project the angle on the plane with which it is parallel.

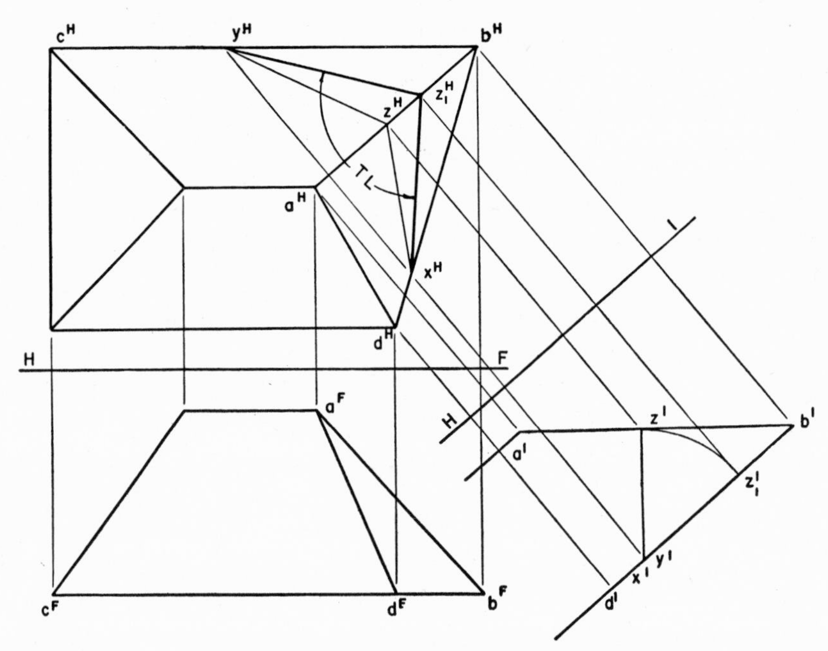

FIG. 5.19. Angle Revolved Parallel to H

Discussion: It is assumed in Figure 5.19 that the H and F projections of the hip roof of a building of irregular shape are given. The planes ABC and ABD of the roof intersect in the line AB. In order to frame the roof, the angle between the planes is required.

The dihedral angle between any two intersecting planes is measured in a plane perpendicular to their line of intersection. Plane *1* of Figure 5.19 is parallel to the line AB and shows that line in true length projection as a^1b^1. A plane perpendicular to AB through the point Z intersects the plane ABC in the line ZY and the plane ABD in the line ZX. The angle XZY is the required angle. This angle projects on H as $x^Hz^Hy^H$ and on plane *1* as $x^1z^1y^1$. The plane of XZY is revolved parallel to H about XY as an axis and shows a true size projection of the angle as $x^Hz_1{}^Hy^H$.

5.15. Application Problems.

5.1. *Layout 3.* The points A, B, and C are: $A(4, 1, \frac{1}{4})$, $B(2, \frac{1}{4}, 1)$, and $C(3, \frac{1}{4}, \frac{1}{4})$.

(a) Find the angle, LH, that the line AB makes with the H plane. Indicate by letters, TL, the true length of the line AB.

(b) Find the angle, LF, that the line AB makes with the F plane. Indicate by letters, TL, the true length of the line AB.
(c) Find the angle, LP, that the line AB makes with the P plane. (Project the line on an auxiliary plane that is parallel to P and revolve the line parallel to F.)
(d) Locate the H and F projections of a point X that is on the line AB and is 1″ from A.

5.2. *Layout 3.* Same points as in Problem 5.1.

(a) Find the angle, L, between the lines AB and BC.
(b) Find the projections on H and F of a line through C and intersecting AB in an angle of 30 degrees. Dimension the distance from the point A to the intersection.
(c) Find the projections on H and F of a line through C and intersecting the line AB in an angle of 90 degrees.
(d) Find the projections on H and F of a line through C and intersecting AB at a point 1″ from B.

5.3. *Layout 1.* Locate the projections of the points A, B, and C: $A(2, 1\frac{1}{2}, 1\frac{1}{2})$, $B(5, 1\frac{1}{2}, 1\frac{1}{2})$, $C(8\frac{1}{2}, 1\frac{1}{2}, 1\frac{1}{2})$.

(a) Draw the H and F projections of a cone of which the point A is the apex and having elements that are $1\frac{1}{2}$″ long that are inclined toward H from point A in an angle of 30 degrees with H.
(b) Draw the H and F projections of a cone of which point B is the apex and has elements $1\frac{1}{2}$″ long that are inclined toward F in an angle of 45 degrees with F.
(c) Assume that the two cones described above have their apexes at the point C.

1. Draw the H and F projections of the cones.
2. Find the H and F projections of two elements that lie on both cones.

5.4. Interchange the angle specifications in the above problem.

5.5. *Layout 1.* Assume the HF axis 3″ above the lower margin. Locate the projections of the points $A(9, 1, 1\frac{1}{2})$, $B(8, 2, 2)$, $C(6, \frac{1}{2}, \frac{1}{2})$, and $D(7, 2, \frac{1}{2})$. The line AD is the center line of a strut attached to the plane surface ABC. Find the angle in which a fitting must be bent to attach the strut to the plane surface.

5.6. Same as Problem 5.5 except that the center line of the strut is the line CD.

5.7. Same as Problem 5.5 except that the center line of the strut is the line BD.

5.8. *Layout 1.* Same points as in Problem 5.5. Find the projections on H and F of a line DX that makes angles of 45 degrees with H and 30 degrees with the plane ABC.

5.9. Same as Problem 5.8 except that the angles are 30 degrees with H and 45 degrees with ABC.

5.10. *Layout 1.* The line AB is the center line of a 6″ square sheet metal duct that slopes upward to the left, and to the rear from the point A in angles of 30 degrees with a floor (H) and 15 degrees with a wall (F). Two edges of any right section of the duct are parallel with H. The point A is located: $A(5, 0, 2\frac{1}{4})$. Scale 1″ = 1′ 0″.

(a) Find the H and F projections of the duct.
(b) Find the intersection of the duct with the floor and the wall.

5.11. Same as Problem 5.10 except that the angle with F is 30 degrees.

5.12. *Layout 1.* The line CD is the center line of a 6″ square sheet metal duct that slopes upward, forward, and to the left from a point D in angles of 30 degrees with a wall (F) and 45 degrees with another wall (P). Two edges of any right section of the duct are parallel to P. The point D is located: $D(0, 2, 4)$. Assume the HF axis line 7″ above the lower margin and the FP axis line $3\frac{1}{2}$″ from the right margin. Scale 1″ = 1′ 0″.

(a) Find the F and P projections of the duct.
(b) Find the intersection of the duct with the two walls.

5.13. Same as Problem 5.12 except that the angles are interchanged and the FP axis is $4\frac{1}{2}$″ from the right margin.

5.14. *Layout 1.* The line AB makes angles of 30 degrees with the side wall (P) and 15 degrees with a horizontal plane (H). The line slopes downward, to the right, and to the rear from the point $A(2, 0, 1)$ and intersects the plane P at the point B. Assume the HF axis line 3″ above the lower margin and the HP axis line 6″ from the right margin of the sheet. Omit the F projection and revolve P into H. Scale 1″ = 1′ 0″.

(a) Find the H and P projections of the line.
(b) Find the H and P projections of a 6″ square sheet metal duct of which AB is the center line. Two edges of the right section of the duct are parallel to P.
(c) Find the intersection of the duct with the F and P planes.
(d) Indicate by dimension the length of the line AB.

5.15. Same as Problem 5.14 except that the line AB is the center line of a ½″ diameter tube.

5.16. Same as Problem 5.14 except that two edges of the right section are parallel to H.

5.17. *Layout 1.* Assume that the H plane has an elevation of 1000′ and is located on the drawing 3½″ above the lower margin. Scale of drawing 1″ = 100′.

The point A is 100′ north of F, 400′ west of P and has an elevation of 800′. A vertical shaft from the 1000′ elevation passes through the point A and reaches the 700′ level. A tunnel 150′ in length bears north 60 degrees east and is inclined to H in an angle of 45 degrees, sloping upward to the rear from the point A to a point B. The point B is the mid-point of a horizontal tunnel 300′ in length that intersects the inclined tunnel and bears north 30 degrees west. A tunnel that is inclined upward to the rear in an angle of 30 degrees joins the horizontal tunnel in an angle of 90 degrees at its right end in a point C and pierces the H plane at the point X. A tunnel that slopes forward and downward joins the left end of the horizontal tunnel in an angle of 90 degrees at a point D and pierces the F plane in a point Y which has an elevation of 700′.

Show by dimensions on the map the locations, relative to the reference planes, of the points B, C, D, X, and Y, and note on the front view their elevations. Indicate the angle of inclination of the tunnel DY. Indicate the bearing and length of a tunnel from A to Y.

5.18. *Layout 1.* A vertical line through D(2½, ½, ¼) is the center line of a radio tower. Two braces are attached to the tower at the point D and to a roof plane ABC at the points X(3¼, ?, ¾) and Y(1¼, ?, 1¾). The indefinite roof plane is determined by the points A(4¾, 1, 1), B(4, 1½, ¼), and C(3¼, 1, 1½).

(a) Find the point E in which the center line pierces the roof.
(b) Find the angle between the center line and the roof plane.
(c) Find the angles between the roof plane and the braces.
(d) Find the lengths of the braces.

5.19. *Layout 1.* The points A(8, ½, 2) and B(8¾, 2½, ½) are two points on the intersection of roof planes, one of which contains the point C(7¼, 2¼, 2), the other the point D(9, ¾, 2). A vertical line through E(9½, 1¼, ½) is the center line of a 2′ square chimney. The top of the chimney is at D and has two edges parallel to F. Scale ¼″ = 1′ 0″.

(a) Find the H and F projections of the intersection of the chimney with the roof.
(b) Find the true size of the opening in the roof.
(c) Find the angle between the roof planes.
(d) Find the angle between the center line and the roof plane that is pierced by it.

5.20. *Layout 1.* The points A, B, and C lie on the plane of a bulkhead which is the mounting surface for a guide pulley of a control cable. The cable runs over a 3″ pulley mounted so that the direction of each segment of cable is such that they would intersect at the mid-point of AB. The locations of the given points are: A(8, ½, 2), B(8¾, 2½, ½), C(7¼, 2¼, 2), D(9, ¾, 2), and E(7, 1½, 2¼). Scale 1″ = 1′ 0″.

(a) Show the location of the pulley on a plane that is parallel to the cable and on a plane that is perpendicular to the plane of the cable.
(b) Find the angle in which the mounting must be bent to attach the pulley to the plane ABC.

CHAPTER VI

NONINTERSECTING LINES

6.1. Problem 6.1. To determine a plane that contains one line and is parallel to another line.

Given: The projections of two lines that are not in the same plane.

Required: To find the projections of two lines that determine a plane that contains one given line and is parallel to the other given line.

Solution: Through some point of one line draw an auxiliary line that is parallel to the other line.

Analysis:

1. Assume any convenient point on one given line.
2. Draw the projections of an auxiliary line through the point and parallel to the second line.

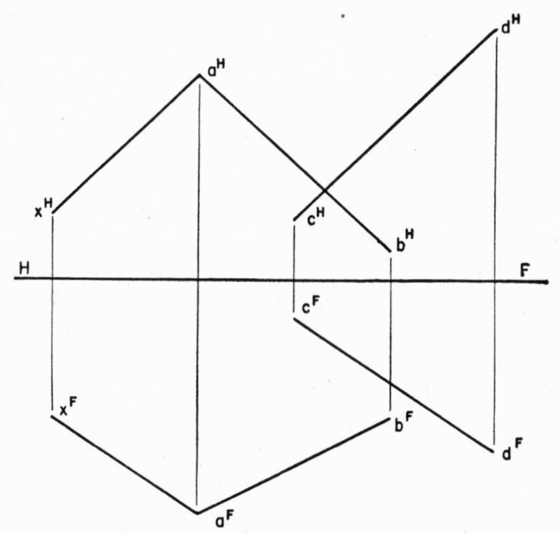

Fig. 6.1. Plane *ABX* Is Parallel to *CD*

Discussion: It should be remembered that two intersecting lines determine a plane, and that parallel lines have parallel projections on any projection plane. In Figure 6.1 the lines *AB* and *CD* are assumed to be given lines. The *H* and *F* projections of an auxiliary line *AX* are drawn parallel to the corresponding projections of the line *CD*. The lines *AB* and *AX* intersect and determine a plane that is parallel to *CD* and that contains the line *AB*.

6.2. Problem 6.2. To find the projections of the shortest line (i.e., common perpendicular) that may be drawn between two given lines.

Case 1: The lines are parallel.

Discussion: Two parallel lines determine a plane. The plane of the lines may be projected in edge view on a plane perpendicular to it, and on a plane that is parallel to it, by using the drafting methods that have been discussed. When the lines have been projected on a plane that is parallel to them, the projection of a common perpendicular may be drawn at any desired location.

Case 2: The lines are not parallel.

Given: The projections of two lines that are not in the same plane.

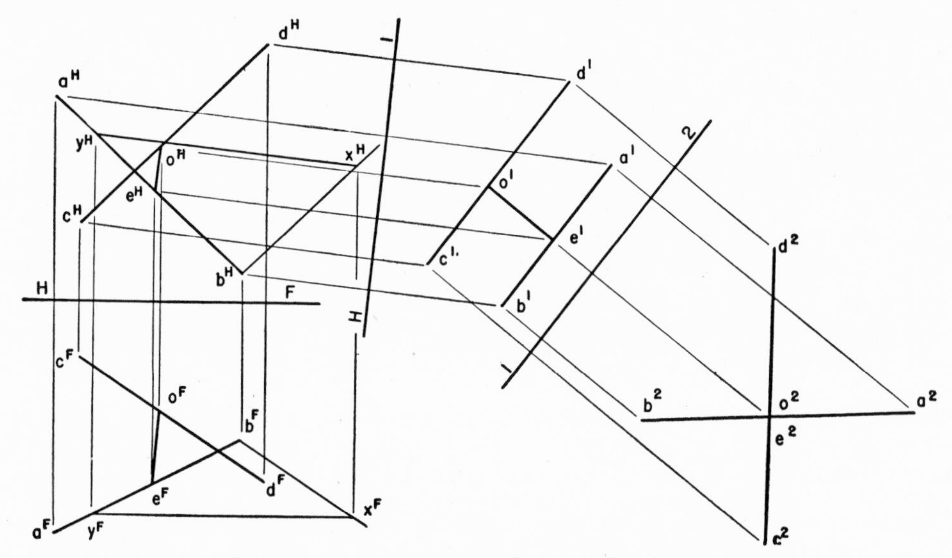

FIG. 6.2. Common Perpendicular. First Method

Required: The projections of a line that intersects and is perpendicular to both given lines.

Solution: Project the required line as a point on a plane that is parallel to both given lines.

Analysis: *Method I.*

1. Determine a plane that contains one line and is parallel to the other given line. (Problem 6.1.)
2. Project the lines on an auxiliary plane that is perpendicular to the plane found in step 1. (Operation III.)
3. Project the lines on a plane that is parallel to the plane found in step 1. (Operation IV.)
4. Locate the projection of the common perpendicular as a point at the intersection of the projections of the lines.
5. Determine any other required projections of the common perpendicular.

Discussion: The lines AB and CD are assumed as the given lines of Figure 6.2. The auxiliary line BX determines a plane ABX that contains AB and is parallel to

CD. The first auxiliary plane is perpendicular to the horizontal line *XY* of the plane *ABX*. The projections of the lines *AB* and *CD* on plane *1* are parallel. A second projection plane that is parallel to both *AB* and *CD* is perpendicular to the required line. The projection of *EO*, the common perpendicular to *AB* and *CD*, must show as a point at the intersection of the projections of the lines. All projections of *EO* may now be determined.

Analysis: *Method II*.

1. Project the given lines on a plane that is perpendicular to one of them. (Operations I and II.)
2. Project the lines on a plane that is parallel to them.
3. Locate the projection of the common perpendicular at the point where the projections of the lines intersect.
4. Determine any other required projections of the common perpendicular.

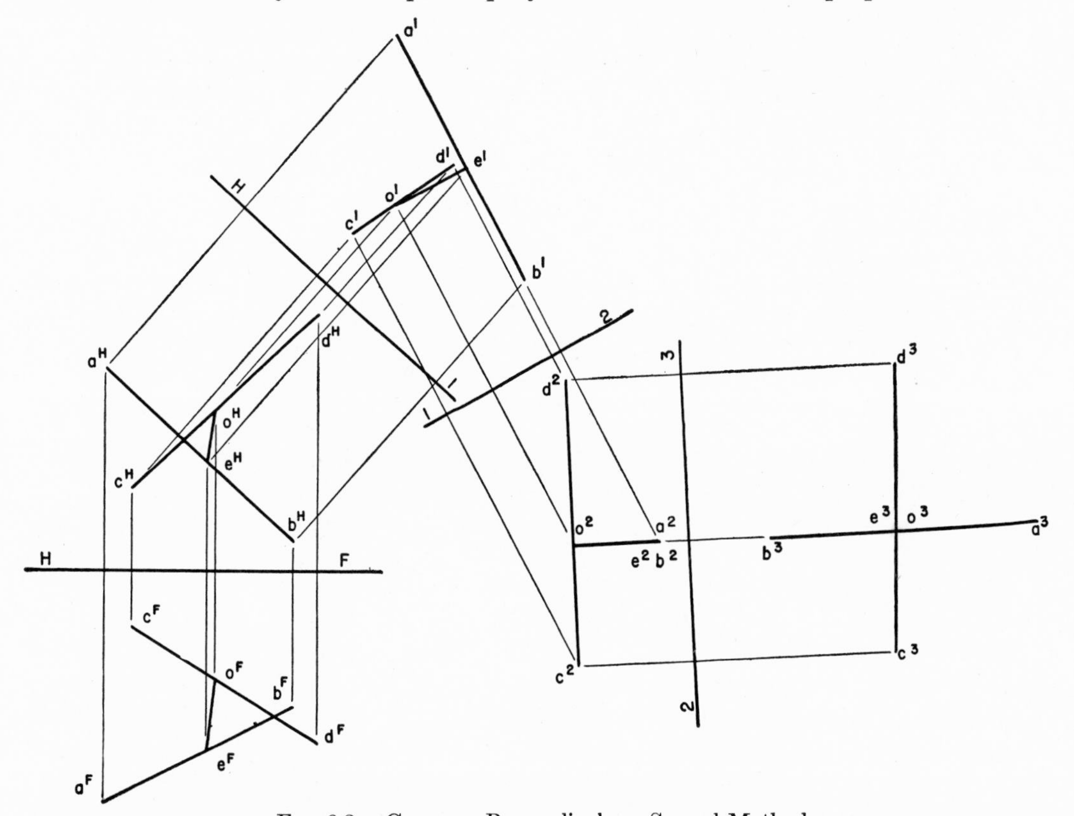

Fig. 6.3. Common Perpendicular. Second Method

Discussion: In Figure 6.3 the lines *AB* and *CD* are assumed to be given. The plane *1* is parallel to *AB* and perpendicular to *H*. The plane *2* is perpendicular to *AB*, and the plane *3* is parallel to both *AB* and *CD*. The required line projects on plane *3* as e^3o^3 at the intersection of a^3b^3 and c^3d^3. The required projections of *EO* may now be found.

6.3. Problem 6.3. To find the shortest line that will join two given lines and be parallel to a given projection plane.

Given: The projections of two lines that are not in the same plane.

Required: To find the projections of the shortest line that intersects both given lines and is parallel to a specified projection plane.

Solution: Project the given lines on a plane that will show the required line as a point.

Analysis:

1. Determine a plane that contains one line and is parallel to the other. (Problem 6.1.)
2. Project the lines on a plane that is perpendicular to the plane found in step 1.
3. Project the lines on a plane that is perpendicular to the known direction of the required line.
4. Locate the projection of the required line at the point where the projections of the given lines intersect.
5. Find any other required projections of the lines.

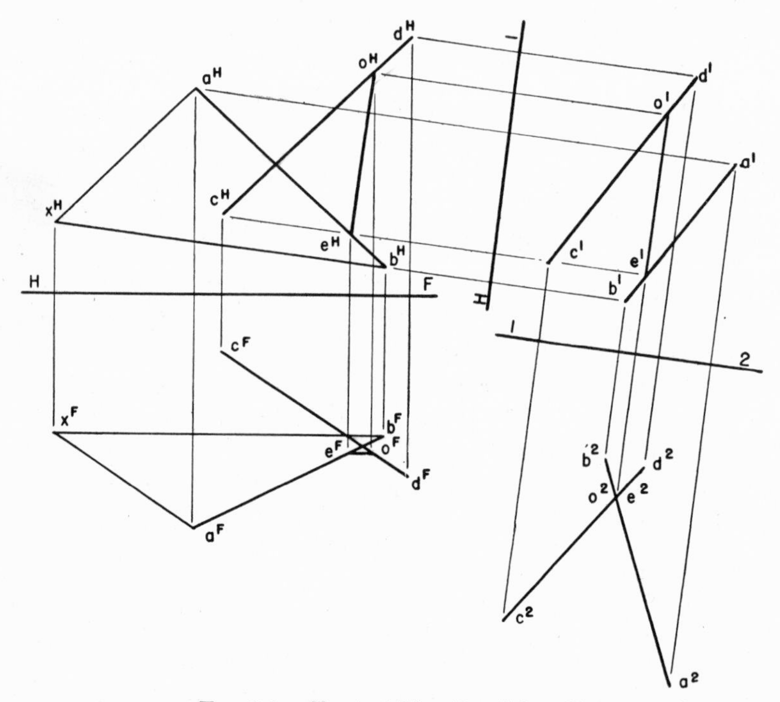

FIG. 6.4. Shortest Line Parallel to *H*

Discussion: The projections of the lines AB and CD are assumed to be given in Figure 6.4. The lines AB and AX determine a plane containing AB and parallel to CD. Plane *1* is perpendicular to the horizontal line BX and is perpendicular to H. Any line that is parallel to H will project on plane *1* as a line parallel to the

$H1$ axis line. Plane 2 is taken perpendicular to this known direction, and the required line, EO, projects as a point e^2o^2 at the intersection of a^2b^2 and c^2d^2 on that plane. Any other required projections of EO may now be found.

It will be noticed that the statement of the problem was that of a general case in which the required line was parallel to any specified projection plane. In the illustration the required line is parallel to H. Should any other projection plane be specified, the analysis and solution would be the same and the drafting operations adapted to the required conditions.

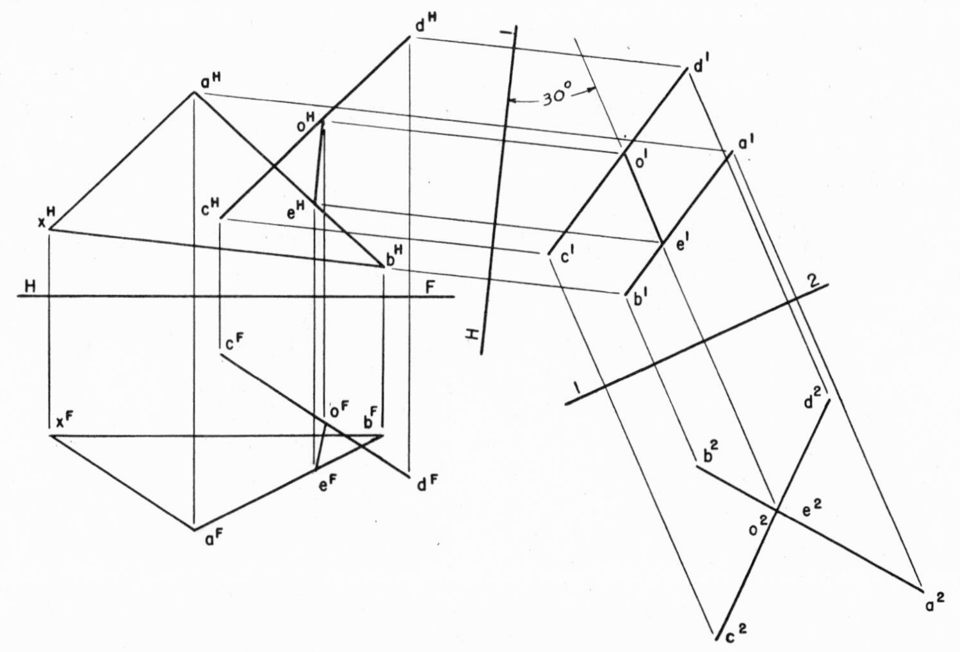

FIG. 6.5. Shortest Line Making 30 Degrees with H

6.4. Problem 6.4. To find the projections of the shortest line that will join two given lines and which makes a given angle with a specified projection plane.

Given: The projections of two lines that are not in the same plane.

Required: The projections of the shortest line that intersects the given lines and that makes a given angle with a specified projection plane.

Solution: Project the required line as a point on a plane that is perpendicular to its given direction.

Analysis:

1. Determine a plane that contains one given line and is parallel to the other line.
2. Project the lines on a plane that is perpendicular to the plane found in step 1.
3. Project the lines on a plane that is perpendicular to the given direction of the required line.
4. Locate the projections of the required line.

Discussion: It will be observed that the solution and analysis are the same in this and the preceding problem. In Figure 6.5 it was assumed that the shortest line sloping upward to the rear and intersecting AB and CD was required. Plane *2* must, therefore, be perpendicular to that specified direction. On plane *2*, the required line projects as the point e^2o^2 at the intersection of a^2b^2 and c^2d^2. From this projection any other projection of the required line may be determined.

6.5. Problem 6.5. To find the projections of a line that intersects two given lines in specified angles with each.

Given: The projections of two lines that are not in the same plane.

Required: The projections of a line that intersects the given lines in specified angles with each.

Solution: Determine the direction of the required line by means of intersecting cones and join the lines with a line of this direction.

Analysis:

1. Project the lines on a plane that is perpendicular to one of them and on a plane that is parallel to both. (Operations I, II and IV.)
2. Through some point of the other line assume an auxiliary line that is parallel to the one shown as a point on plane *2*.
3. Draw the projections on auxiliary planes *2* and *3* of a cone with its apex at the assumed point and having the auxiliary line as its axis. The elements of the cone may be of any convenient length and making the specified angle with the axis.
4. Draw the projections on the auxiliary plane *3* of another cone having the assumed point as an apex and the given line as an axis. The elements must be of the same length as those of the first cone and making the required angle with the axis.
5. Find the projections of the element (or elements) common to both cones.
6. Draw the projections of the required line parallel to an element that is common to both cones.

Discussion: Let it be assumed that the lines AB and CD of Figure 6.6 are the given oblique lines and that the required line is to make angles of 60 degrees with CD and 45 degrees with AB. Plane *1* is parallel to AB and plane *2* is perpendicular to that line. The line AB projects on plane *2* as a^2b^2 and CD as c^2d^2.

An auxiliary line through D and parallel to AB projects on plane *1* as d^1o^1 and on plane *2* as d^2o^2. The lines CD and DO project on a plane *3* that is parallel to them as c^3d^3 and d^3o^3. A 45-degree cone with DO as its axis intersects a 60-degree cone with CD as its axis in the line DZ. The projection of DZ on plane *2* is d^2z^2 and on plane *1* is d^1z^1. The direction of the projection of the required line (XY) on plane *2* is determined by d^2z^2 to which it must be parallel. The direction of the projection of XY on plane *1* is determined by d^1z^1. The line XY intersects AB at the point X and the line CD at the point Y. The projections of the required line may now be determined on all projection planes.

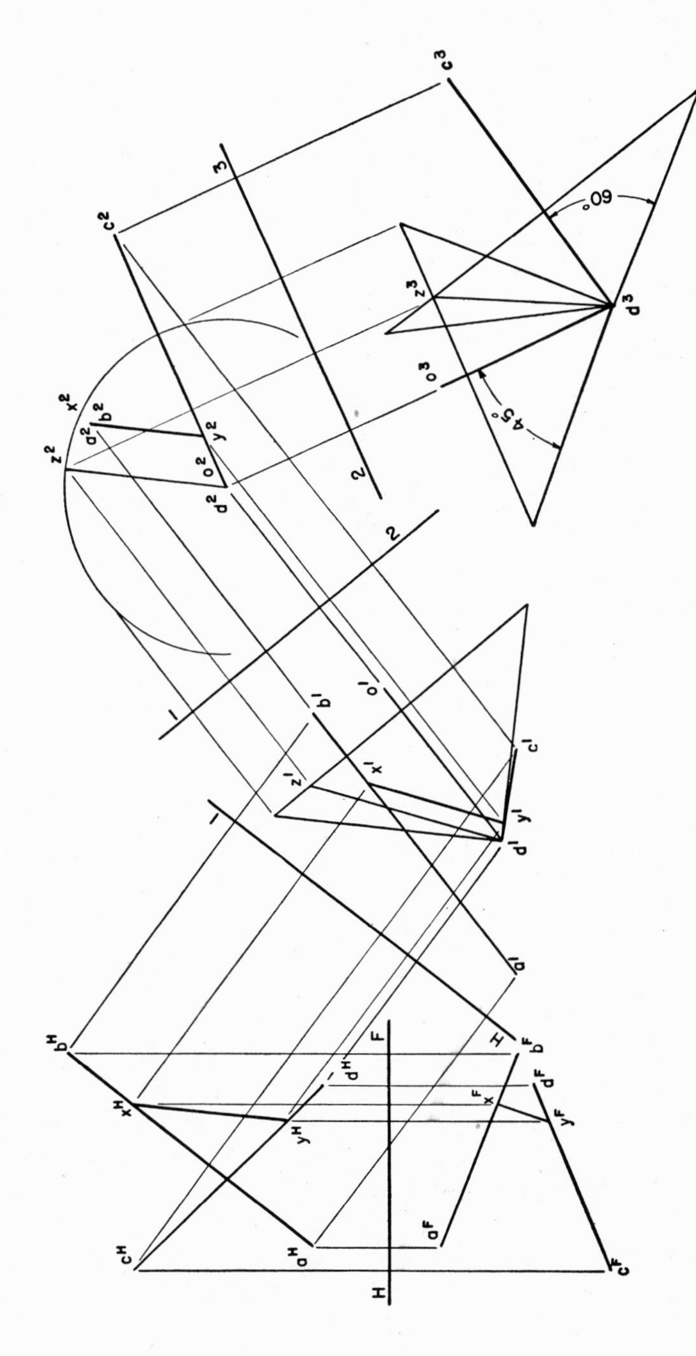

Fig. 6.6. Line Makes Specified Angles with AB and CD

It should be noticed that the cones of Figure 6.6 intersect in two elements and that only one is shown in that illustration. If the other element had been used to determine the direction of the required line, a different location of that line would have been found. It should be observed also that the cones might be reversed on their extended axes to determine the direction of the required line. The problem as stated is general and a definite solution would depend on other more specific data.

6.6. Application Problems.

SERIES A. *Parallel Lines. Layout 1.* The coordinate location of the points A, B, C, and D are: $A(9\frac{1}{2}, 2\frac{1}{2}, 1)$, $B(7\frac{1}{2}, \frac{1}{2}, 2)$, $C(8\frac{1}{2}, 3, \frac{1}{2})$, and $D(6\frac{1}{2}, 1, 1\frac{1}{2})$. The HF axis line is $3\frac{1}{4}''$ above the lower margin.

6.1. The lines AB and CD are the center lines of $\frac{1}{2}''$ circular tubes of an aircraft structure. A similar tube is perpendicular to both and intersects AB $1''$ from B.

(a) Find the H and F projections of the center line of the connecting tube.
(b) Project the tubes on a plane parallel to both and show welded intersections.
(c) Project the tubes on a plane perpendicular to both.

6.2. The lines AB and CD are the center lines of two shafts of $2''$ diameter. Power is transmitted between the shafts by means of spur gears of equal diameters and having $2''$ face widths. The central plane of the gears intersects the line AB $12''$ from B. Scale $1'' = 1'\,0''$.

(a) Project the shafts and gears on a plane parallel to both shafts. (The gears may be drawn as friction cylinders.)
(b) Project the shafts and gears on a plane perpendicular to the shafts.

6.3. Power is transmitted between the shafts AB and CD by means of a third shaft and bevel gears of $8''$ maximum diameter and $2''$ face width. The center line of the third shaft is the common perpendicular between AB and CD that intersects CD at the mid-point of CD. The gears may be drawn as friction cones. All shafts are $2''$ in diameter. Scale $1'' = 1'\,0''$.

(a) Find the H and F projections of the center line of the third shaft.
(b) Project the shafts and gears on a plane parallel to AB and CD.
(c) Project the shafts and gears on a plane that is perpendicular to AB and CD.

6.4. The point $E(6\frac{1}{2}, 3, 2\frac{1}{2})$ is a point on the center line of a $1''$ cylinder that intersects the plane of AB and CD. The center line is the shortest line that may be drawn from point E and inclined to H in an angle of 30 degrees. The base at E is a right section.

(a) Find the H and F projections of the cylinder.
(b) Indicate the angle in which the cylinder is cut to fit the plane.

6.5. A power plant installation includes two penstocks (i.e., pipes) of $2'$ diameter, having AB and CD as center lines, that are joined by a horizontal by-pass of the same diameter. The center line of the by-pass intersects the line CD, $3'$ from D. Scale $\frac{1}{4}'' = 1'\,0''$.

(a) Find the H and F projections of the center lines.
(b) Project the penstocks on a plane parallel to them.
(c) Project the penstocks on a plane perpendicular to them.
(d) Indicate the bearing of the by-pass.

6.6. The lines AB and CD are the center lines of two $4'$ square tunnels. A line drawn on the floor and in a right section of either tunnel is horizontal. Scale $\frac{1}{8}'' = 1'\,0''$.

(a) Find a projection of the tunnels on a plane parallel to their center lines.
(b) Find a projection on a plane perpendicular to them.

SERIES B. *The lines are not parallel. Layout 1.* The coordinate location of the points A, B, C, and D are: $A(9\frac{1}{2}, 1, \frac{1}{2})$, $B(7\frac{1}{2}, 3, 1\frac{3}{4})$, $C(9\frac{1}{2}, 1\frac{1}{2}, 2\frac{1}{2})$, and $D(7\frac{1}{2}, \frac{1}{2}, 1\frac{1}{2})$. The HF axis line should be drawn $3\frac{1}{2}''$ above the lower margin.

6.7. Computations indicate a danger of arcing between two wires carrying electric current if the distance between them is less than 1″. If two wires have the location of the lines *AB* and *CD*, will they be safe in this respect?

(a) Indicate by dimensions the distance between the wires at their closest points.
(b) Draw the *H* and *F* projections of the line drawn between their closest points.
(c) Dimension the distance from *C* on *CD* to the intersection with the connecting line.

6.8. The lines *AB* and *CD* are the center lines of two tunnels of a mine which are to be joined by the shortest horizontal tunnel that may be constructed between them.

(a) Find the *H* and *F* projections of the center line of the connecting tunnel.
(b) Indicate by dimension the length of the connecting tunnel.
(c) Locate by dimension the point of intersection on line *CD*.
(d) Indicate the angle of bearing.

6.9. Assume that the tunnels of Problem 6.8 are to be connected by the shortest shaft that is parallel to *F*.

(a) Find the *H* and *F* projections of the center line of the shaft.
(b) Dimension the length of the center line of the shaft.
(c) What angle does the shaft make with the vertical?
(d) Dimension the distance from the point *C* to the intersection of line *CD* with the shaft.

6.10. The tunnels *AB* and *CD* of Problem 6.8 are joined by the shortest tunnel that is inclined to *H* in an angle of 30 degrees. The connecting tunnel slopes upward to the rear.

(a) Find the *H* and *F* projections of the center line of the connecting tunnel.
(b) Dimension its length.
(c) Indicate the bearing angle.
(d) Locate by dimension the distance from *C* to the intersection of the connecting tunnel with *CD*.

6.11. The lines *AB* and *CD* are joined by a line *XY*. The line *XY* intersects the given lines in an angle of 60 degrees with each.

(a) Find the *H* and *F* projections of any line *XY* that will satisfy its descriptions. (Make the first auxiliary plane perpendicular to *H* and parallel to *AB*.)
(b) Check your results to determine if the angles are correct.

6.12. The lines *AB* and *CD* are the center lines of two ½″ diameter tubes of an airplane structure. A line *XY* is the center line of a similar tube that intersects *AB* and *CD* in an angle of 90 degrees with each.

(a) Draw the *H* and *F* projections of *XY*.
(b) Project the structure on a plane that is parallel to the lines *AB* and *CD*.
(c) Project each tube on a plane that is perpendicular to its center line.

6.13. Power is transmitted between the shafts, whose center lines are *AB* and *CD*, by a shaft whose center line is *XY*. The line *XY* is perpendicular to both *AB* and *CD*. The shafts are 2″ in diameter. The bevel gears have a maximum diameter of 9″ and face widths of 3″. The gears may be drawn as friction cones, i.e., the teeth may be omitted. Scale 1″ = 1′ 0″.

(a) Find the *H* and *F* projections of line *XY*.
(b) Project the shafts and gears on a plane parallel to *AB* and *CD*.
(c) Project each shaft, the attached gear, and its mating gear on a plane perpendicular to the center line of that shaft.

6.14. *Layout 1*. Assume points *A*(9½, 1½, ½), *B*(7½, 3, 1¾), *C*(9½, 1¼, 2½), and *D*(7½, ½, 1½). The *HF* axis line is 3½″ above the lower margin.

The lines *AB* and *CD* are the center lines of two timbers of 1″ square right section, and they are intersected by a third timber that is perpendicular to both. The right section of the third timber is such that its faces are flush with the faces of the timbers *AB* and *CD*. Find the plan and elevation of the timbers.

CHAPTER VII

SURFACES

7.1. Surfaces. In general, a surface may be conceived to be generated by a moving straight or curved line. The positions that the line may assume in its movement are infinite in number. Hence, a surface may be regarded as consisting of an infinite number of lines or elements that lie in the successive positions that the moving line assumes in its movement.

The line that generates a surface is called the generatrix of that surface. In its movement the generatrix may be assumed to be guided by a line called the directrix or by two such lines. In the generation of some surfaces the generatrix must also be guided in its movement in such a manner that its relation to a reference plane is constant. Such a plane is known as a director.

7.2. Classification of Surfaces. In accordance with their method of generation, surfaces may be classified as ruled surfaces and double curved surfaces.

A ruled surface is one that may be generated by a moving straight line. It may be conceived to consist of an infinite number of straight line elements.

A double curved surface can be generated by a curved line only. It contains no straight line elements and is composed of all the positions that the generatrix assumed in its movement.

7.3. Ruled Surfaces. The simplest of the ruled surfaces is the plane. It may be generated by a straight line that is moved in such a manner that it is continually in contact with two parallel or intersecting lines. A plane may also be generated by a straight line that is revolved about an axis that intersects it at right angles. A plane curve may also be moved or revolved in such a manner that a plane would be generated.

A single curved surface is a ruled surface in which the consecutive straight line elements are either parallel or intersecting. The most common of the single curved surfaces are the cone and cylinder. The convolute is also a single curved surface, but is frequently classified as a warped surface because of its similarity to the other surfaces of that group.

A warped surface is a surface in which the consecutive elements are neither parallel nor intersecting. Such surfaces are very frequently encountered in the design of structures and mechanisms. The bearing surface of the tile or stone used in the construction of a skew arch are hyperbolic paraboloids. The face of the tooth of a worm gear is, in general, a helicoid. The forms of the vaulted ceilings and domes, or the surfaces of mouldings used in architectural design, are limited only by the ingenuity of the designer. A study of the warped surfaces and their application is both interesting and profitable, but is not within the scope of this volume.

7.4. Surfaces of Revolution. Another classification of surfaces includes surfaces of revolution. To a very large extent the surfaces with which the draftsman is concerned are surfaces of revolution. The plane may be defined as a surface generated by a straight line revolved about an axis that is perpendicular to and intersecting that generatrix. The form of cone that is most frequently used in design may be generated by a straight line which is revolved about an axis that intersects that generatrix at any angle other than 90 degrees. The circular cylinder is generated by a straight line generatrix that is revolved about an axis and is parallel to and a constant distance away from that axis. Such surfaces as the sphere, torus, ellipsoid, and other double curved surfaces common in the design of machines and structures are surfaces generated by the revolution of a curve about an axis. In general, the surfaces of objects that are manufactured in a lathe will be surfaces of revolution. By virtue of the method of their generation, a section of a surface of revolution cut perpendicular to the axis of revolution will be a circle.

The succeeding paragraphs of the chapter are devoted to a brief study of a few of the most commonly used ruled and double curved surfaces. The study of the principles that are discussed in these paragraphs will suggest to the student their application to other surfaces that are not mentioned.

7.5. A Cone. The generation of the cone has been described in a previous paragraph to consist of a straight line moving in such a manner that one point of the line remains stationary while it is guided in its movement by a curved line directrix. In the cones that have practical application the directrix is, in general, an ellipse or circle. In the case of a right circular cone the directrix is a circle lying in a plane perpendicular to the axis of the surface. Such a cone is a surface of revolution.

7.6. Problem 7.1. To find the projections of an element of a given cone.

Given: The projections of a cone on adjacent planes.

Required: The projections of an element of the given cone.

Solution: Find two points of an element.

Analysis:

1. Locate the projections of a point in the base of the cone.
2. Draw a straight line through this point and the apex of the cone.

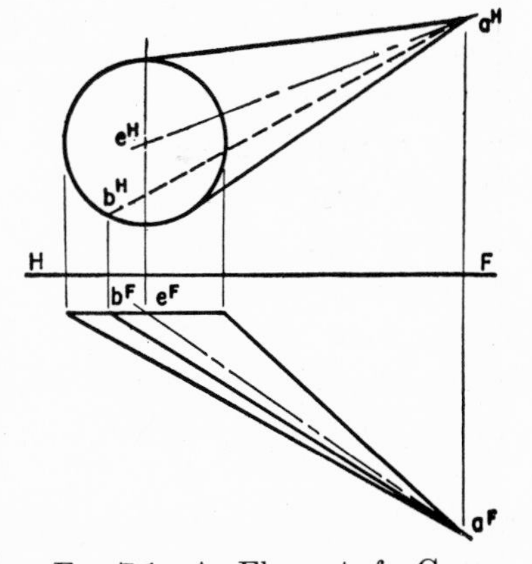

FIG. 7.1 An Element of a Cone

Discussion: In Figure 7.1 it is assumed that the given cone has its apex at the point A and that it is elliptical in right-section, with its circular base parallel to H. In the generation of the cone the point A of the generatrix was stationary while the line moved in such a manner that it was continually in contact with the curve of the base. The point B is a point of the base having its H projection at b^H and its F projection at b^F. The line AB is one position of the generating line and is, therefore, an element of the cone.

7.7. Problem 7.2. To find the projections of a point that lies on a given cone if one projection of the point is given.

Given: Two projections of a cone and one projection of a point on that cone.

Required: The unknown projection of the point.

Solution: Determine a line of the cone that passes through the point.

Analysis: *Method I.*

1. Find the projections of an element of the cone that passes through the point.
2. Locate the required projection of the point in the corresponding projection of the element.

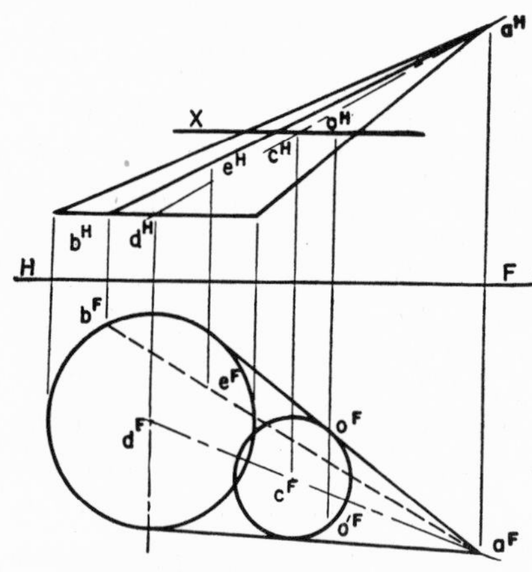

Fig. 7.2. A Point of a Cone

Discussion: Let it be assumed, as in Figure 7.2, that the cone is elliptical in section and has its circular base parallel to F; also that the F projection of the point E is located at e^F. The F projection of an element of the cone that passes through the point E intersects the base of the cone at b^F. The element AB projects on H as $a^H b^H$. Since point E is a point of AB, its H projection will lie at e^H.

Analysis: *Method II.*

1. Assume a plane through the point that intersects the cone in a circle or other simple geometric curve.
2. Draw the projections of the curve cut from the cone by the assumed plane.
3. Locate the required projection of the point on the corresponding projection of the curve.

Discussion: Referring again to Figure 7.2, it will be seen that a plane X, taken parallel to F through the given H projection of point O, cuts from the cone a curve parallel to the base of the cone. The F projection of this curve is a circle with center at c^F. The F projection of the point O lies in the F projection of the circle at o^F or o'^F.

The use of Method II is convenient only when the cone is right circular or when an oblique base of the cone is a circle or other simple geometric curve. In general, Method I is preferred.

7.8. The Cylinder. In a preceding paragraph a cylinder was defined as a surface generated by a straight line generatrix that moved in such a manner that its successive positions were parallel with each other and in contact with a curved directrix. In the case of the right circular cylinder the surface may be assumed to be generated by a straight line generatrix that is revolved about an axis that is parallel to and a constant distance from that axis. The cylinder may be conceived to consist of all of the positions that the generatrix assumed in its movement. The successive positions of the generatrix are called elements of the cylinder.

7.9. Problem 7.3. To determine the projections of an element of a given cylinder.

Given: The projections of a cylinder on adjacent planes.

Required: The projections of an element of the cylinder.

Solution: Determine one point of the element and its direction.

7.10. Problem 7.4. To find the projection of a point that lies on a given cylinder when one projection of the point is given.

Given: Two projections of a cylinder and one projection of a point that lies on that cylinder.

Required: The unknown projection of the point.

Solution: Find the projections of a line of the surface that contains the point. (Two methods as in Problem 7.2.)

7.11. Problem 7.5. To find the projection of a point that lies on any given ruled surface when one projection of the point is given.

Given: Two projections of a ruled surface and one projection of a point of that surface.

Required: The unknown projection of the point.

Solution: Draw the projections of a line of the surface that contains the point.

7.12. The Sphere. A sphere is a surface generated by a circle that is revolved about one of its diameters. The sphere is, therefore, a surface of revolution. The intersection of a plane with a surface of revolution is necessarily a circle if the plane is perpendicular to the axis of the surface. The sphere may therefore be conceived to be composed of all the circles that may be cut by such planes.

7.13. Problem 7.6. To find the projection of a point that lies on a given sphere when one projection of the point is known.

Given: Two projections of a sphere and one projection of a point on that sphere.

Required: The unknown projection of the point.

Solution: Determine the projections of a line of the surface that contains the point.

7.14. The Torus. The torus is a surface generated by revolving a circle about an axis that lies in the plane of the circle but does not intersect it. The intersection of the torus with any plane perpendicular to its axis is two circles cut from that surface. A plane tangent to the surface and perpendicular to the axis will cut a circle from the torus. The torus may be conceived to consist of all of the circles that may be cut from it by the intersecting and tangent planes.

7.15. Problem 7.7. To find the projections of a point on a given torus when one projection of the point is given.

Given: Two projections of a torus and one projection of a point of that surface.

Required: The unknown projection of the point.

Solution: Locate a curve of the surface that contains the point.

7.16. Problem 7.8. To draw the projections of a hyperboloid of revolution.

Given: The location in space of an axis and the dimensions of a hyperboloid of revolution.

Required: The projections of the hyperboloid on adjacent planes.
Solution: Draw a sufficient number of elements of the surface.
Analysis:

1. Draw the projections of the circular bases and of the gorge circle.
2. Assume the projections of elements that are tangent to the projection of the gorge circle and intersect the projections of the base circles.

Discussion: It is assumed that the conditions of the problem specify that the base circles are parallel to H, that the axis is perpendicular to H, and that the gorge and base circles are of the diameters and located as in Figure 7.3.

The hyperboloid of revolution is generated by a straight line generatrix that is revolved about an axis not parallel to, nor intersected by, the generatrix. Any point of the generatrix will describe in its revolution a circle that lies in a plane perpendicular to the axis. The smallest of the circles is known as the gorge circle. The projections of the elements of the surface on a plane perpendicular to the axis are tangents to the projection of the gorge circle. Hence, a representation of the surface and an approximate contour of it may be drawn by assuming a sufficient number of elements. In Figure 7.3 the elements are taken at 30-degree intervals.

The method of locating the projections is shown by the element AB of which the H projection is tangent to the H projection of the gorge circle at c^H and cuts the H projections of the base circles at a^H and b^H. The F projection of A is in the lower base at a^F and of B at b^F in the upper base.

7.17. Problem 7.9. To find the projections of a point that lies on a given hyperboloid of revolution when one of those projections is given.

Given: Two projections of a hyperboloid of revolution and one projection of a point of that surface.

Required: The unknown projection of the point.

Solution: Find the projections of an element of the surface that passes through the given point.

Analysis:

1. Draw the projections of an element that contains the point.
2. Locate the unknown projection of the point on the corresponding projection of the element.

Discussion: The H and F projections of the hyperboloid and the H projection of D are assumed to be given in Figure 7.4. The H projection of the element AB that contains D is drawn through d^H and tangent to the gorge circle of the surface. The F projection of the element is found at a^Fb^F. Since D is a point of this element, the F projection is at d^F in a^Fb^F. The point d'^F on the element $a'^Fb'^F$ is the F projection of another point of the surface, whose H projection is d^H.

Since the surface is a surface of revolution, a point may be located by the second method of Problem 7.2. The plane W passed through the point O cuts a circle from the surface. The projections of O must lie on the projections of that circle.

7.18. Developments. A development may be visualized as a pattern, drawn on a plane, which would form the given surface when properly folded or bent into shape. The patterns used by the tinsmith in the construction of objects made of sheet metal are developments of the surfaces that form the object. Most objects so constructed are geometric surfaces or combinations of surfaces such as cylinders, cones, prisms, and pyramids.

7.19. Developable Surfaces. Single curved surfaces and such surfaces as the pyramid or prism that are made up of planes can be developed. Warped surfaces

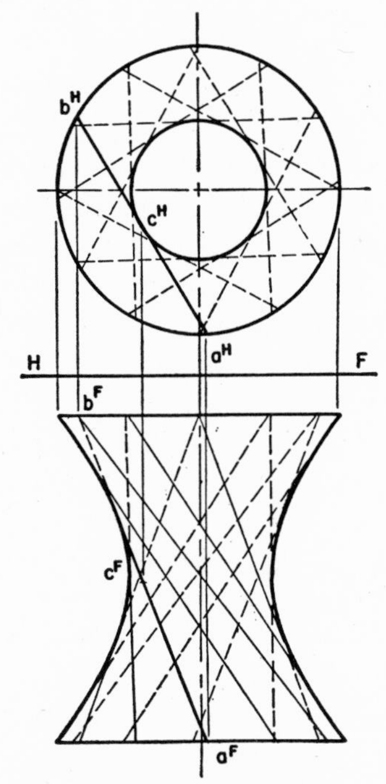

FIG. 7.3. A Hyperboloid of Revolution

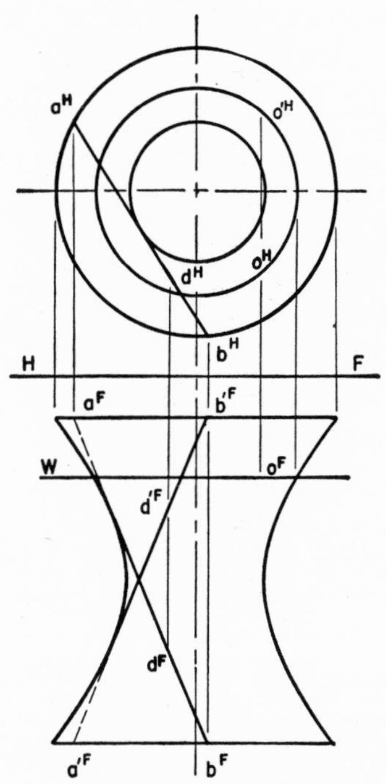

FIG. 7.4. A Point of a Hyperboloid of Revolution

and double curved surfaces cannot be developed. The leather in a baseball cover or the metal that forms the body of an automobile must be distorted to form those surfaces; hence they are not true developments.

7.20. Problem 7.10. To develop the surface of a right prism.

Given: The description of a right prism.

Required: The development of the prism.

Solution: Determine the shape and size of each of the plane surfaces that form the prism.

Analysis:

1. Draw the projections of the prism on adjacent planes.
2. Determine the exact form and size of each of the plane surfaces that bound the prism.

3. Join the edges of the plane surfaces so that they may be folded to form the prism.

Discussion: Figure 7.5 shows the front and top views of a right prism having as its base the polygon *ABCD*. Since the vertical edges are at right angles to the base the perimeter of the base will develop as a straight line. Starting at a', on the line $a'a''$ of Figure 7.5, the distances $a'b'$, $b'c'$, $c'd'$, and $d'a''$ are laid off equal to *AB*, *BC*, *CD*, and *DA*. The edges are drawn perpendicular to the base line at the points a', b', c', and d'. The lengths of the edges may be projected from the front view or measured with the dividers. The points *E* and *O* are located on auxiliary lines drawn on the faces *AB* and *DC*.

7.21. Problem 7.11. To develop the surface of an oblique prism.

Given: An oblique prism.

Required: The development of the prism.

Solution: Determine the shape and size of each of the faces of the prism and join them in the proper sequence.

Analysis:

1. Draw the projections of the prism on adjacent planes.
2. Assume a plane perpendicular to the edges of the prism.
3. Develop the perimeter of the right section as a straight line.
4. Locate the edges of the surfaces on the developed perimeter.
5. Measure the lengths of the edges above and below the right section.

Discussion: An oblique hexagonal prism is shown in Figure 7.6. A plane through the points *1* and *4* and taken perpendicular to the axis line and the edges cuts the section *1–2–3–4–5–6* from the prism. The perimeter of the right section will develop as a straight line. In Figure 7.6 the distances *1′–2′*, *2′–3′*, *3′–4′*, etc., are laid off on this line equal to the distance *1–2*, *2–3*, *3–4*, etc. The edges of the prism are drawn perpendicular to the developed perimeter, and their lengths above and below the right section are measured with the dividers.

7.22. Problem 7.12. To develop the surface of a right cylinder.

Given: A right cylinder.

Required: The development of the cylinder.

Solution: Develop the right section, and locate and measure any numbers of assumed elements.

Analysis:

1. Draw the projections of the cylinder on adjacent planes.
2. Develop the perimeter of the base as a straight line.
3. Locate and measure elements of the cylinder on the development.

Discussion: The development of a right cylinder is a rectangle, one dimension of which is the length of the perimeter of the base of the cylinder, the other the length of the elements of the cylinder. For convenience in making its development

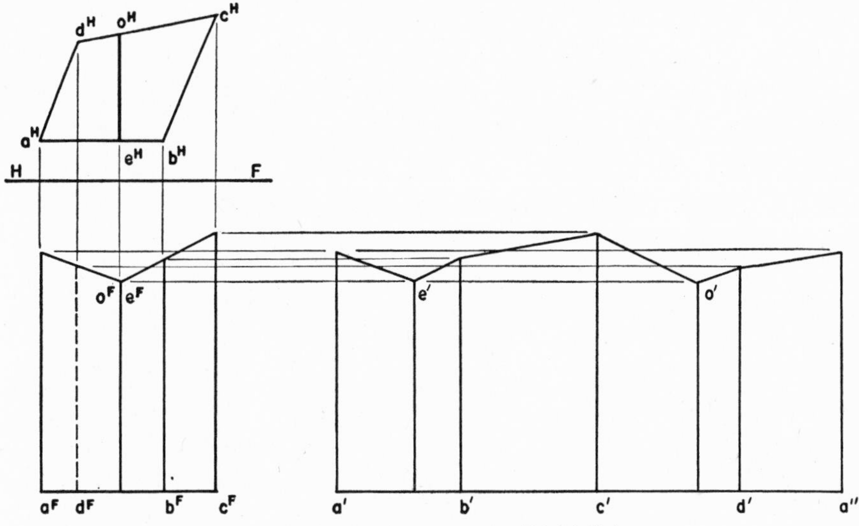

Fig. 7.5. Development of a Right Prism

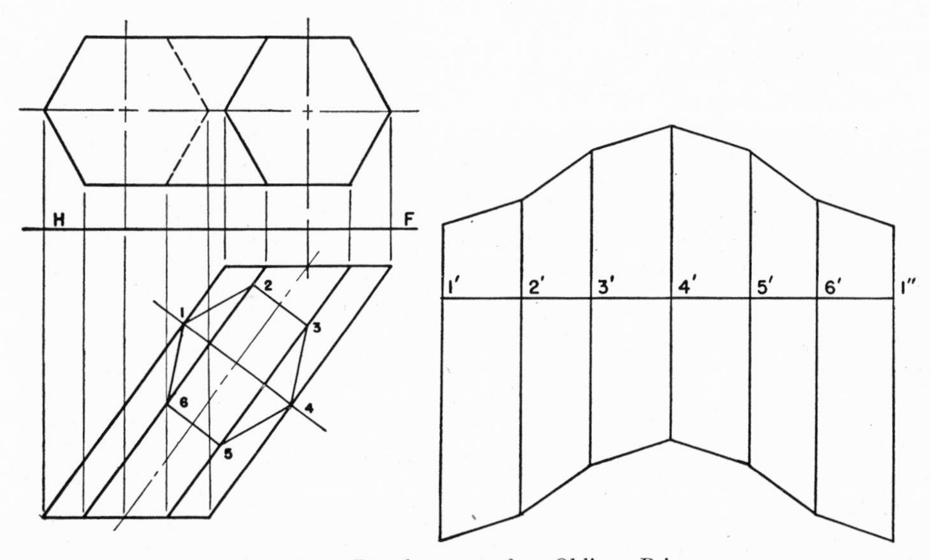

Fig. 7.6. Development of an Oblique Prism

a cylinder may be imagined to be a prism having an infinite number of faces. The method then becomes that used in developing the prism. The perimeter develops into a straight line and is shown as the line *1′ 1″* in Figure 7.7. Any number of elements may be drawn on the *H* and *F* projections of the cylinder and on the development. In the figure the elements are spaced at 30-degree intervals. These elements are drawn perpendicular to the development of the perimeter and spaced at intervals equal to the length of a 30-degree arc of the base.

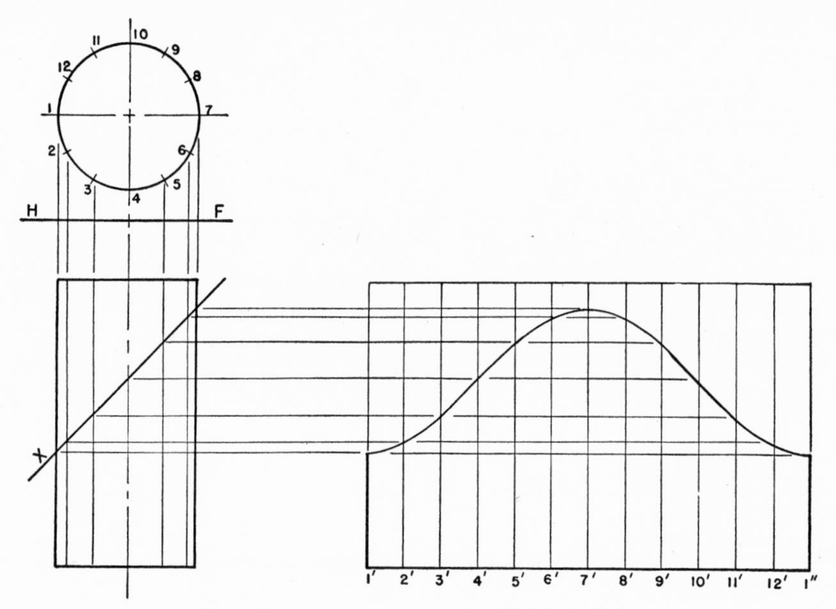

FIG. 7.7. Development of a Right Cylinder

Figure 7.7 shows an oblique plane cutting the cylinder. The intersection of the plane and cylinder is an ellipse that projects on *F* as a straight line and on *H* as a circle. Since the elements of the cylinder are parallel to *F*, they project their true lengths on *F*. The point in which each element is cut by the plane is shown on *F* and may be located on the development by measurements taken from the front view. A smooth curve drawn through the points so located will be an approximation of the intersection. The curve would be exact if accurate measurements were made on a very large number of elements.

7.23. Problem 7.13. To develop the surface of an oblique cylinder.

Given: An oblique cylinder.

Required: The development of the cylinder.

Solution: Develop the right section and locate and measure any number of elements.

Analysis:

1. Draw the projections of the cylinder on adjacent planes.
2. Assume a plane perpendicular to the axis of the cylinder.

3. Develop the perimeter of a right section.
4. Locate on the developed perimeter and measure the lengths of the elements of the cylinder.

Discussion: Figure 7.8 is the top and front views of an oblique cylinder. A plane *X* perpendicular to the axis and to the elements cuts an elliptical right section from the cylinder. The development of the perimeter of the ellipse is a straight line, shown as line *x–x′* in Figure 7.8. The spacing of the elements along this line are

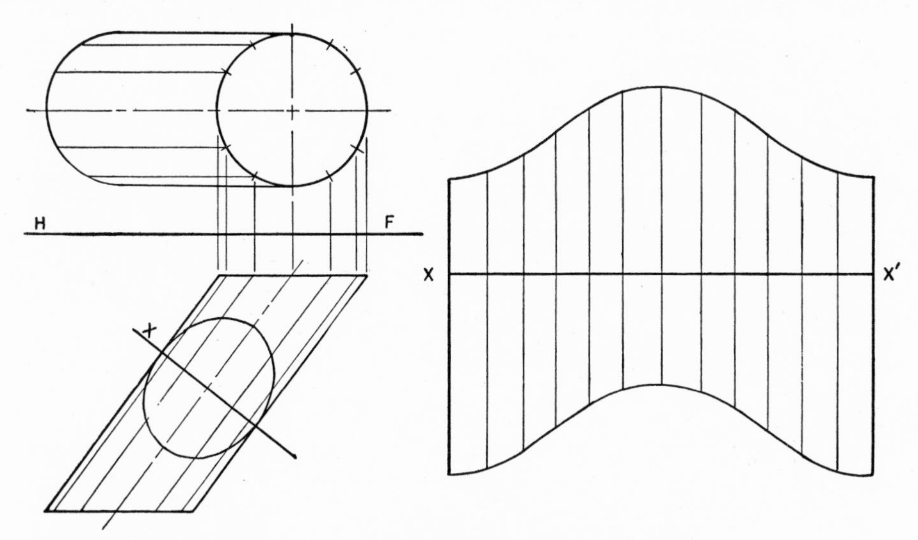

Fig. 7.8. Development of an Oblique Cylinder

the same as on the elliptical curve, and the lengths of the elements above and below the line are shown in the front view of the cylinder.

7.24. Problem 7.14. To find the development of a right pyramid.

Given: A right pyramid.

Required: The development of the pyramid.

Solution: Determine the shape and size of the planes that form the pyramid and join them in proper sequence.

Analysis:

1. Draw the projections of the pyramid on adjacent planes.
2. Develop the perimeter of the base.
3. Locate the edges of the pyramid on the development.

Discussion: The oblique edges of a right pyramid are of equal lengths and all have a common point. Figure 7.9 shows the top and front views of a right rectangular pyramid and the method used in finding the length of the edge *0–1*. The directions of the lines that form the base of the pyramid are found by drawing an arc having its center at *o′* and a radius equal to the length of the edge of the pyramid. From any convenient point of the arc lay off the chords *1′–2′*, *2′–3′*, *3′–4′*, and *4′–1″* equal to the edges *1–2, 2–3, 3–4,* and *4–1,* of the pyramid. Lines drawn from the ends of the chords to the point o' are the oblique edges of the pyramid.

If the pyramid be cut by a plane W, two of the oblique edges will be cut at a distance $o^F y'^F$ from the point O and two edges at the distance $o^F z'^F$ from the point O. These distances may be laid off in the development to show the lines of intersection of the plane with the pyramid.

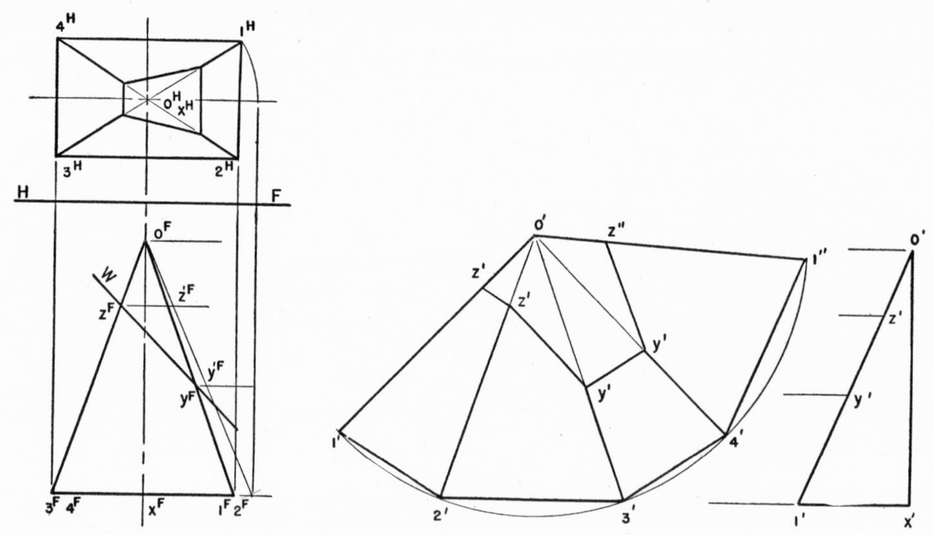

FIG. 7.9. Development of a Right Pyramid

Another method of measuring the lengths of the edges is sometimes preferable. It will be seen that an oblique edge of the pyramid is the hypotenuse of a right triangle of which $o^F x^F$ is the altitude and $o^H 1^H$ is the base. The length of the oblique edge *0–1*, and the locations of y' and z' as found by this method are shown in the figure.

7.25. Problem 7.15. To find the development of an oblique pyramid.

Given: An oblique pyramid.

Required: The development of the pyramid.

Solution: Determine the shape and size of the planes that form the pyramid and join them in the proper sequence.

Analysis:

1. Draw the projections of the pyramid on adjacent planes.
2. Determine the lengths of the edges of the pyramid.
3. Draw the triangular planes that form the pyramid with their common lines coincident.

Discussion: The lengths of the edges AC and AD of the pyramid of Figure 7.10 are $a^F c'^F$ and $a^F d'^F$. The triangular surface AED of the pyramid is drawn in its true shape and size as $a'e'd'$. The surfaces ADC and AEB of the pyramid have edges AD and AE coincident with the corresponding edges of surface ADE. With

a' as center and radius equal to $a^F c'^F$ strike arcs at b' and c'. With centers at d' and e' and radius equal to $e^F b^F$ or $c^F d^F$, strike arcs at c' and b'. The intersections of the arcs at c' and b' determine the location of those points on the development. One-half of the surface ABC is joined in the development to $a'c'$ and the other half to $a'b'$. In the construction of a sheet metal object of this form the joint of the material would be along the line $a'x'$.

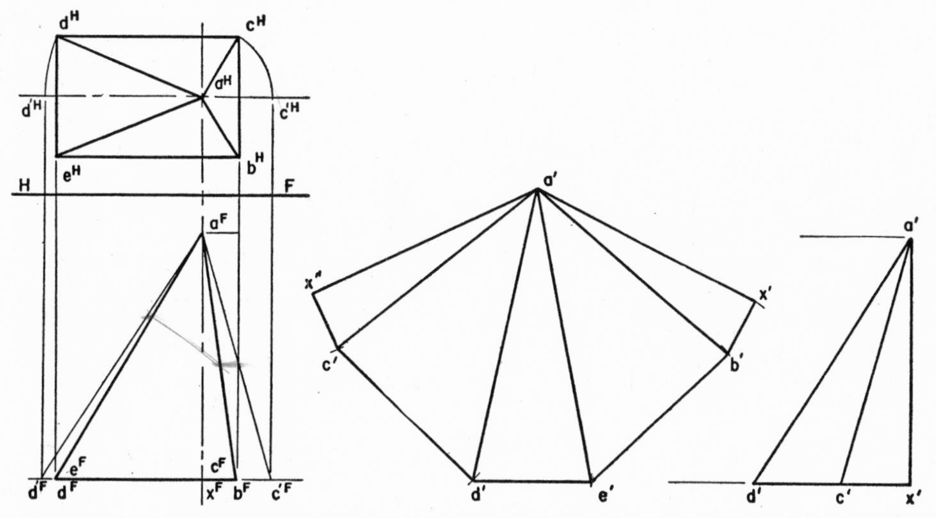

FIG. 7.10. Development of an Oblique Pyramid

The use of a right triangle to find the length of the edges is shown at the right side of the figure.

7.26. Problem 7.16. To find the development of a right circular cone.

Given: A right circular cone.

Required: The development of the cone.

Solution: Develop the perimeter of the base and join its extremities with the point that is the development of the apex.

Analysis:

1. Draw the projections of the cone on adjacent planes.
2. Determine the length of the elements of the cone.
3. Draw from any assumed center an arc having a radius equal to the length of the elements.
4. Lay off the length of the perimeter of the base on the arc and join the ends of the arc with lines drawn to the center.

Discussion: The length of the elements of the cone of Figure 7.11 is equal to the length of the projection $a^F o^F$. With a' as a center and radius $a^F o^F$, draw the arc $o'–o''$ and space on this arc the location of the elements. The development of the cone may be completed by joining the extremities of the arc with the point a'.

If the cone be cut by the plane as shown in Figure 7.11, the line of intersection may be found on the development by locating the points in which the elements are cut by the plane. The method of measuring the length of the elements above or below the plane is indicated in the figure. Since the projection a^Fo^F is the true length of each of the elements, the points in which each are cut may be projected horizontally to a^Fo^F to determine the distance along the elements from the point A to the plane. The lengths as here determined may now be measured on the development.

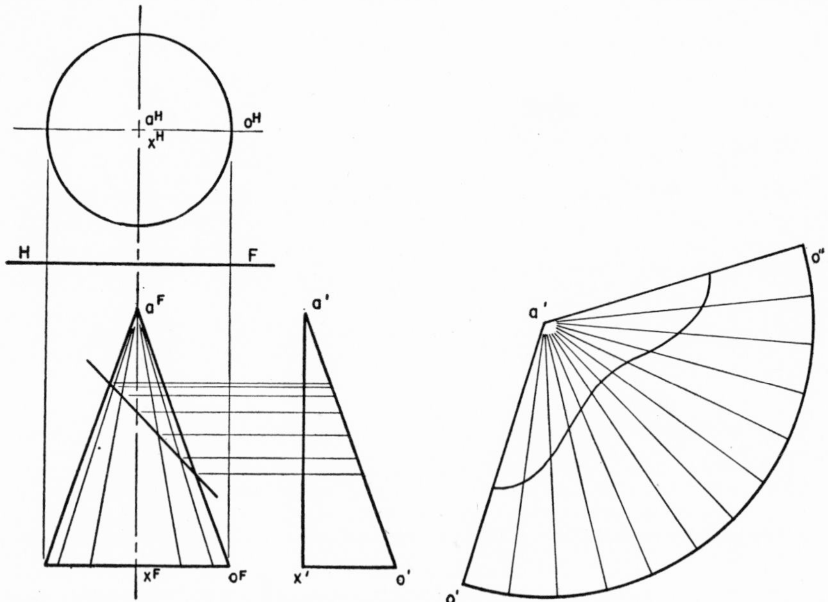

FIG. 7.11. Development of a Right Cone

The right-angled triangle $a'x'o'$ is merely a duplication of $a^Fx^Fo^F$ and is not necessary in this drawing. In the case of an oblique cone or a more complicated problem a similar triangle serves to segregate the work and to clarify it.

7.27. Problem 7.17. To find the development of an oblique cone.

Given: An oblique cone.

Required: The development of the cone.

Solution: Assume the surface to be composed of a large number of plane surfaces and then develop those surfaces in proper sequence.

Analysis:

1. Draw the projections of the cone on adjacent planes.
2. Locate the projections of the elements of the cone.
3. Determine the lengths of the elements and the length of the arcs of the base between elements.
4. Lay off the development of the perimeter of the base and join its extremities to the point that is the development of the apex.

Discussion: A conical surface may be visualized as a pyramid having an infinite number of sides. The development of a conical surface may therefore be made by the same methods as for a pyramid. The base of the oblique cone of Figure 7.12 is divided into 30-degree segments, and the development is constructed as if the base were a polygon of 12 sides. The development of the perimeter of the base is drawn as a smooth curve rather than as a broken line. As in the case of the oblique pyramid each element of an oblique cone must be measured. They may be revolved parallel to the *F* plane or laid off on a right-angled triangle.

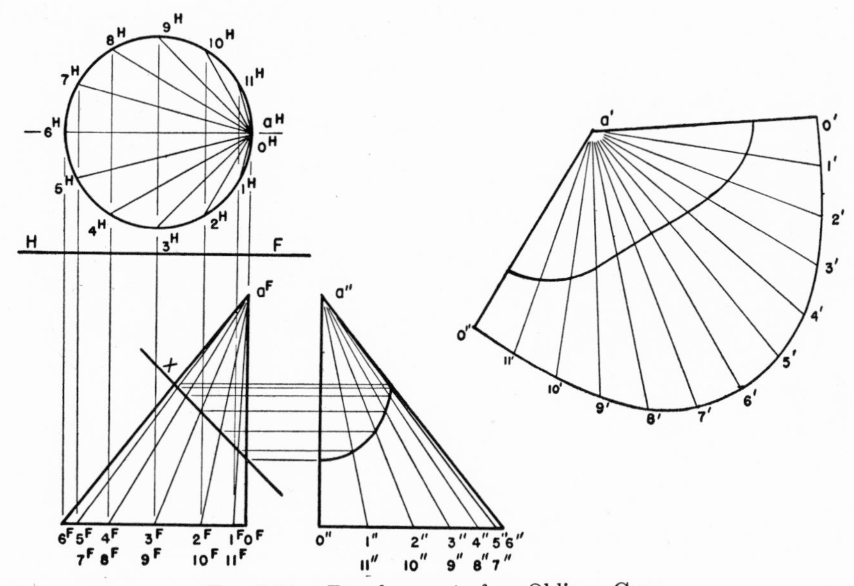

FIG. 7.12. Development of an Oblique Cone

To construct the development, lay off any line as a'–$6'$ of Figure 7.12. With point a' as a center, strike an arc having a radius of $a''7''$ that will intersect an arc drawn with point $6'$ as a center and radius equal to the length of the arc between elements. By similar construction each of the points of the base may be located on the development. A smooth curve drawn through these points is a close approximation of the development of the perimeter of the base.

If the cone be cut by an oblique plane as indicated in the figure, the intersection of the plane and cone may be laid off on the development as in Problem 7.16. The method of measuring the elements is indicated in the figure.

7.28. Problem 7.18. To find the development of a transition piece.

Given: A transition piece.

Required: The development of the surface.

Solution: Segregate and develop the surfaces of which the transition is composed.

Analysis:

1. Draw two projections of the surface to be developed.

2. Segregate by lines the various surfaces of which the object is composed.
3. Develop each surface and join them in proper sequence.

Discussion: A transition from a rectangular to a circular section and its development is shown in Figure 7.13. The rectangular portion is a prism and develops into the rectangle *abcd*. The circular portion is a cylinder and develops as the rectangle *efgh*. The surfaces *1*, *2*, *3*, and *4* are planes that show their true shape and size in the development. The rounded portions of the transition are segments of oblique

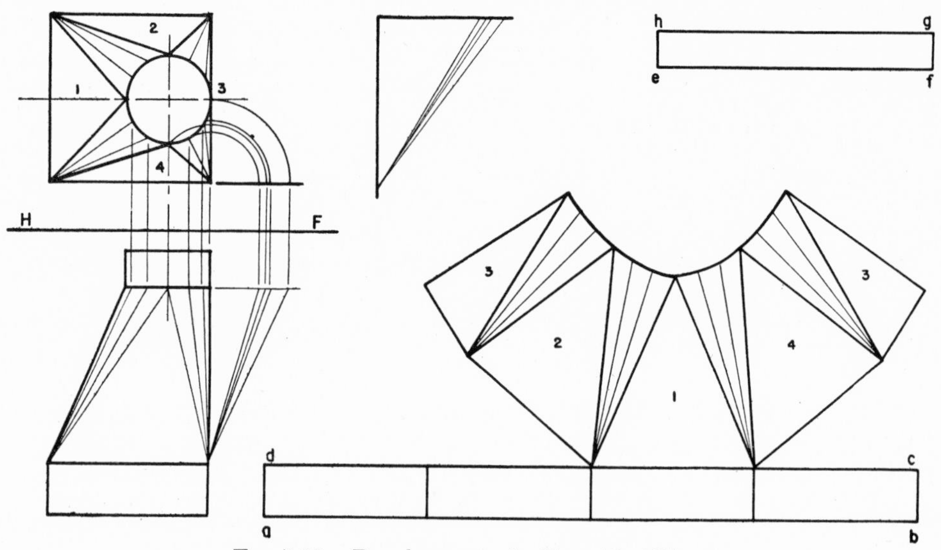

FIG. 7.13. Development of a Transition Piece

cones having coincident circular bases. Two methods of finding the lengths of the elements of the cones are indicated. The developments of the conical segments join the developments of the plane surfaces as shown in the figure.

7.29. Problem 7.19. To develop the surface of a sphere. *Method I.*

Given: The diameter of the sphere.

Required: The development of the surface of the sphere.

Solution: Assume that the sphere is composed of an indefinite number of right circular cones that have their bases in the surface of the sphere.

Analysis:

1. Divide the sphere into zones.
2. Assume cones that intersect the sphere in the circles that bound the zones.

Discussion: The sphere is a double curved surface and as such can not be developed. If the sphere is large, and a small amount of distortion is permitted, an approximation may be made that gives satisfactory results. In any case, the material used to construct any engineering project of spherical form must be more or less distorted.

The method shown in Figure 7.14 and discussed here is called the zone method. It will be seen that the upper half of the sphere has been divided into three zones. A cone, with its apex in the vertical center line, intersects the sphere in circles that pass through the points *A* and *B*. The development of that portion of the conical surface that lies between these circles is indicated as zone *1* of the development.

The development of the cone that intersects the sphere in the circles through *B* and *C* is found by similar construction to be zone *2* of the development. The development of the cone with its apex at *D*, and intersecting the sphere in a circle through *C*, completes the approximation and is indicated as zone *3*.

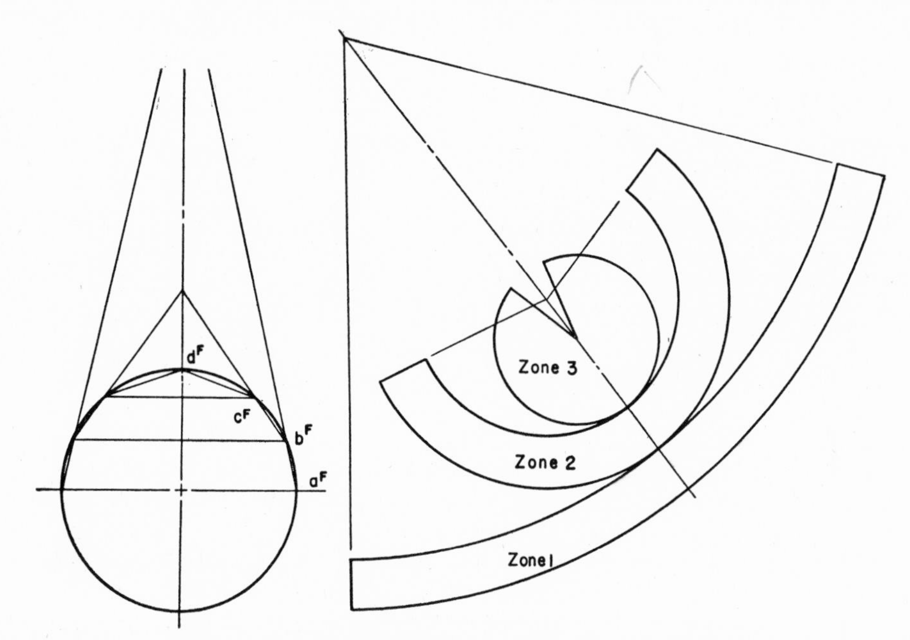

Fig. 7.14. The Development of a Sphere. Zone Method

It will be noticed that a considerable distortion of the material would be necessary to construct a sphere of this size if only three zones were assumed. In engineering applications, such as storage tanks, the spheres are frequently large and the material used is made in narrow widths. The development of such a surface would involve a large number of cones and the distortion of the material would be correspondingly small.

7.30. Problem 7.20. To develop the surface of a sphere. *Method II.*

Given: The diameter of the sphere.

Required: The development of the surface.

Solution: Assume that the sphere is composed of an indefinite number of gores that are determined by planes cutting through a diameter of the sphere.

Analysis:

1. Draw the projections of the sphere on any two adjacent planes.

2. Cut any number of planes through a diameter of the sphere.
3. Develop the gores cut from the sphere by the planes.

Discussion: In Figure 7.15, the sphere has been cut by planes taken at 30-degree intervals and through its vertical diameter. The development of the surface consists of twelve gores cut from the sphere by the planes. Since the gores are identical in shape, it is not necessary that all be shown in the development. Six gores, or a half development, are shown in the figure.

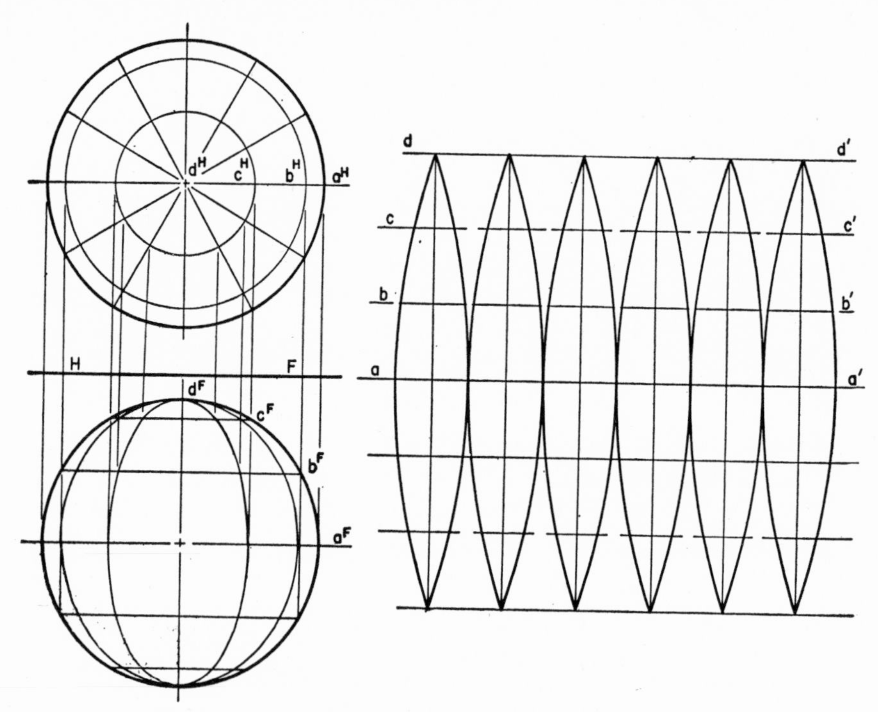

FIG. 7.15. The Development of a Sphere. Gore Method

The location of the curved edges of the gores on the front view and on the development may be determined by their intersection with planes taken perpendicular to the vertical diameter. In the figure, a plane through a point A on the great circle of the sphere develops as the line aa'. A plane through B develops as the broken line bb', and through C as the broken line cc'. A plane tangent to the sphere at the point D locates the points of the gores on their center lines. The vertical distances between the lines aa', bb', and cc' of the development are the lengths of arcs AB, BC, and CD. The lengths of the arcs cut by the planes on the gores are shown in the top view and may be transferred to the development with the dividers. The lower half of the gores may be constructed in a similar manner to complete the half-development of the sphere.

7.31. The Helix. The helix is probably the most used space curve in engineering and architectural design. The threads on bolts and screws, the screw threads of machine tools, the blades of screw conveyors, all are examples of its use in engineering constructions. The spiral stairway or ramp are architectural adaptations of helical surfaces.

The helix may be defined as the path of a point that revolves about an axis and moves at the same time in a direction parallel to the axis. Both movements are usually assumed to be constant. If the radius of revolution is constant the curve may be called a cylindrical helix. If the radius increases or decreases at a constant

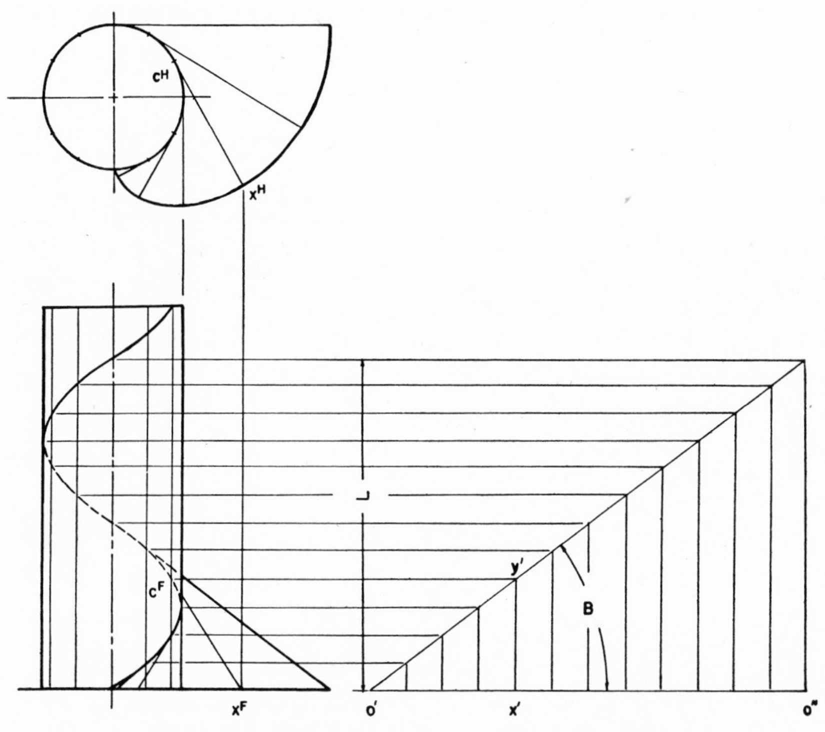

FIG. 7.16. Helical Convolute—Limited by a Plane

rate, it may be called a conical helix. The cylindrical helix is more common in constructions, and attention is directed to it.

In Figure 7.16 the generating point is assumed to move on the surface of a cylinder of the diameter shown. In making one revolution it moves in the direction of the axis a distance L, which is called the lead of the helix. The movement due to one revolution is equal to the circumference of the cylinder. The combined movement may be represented graphically by the hypotenuse of the triangle of which L is the altitude and the circumference of the cylinder, $o'o''$, is the base. The length of the helix is equal to that of the hypotenuse of the triangle. The angle of the tangent of the curve at any point is the angle B indicated in the figure.

It should be noticed that, if the triangle was assumed to be wrapped around the directing cylinder, the line $o'o''$ would form the base of the cylinder and the hypotenuse would coincide with the helix.

7.32. Problem 7.21. To draw a helical convolute. *Case 1. The surface is limited by a plane.*

Given: A description of a helical convolute.

Solution: Draw the projections of the elements of the surface.

Analysis:

1. Draw the projections of the directing helix.
2. Draw the H projections of the elements.
3. Find the points in which the elements pierce the limiting plane.
4. Draw the F projection of the elements.

Discussion: The helical convolute is a surface generated by a line that moves along a helix and is always tangent to the helix. Such a surface is indefinite in extent and for practical application must be limited. The usual assumptions are: (*Case 1*) That it intersects a plane surface perpendicular to the axis of the helix; or (*Case 2*) by a cylinder whose axis is coincident with that of the helix. The latter case is much more common in engineering projects and will be discussed in the next problem.

It is assumed that the diameter of the cylinder on which the helix is drawn and the lead, or pitch, of the helix are as shown in Figure 7.16. The limiting plane is the lower base of the cylinder.

To find the projection of the helix equally spaced elements are drawn on the cylinder and on the triangle which is the development of that portion of the cylinder that lies below the helix. Projection may be made from an element of the development to the corresponding element of the cylinder to determine points of the curve. A smooth curve drawn through the points on the cylinder is the required helix.

The H projection of the tangent element at the point C of the curve is tangent to the H projection of the curve at c^H. The F projection of the element is tangent to the F projection of the curve at the point c^F. It will be seen in the figure that the length of the element from the point C to the limiting plane is $o'y'$ and that the length of its H projection is $o'x'$. This length measured on the H projection of the tangent locates x^H. Since X lies in the limiting plane, a vertical projector from x^H locates x^F. The F projection of the element can now be drawn from c^F to x^F. The same procedure may be used to determine any number of elements of the surface.

It is interesting to note that the intersection of the helical convolute with the limiting plane is the involute of the circular path of revolution.

7.33. Problem 7.22. To draw a helical convolute. *Case 2. The surface is limited by a cylinder.*

Given: A description of the surface.

Required: The projections of the surface.

Solution: Draw the projections of the elements of the surface.

Analysis:

1. Draw the projections of the directing helix.

2. Draw the H projection of the elements.
3. Find the points in which the elements pierce the limiting cylinder.
4. Draw the F projections of the elements.

Discussion: It is assumed that the directing helix and the limiting cylinder are of the diameters shown in Figure 7.17. The H projections of the elements are drawn

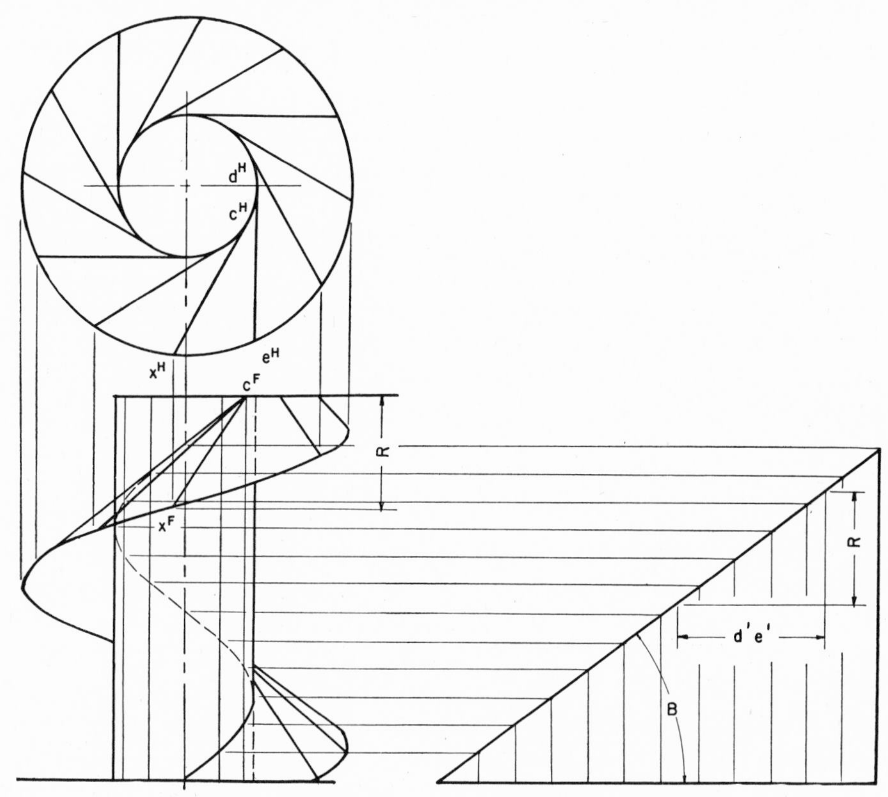

Fig. 7.17. Helical Convolute—Limited by a Cylinder

tangent to the H projection of the helix. The length of the H projection of any element is determined by the H projection of the limiting cylinder. The length and rise of any element, DE, are found by laying off the length of the H projection of an element in the triangular development. In the figure, $d'e'$ is equal to d^He^H, and R is the rise of any element of the surface.

To find the F projection of the element, CX, locate the F projection of C at c^F on the F projection of the helix, and the F projection of X at x^F a distance R below c^F. Any other element may be located by following a similar procedure. A sufficient number of elements may be drawn in this manner to show the contour of the surface.

7.34. Problem 7.23. To develop the surface of a helical convolute that is limited by a cylinder. *Method I.*

Given: The projections of a helical convolute.

Required: The development of the surface.

Solution: Assume that the surface is composed of a series of triangles that are bonded by the elements and the limiting cylinder.

Analysis:

1. Extend each element to its intersection with another element.
2. Determine the length of the extended element.
3. Determine the length of the arc on the limiting cylinder.
4. Lay off in succession the triangles determined by the elements and the arc.

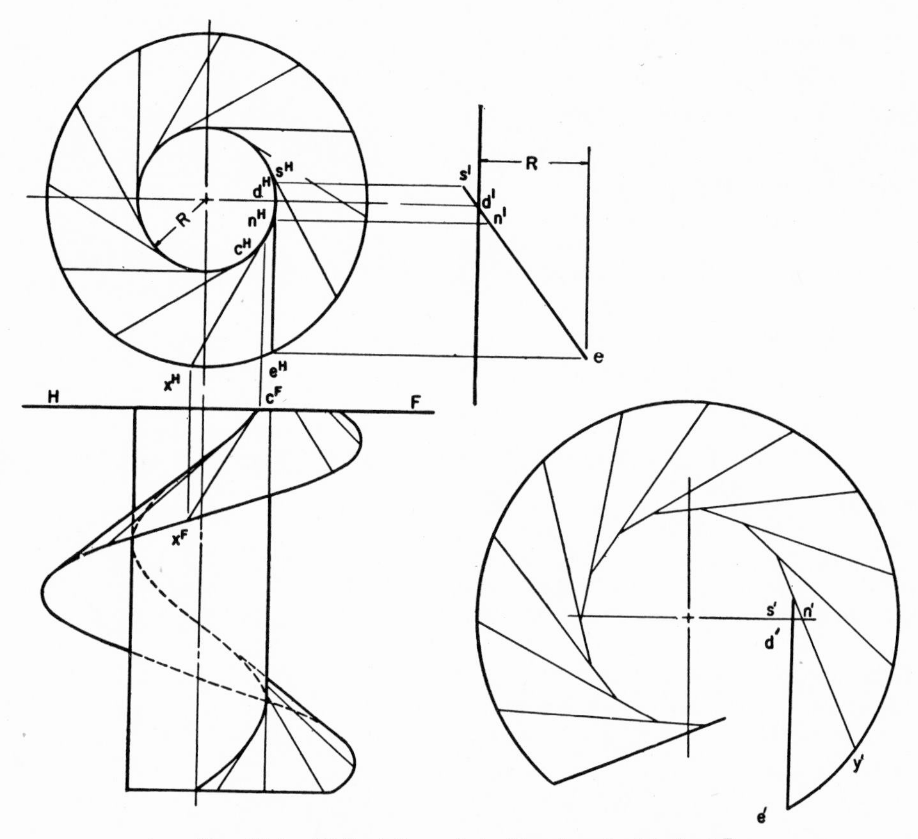

Fig. 7.18. Helical Convolute Developed—Method I

Discussion: The H and F projections of the elements of the helical convolute of Figure 7.18 are assumed to be given. The element ED extended intersects the next adjoining element at the point S and is intersected by the extended element CX at the point N. The true lengths of EN, ED, and ES are projected on the plane *1* as e^1n^1, e^1d^1, and e^1s^1.

The length of the helical curve between the points E and X may be closely approximated by measuring on a triangle similar to that of Figure 7.17, or by computations based on such a triangle. The computed length for this figure is the distance $e'y'$ as shown on the development.

The development of the surface is constructed by the method of triangulation used in the development of the oblique pyramid and cone. The lengths of the extended element, $e's'$, and the point of intersection of elements, n', may be located on any assumed line. An arc of radius e^1n^1 and center at s' intersects another arc of radius $e'y'$ and center at e' at the point y'. An element of the development through $n'y'$ completes the first triangle of the developed surface. Similar triangles of the surface may now be joined as indicated in the figure. The inside circle is drawn tangent to the extended elements. The outside curve (also a circle) is drawn through the ends of the elements.

7.35. Problem 7.24. To develop the surface of a helical convolute. *Method II.*

Given: The projections of a helical convolute.

Required: A development of the surface.

Solution: Compute the radius of the developed helix and determine the lengths and locations of the elements.

Analysis:

1. Compute the radius of the developed helix.
2. Draw the developed helix and locate the tangent points on it.
3. Draw tangent elements of the required length.
4. Draw the outside circle.

Discussion: The method of Problem 7.23 is laborious and subject to the usual inaccuracies of graphical construction. Time may be saved and some errors eliminated if certain formulas are borrowed from mathematics. In Problem 7.23 the inside curve of the development was found to be a circle. The formula $R = \frac{r}{\cos^2 B}$ may be used to determine the radius of that circle. In this formula, R equals the radius of the developed helix, r the radius of the directing cylinder, and B the tangent angle of the helix. See Figure 7.17.

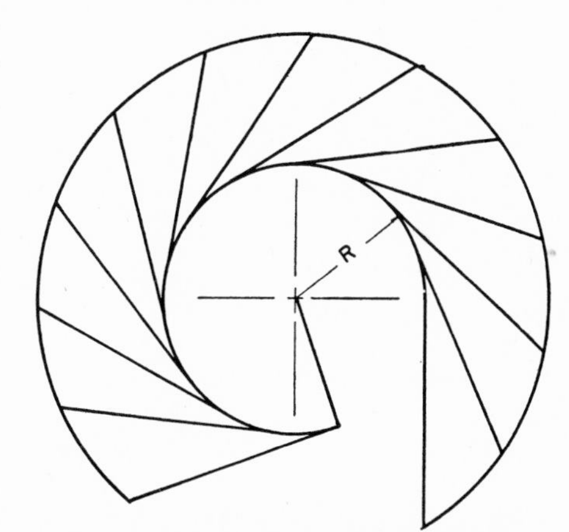

FIG. 7.19. Helical Convolute Developed —Method II

The angle B may be found by the formula $\cot B = \frac{\pi d}{L}$ in which L equals the lead of the helix and d the diameter of the directing cylinder.

The length of the helix is equal to the hypotenuse of the triangle of which L is the altitude and πd the base. The formula $M = \sqrt{L^2 + (\pi d)^2}$ may be used to determine the length of the circular development of the helix. The length of the elements may be found by projection as in Problem 7.23.

With these values known the development may be quickly and accurately drawn. A circular arc of radius R may be drawn at any convenient location, and the points of tangency located on it. The elements of the development may be drawn tangent to the arc, and another circle drawn through their ends. Since the elements are of the same length, only the first and last need to be drawn. See Figure 7.19.

The development shown in the figure is for one complete turn of the helix. A somewhat greater amount could have been drawn. The largest amount being determined by the formula $N = \frac{1}{\cos B}$ in which N is the total number of turns and B the tangent angle. Assuming the dimensions used in the figure $N = 1.245$ turns.

7.36. Application Problems.

7.1. *Layout 1.*

(a) The line $A(9, \frac{1}{4}, 1\frac{1}{4})$, $B(7, 2\frac{3}{4}, 2\frac{3}{4})$ is the center line of an elliptical cylinder having 2″ circular bases, parallel to F. A hole in the upper surface projects on H as a 1″ square with its center at $C(8, 1\frac{1}{2}, ?)$. Two sides of the square are parallel to F. Find the F projection.

(b) The line $X(1\frac{3}{4}, 2\frac{1}{2}, \frac{3}{4})$, $Y(4, 1, 3)$ is the center line of an elliptical cylinder having 2″ circular bases parallel to H. A hole in the front surface of the cylinder projects on H as a ¾″ square with its center at $Z(3, 1\frac{1}{4}, ?)$. Two sides of the square are parallel to F. Find the F projection.

7.2.

(a) Same as Problem 7.1 (a) except that the diagonal of the square is parallel to F.

(b) Same as Problem 7.1 (b) except that the diagonal of the square is parallel to F.

7.3. *Layout 1.*

(a) The line $A(8, 1\frac{1}{2}, \frac{1}{2})$, $B(8, 1\frac{1}{2}, 3\frac{1}{4})$ is the center line of a right circular cone having a 3″ base at the point B. A 1″ square hole is cut through the cone. The center line of the hole is perpendicular to F and passes through the point $C(8, 1\frac{1}{2}, 2)$. Two surfaces of the hole are parallel to H. Find the H and F projections.

(b) The line $X(4\frac{1}{2}, \frac{1}{2}, \frac{1}{2})$, $Y(1\frac{3}{4}, 3\frac{1}{4}, 2)$ is the center line of an elliptical cone having a 2″ circular base parallel to F at the point Y. The center line of a ½″ square hole through the cone is perpendicular to H through the point $Z(2\frac{1}{2}, 2\frac{1}{2}, 1\frac{1}{2})$. Two surfaces of the hole are parallel to F. Find the H and F projections.

7.4.

(a) Same as Problem 7.3 (a) except that the 1″ square hole is parallel to F.

(b) Same as Problem 7.3 (b) except that the ½″ square hole has one diagonal of its right section parallel to F.

7.5. *Layout 1.*

(a) The center of a 2½″ sphere is at the point $A(8, 1\frac{1}{2}, 2)$. A vertical line drawn through $B(8, \frac{7}{8}, 1\frac{3}{8})$ is the center line of a ¾″ square hole cut through the sphere. One diagonal of the square right section is parallel to F. Find the H and F projections.

(b) The center of a sphere is at the point $C(3, 1\frac{1}{2}, 1\frac{1}{2})$. A vertical line drawn through $D(3, \frac{7}{8}, \frac{7}{8})$ is the center line of a 1″ round hole through the sphere. Find the H and F projections.

7.6.

(a) Same as Problem 7.5 (a) except that the center line of the hole is perpendicular to F and the diagonal is parallel to H.

(b) Same as Problem 7.5 (b) except that the center line of the hole is perpendicular to F.

7.7. *Layout 1.* The *HF* axis line is 3½″ above the lower margin. The point *A*(7, 1½, 1½) is the center of a 2½″ sphere. A line drawn from point *X*(6½, ?, ¾) on the surface of the sphere to the point *A* is the center line of a 1″ diameter hole in the sphere. Find the *H* and *F* projections.

7.8. Same as Problem 7.7 except that the hole is a ¾″ square with the diagonal of its right section parallel to *H*.

7.9. *Layout 1.* The line *A*(7½, 1¾, ¼), *B*(7½, 1¾, 3¼) is the center line of a right circular cone with its 3″ base at the point *B*. A line drawn through *X*(7, ?, 2¼) and perpendicular to *AB* is the center line of a 1″ diameter hole. Find the *H* and *F* projections.

7.10. Same as Problem 7.9 except that the hole is a ¾″ square with the diagonal of its right section parallel to *H*.

7.11. *Layout 1.* Power is transmitted between the shafts, whose center lines are *AB* and *CD*, by means of two friction cones having their apexes at the point *C*. The diameter of the base of each cone is 2″. Draw the *H* and *F* projections of the cones showing the line of contact between them. Line *AB*: *A*(7½, 1½, ½), *B*(7½, 1½, 3¼). Line *CD*: *C*(7½, 1½, 3), *D*(6, 3½, 1).

7.12. *Layout 1.*

(a) The line *A*(7½, 2, ½), *B*(7½, 2, 2½) is the axis of a torus generated by revolving a 1″ circle about the axis. The radius of revolution is 1″ measured from the axis to the center of the generatrix. The center of the generatrix revolves in a plane that passes through the mid-point of *AB*. A vertical line through the point *C*(7, 1, 2½) is the center line of a ¾″ circular hole through the torus. Draw the *H* and *F* proportions.

(b) The line *X*(3, 2, ½), *Y*(3, 2, 2½) is the axis of a torus of the same description as in Problem 7.12(a). The surface is cut by a plane that is perpendicular to *F* and slopes upward in an angle of 30 degrees with *H* through the point *Z*(2, 2, 1½). Draw the *H* and *F* projections.

7.13.

(a) Same as Problem 7.12 (a) except that the hole is a ½″ square having two surfaces parallel to *F*.

(b) Same as Problem 7.12 (b) except that the plane makes an angle of 45 degrees with *H*.

7.14. *Layout 1.* The *HF* axis line is 4½″ above the margin. The line *A*(8½, 1½, ¼), *B*(8½, 1½, 3¼) is the center line of a right rectangular prism having 2″ × 1½″ bases at *A* and *B*. The longer edges of the bases are parallel to *F*. Assume that the prism is cut by a plane that is perpendicular to *F* and slopes upward to the left in an angle of 30 degrees with *H* through the point *C*(7½, 1½, 1½). Find the development of the truncated prism.

7.15. Same as Problem 7.14 except that the prism is cut by a semicircular hole of 1″ radius having its center line perpendicular to *F* through the point *C*.

7.16. *Layout 1.* The *HF* axis is 4½″ above the lower margin. The line *A*(8½, 1½, ¼), *B*(8½, 1½, 3¼) is the center line of a right hexagonal prism. The bases are 2″ in maximum diameter with two edges parallel to *F*. The prism is cut by a plane that is perpendicular to *F* and slopes upward to the left in an angle of 30 degrees with *H* through the point *C*(7½, 1½, 1½). Find the development of the truncated prism.

7.17. Same as Problem 7.16 except that the prism is cut by a semicircular hole of 1″ radius having its center line perpendicular to *F* through the point *C*.

7.18. Same as Problem 7.16 except that the prism is revolved so that two edges of the base are perpendicular to *F*.

7.19. Same as Problem 7.18 except that the prism is cut by a semicircular hole of 1″ radius, having its center line perpendicular to *F* through the point *C*.

7.20. *Layout 1.* The *HF* axis line is 4½″ above the margin. The line *A*(8½, 1½, ¼), *B*(8½, 1½, 3¼) is the center line of a right octagonal prism. The bases are 2″ in minimum diameter with two edges parallel to *F*. The prism is cut by a plane that is perpendicular to *F* and slopes downward to the left in an angle of 30 degrees with *H* through the point *X*(7½, 1½, 1½). Find the development of the truncated prism.

7.21. Same as Problem 7.20 except that a 1¾″ circular hole is cut through the prism. The center line of the hole is perpendicular to *F* through the mid-point of *AB*. Find the development of the prism.

7.22. *Layout 1.* The line $A(8\frac{1}{2}, \frac{1}{4}, 2)$, $B(6, 2\frac{1}{2}, 2)$ is the center line of an oblique hexagonal prism. The bases at A and B are parallel to F and are $1\frac{1}{2}''$ in maximum diameter. Two edges of the bases are parallel to H. Find the development of the prism.

7.23. Same as Problem 7.22 except that two edges of the bases are perpendicular to H.

7.24. Same as Problem 7.22 except that the bases are octagonal and are $1\frac{1}{2}''$ in minimum diameter.

7.25. *Layout 1.* The HF axis line is $4\frac{1}{2}''$ above the margin. The line $A(8\frac{1}{2}, 1\frac{1}{2}, \frac{1}{4})$, $B(8\frac{1}{2}, 1\frac{1}{2}, 3\frac{1}{4})$ is the center line of a right circular cylinder. The bases at A and B are $2''$ in diameter. The cylinder is cut by a plane that is perpendicular to F and slopes upward to the left in an angle of 45 degrees with H through the mid-point of AB. Find the development of the truncated cylinder.

7.26. Same as Problem 7.25 except that a $1\frac{1}{4}''$ square hole is cut through the cylinder. The center line of the hole is perpendicular to F through the mid-point of AB. One diagonal of the square right section is parallel to H.

7.27. Same as Problem 7.26 except that the hole is circular and $1\frac{3}{4}''$ in diameter.

7.28. *Layout 1.* The line $A(9, \frac{1}{4}, 1\frac{1}{4})$, $B(7, 2\frac{3}{4}, 1\frac{1}{4})$ is the center line of an oblique cylinder having $2''$ circular bases parallel to F at the points A and B. The point $C(8, 1\frac{1}{2}, 1\frac{1}{4})$ is a point on the vertical center line of a $1''$ square hole cut through the cylinder. Two faces of the square hole are parallel to F. Make a development of one-half of the cylindrical surface.

7.29. Same as Problem 7.28 except that the hole is circular and $1\frac{3}{8}''$ in diameter.

7.30. *Layout 1.* The HF axis line is $4\frac{1}{2}''$ above the margin. The line $A(8, 1\frac{1}{2}, \frac{1}{4})$, $B(8, 1\frac{1}{2}, 3\frac{1}{4})$ is the center line of a right rectangular pyramid. The $2'' \times 1\frac{1}{2}''$ base at B has its longer edges parallel to F. The center line of a $\frac{3}{4}''$ circular hole is perpendicular to F and passes through the point $C(8, 1\frac{1}{2}, 2)$. Find the development of the pyramid. Assume that the surface is joined in the center of one of the narrow sides.

7.31. Same as Problem 7.30 except that the pyramid is truncated by a plane that is perpendicular to F and slopes upward to the left in an angle of 45 degrees with H through the point C.

7.32. *Layout 1.* The HF axis is $4\frac{1}{2}''$ above the margin. The line $A(8, 1\frac{1}{2}, \frac{1}{4})$, $B(8, 1\frac{1}{2}, 3\frac{1}{4})$ is the center line of a right hexagonal pyramid. The base at B is $2''$ in minimum diameter with two edges parallel to F. The pyramid is truncated by a plane that is perpendicular to F and slopes upward to the left in an angle of 45 degrees with H through the mid-point of AB. Find the development of the truncated pyramid.

7.33. Same as Problem 7.32 except that two edges of the base are perpendicular to F.

7.34. *Layout 1.* The HF axis line is $4\frac{1}{2}''$ above the margin. The line $A(6, 1\frac{1}{2}, \frac{1}{4})$, $B(8, 1\frac{1}{2}, 3\frac{1}{4})$ is the center line of an oblique hexagonal pyramid. The hexagonal base at B is parallel to H, $2''$ in minimum diameter, and having two edges parallel to F. The pyramid is truncated by a plane that is perpendicular to F and to its center line through the mid-point of AB. Find the development of the truncated pyramid.

7.35. Same as Problem 7.34 except that two edges of the base are perpendicular to F.

7.36. Same as Problem 7.34 except that the base is octagonal.

7.37. *Layout 1.* The HF axis line is $4\frac{1}{2}''$ above the margin. The line $A(8, 1\frac{1}{2}, \frac{1}{4})$, $B(8, 1\frac{1}{2}, 3\frac{1}{4})$ is the center line of a right circular cone. The base at B is $2\frac{1}{2}''$ in diameter. The cone is truncated by a plane that is perpendicular to F and that slopes upward to the left in an angle of 45 degrees through the mid-point of AB. Find the development of the truncated cone.

7.38. Same as Problem 7.37 except that a $1''$ circular hole is cut through the cone. The center line of the hole is perpendicular to F through the mid-point of AB.

7.39. *Layout 1.* The HF axis line is $4\frac{1}{2}''$ above the margin. The line $A(6, 1\frac{1}{2}, \frac{1}{4})$, $B(8, 1\frac{1}{2}, 3\frac{1}{4})$ is the center line of an oblique cone that is truncated by a plane parallel to H through the mid-point of AB. The base at B is a $2''$ circle and is parallel to H. Find the development of the truncated cone.

7.40. Same as Problem 7.39 except that the plane is perpendicular to F and slopes upward to the left in an angle of 45 degrees with H.

7.41. Find the development of the cone of Problem 7.3 (b).

7.42. Find the development of the cone of Problem 7.4 (b).

7.43. *Layout 1.* The point $A(8, 1\frac{1}{2}, 1\frac{1}{2})$ is the center of a sphere of $2\frac{1}{2}''$ diameter. Find the development of one-half of the sphere. Assume three zones.

7.44. Find the development of one-half of the sphere of Problem 7.5 (a). Use gore method.

7.45. *Layout 1.* The HF axis is $4\frac{1}{2}''$ above the margin. The line $A(8\frac{1}{2}, 1\frac{1}{2}, 1)$, $B(8\frac{1}{2}, 1\frac{1}{2}, 3)$ is the axis of a transition piece. The opening at A is a circle $1\frac{1}{4}''$ in diameter and the opening at B is a

2″ × 1½″ rectangle with the longer edges parallel to F. Both openings are parallel to H. Find the development of the transition piece.

7.46. Same as Problem 7.45 except that the H projection of the rectangle is 2″ × 1½″ and that the F projection makes an angle of 30 degrees with H through the point B.

7.47. *Layout 1.* The HF axis is 4½″ above the margin. The point A(7½, 1½, ¾) is the center of a 1¼″ circular opening that is parallel to H. The point B(8½, 1½, 3) is the center of a 2″ × 1½″ rectangular opening that is parallel to H with its longer edges parallel to F. Find the development of the transition piece that will join the openings.

7.48. *Layout 1.* Given points are: A(8, 1½, ½), B(8, 1½, 3¼), C(8½, 3, 3), and D(9½, 1, ¾).

Power is transmitted between the shafts, whose center lines are AB and CD, by means of a friction drive consisting of two hyperboloids of revolution. The hyperboloids are of equal diameter and heights. Their bases are not necessarily at the given points. (The line of contact is the generatrix of both surfaces.) Find the projections of the hyperboloids on a plane that is parallel to both AB and CD and on planes that are perpendicular to each.

7.49. *Layout 1.* The line A(8, 1¾, ¼), B(8, 1¾, 3) is the center line of a 1¼″ shaft of a helical convolute conveyor that has an outside diameter of 3″. The lead of the helix is 2½″. Draw the projections of one turn of the helix. Assume that the helix is right-hand, that is, it turns clockwise as seen from a position in which the generating point moves away from the observer. Develop one turn of the conveyor blade, using Method II.

7.50. Same as Problem 7.49 except the helix is left-hand.

7.51. Same as Problem 7.49 except that Method I is used to make the development.

7.52. *Layout 1.* Omit axis lines. Scale ½″ = 1′ 0″. Place the drawing sheet with the shorter edges parallel with the T square.

Draw the plan and elevation of a spiral stairway that is supported in the center by a cylindrical column 2′ in diameter. The outer ends of the treads and risers are supported on the inside surface of a cylinder 8′ in diameter. Each tread is a 22½ degree sector of a circle, is 1″ thick, overlaps the tread beneath it, and is butted against the next riser. The risers are 6″ high and 1″ thick. Assume, when making the drawing, that the front half of the large cylinder has been removed.

CHAPTER VIII

TANGENTS TO SURFACES

8.1. Tangency. In the construction of drawings or in the graphic solution of problems, the draftsman frequently uses tangent lines or planes. Inaccurately drawn tangents are very objectionable on a drawing. They destroy any beauty that the design might otherwise possess. The graphic solution of many problems depends upon an accurate visualization and construction of tangents. The intent of the following paragraphs and problems is to develop the ability to visualize tangency and to suggest its use in the solution of problems.

8.2. Tangent Lines. A straight line that is tangent to a plane curve lies in the plane of the curve and is perpendicular to the radius of curvature at the point of tangency. One point, the point of tangency, is common to the curve and its tangent. If the curve and its tangent be projected on any plane, the projection of the line will be tangent to the projection of the curve.

A straight line that is tangent to a curved surface is tangent to the curve cut from the surface by a plane passing through the line and intersecting the surface. The tangent line and surface have one point in common.

8.3. Tangent Planes. A plane that is tangent to a ruled surface is in contact with it in one element of the surface. The tangent plane is determined by an element of the surface and a line tangent to the surface at some point of that element.

A plane that is tangent to a double curved surface of revolution has, in general, point contact with that surface. Such a plane is perpendicular to a plane passed through the axis of revolution and to the radius of curvature of the generating curve. The plane that is tangent to a surface at one point may intersect the surface at some other point.

8.4. Problem 8.1. To find the projection of a plane that is tangent to a cylinder in a given line of the cylinder.

Given: The location in space of a cylinder of given size and form, and of an element of that cylinder.

Required: The projections of the plane that is tangent to the cylinder in the given element.

Solution: Find the projections of two lines of the required plane.

Analysis:

1. Draw the projections of the cylinder and of the given element.
2. Draw the projections of a tangent to the cylinder at some point of the element.

Discussion: The oblique elliptical cylinder of Figure 8.1 and the element *BC* of that cylinder are assumed to be given. The line *DE* is a tangent of the surface and lies in the plane of the base of the cylinder. This tangent is perpendicular to the radius of curvature of the base at the point *C* of the given element. The lines *BC* and *DE* intersect at the point *C* and determine a plane that is tangent to the cylinder in the line *BC*.

It is obvious that the projections of the cylinder and the tangent plane on the auxiliary plane *1* as shown in the figure are not necessary for the solution of the

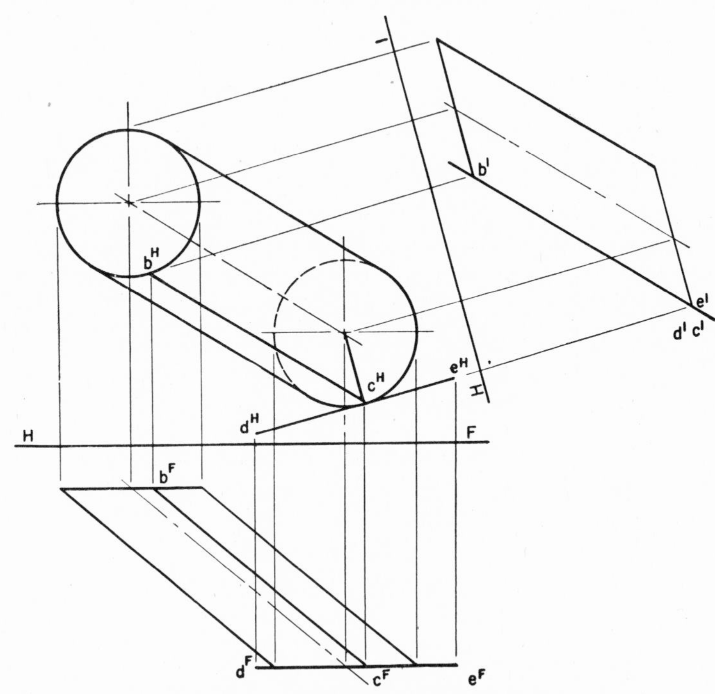

FIG. 8.1. Plane Tangent to a Cylinder

problem. The *H* and *F* projections of the lines determine the required plane, and the auxiliary projection merely serves to indicate the relative positions of the plane and cylinder.

8.5. Problem 8.2. To find the projections of a plane that contains a given point and its tangent to a given cylinder.

Given: The location in space of a cylinder and a point.

Required: The projections of a plane that contains the point and is tangent to the cylinder.

Solution: Determine two lines of the required plane.

Analysis: (*Case I. The point lies in the cylinder.*)

1. Draw the projections of the point and cylinder.
2. Draw the projections of an element of the cylinder through the given point.
3. Draw the projections of a tangent to the cylinder through some point of the element.

Discussion: The solution of this problem in accordance with the analysis involves nothing new. The method of finding an element of the cylinder and the method of finding the projections of lines that determine a tangent plane have been illustrated and discussed in the preceding problems.

Analysis: (*Case II. The point is not in the surface.*)

1. Draw the projections of the cylinder and point.
2. Draw the projections of an auxiliary line that passes through the given point and is parallel to the axis of the cylinder.
3. Draw a tangent of the surface that intersects the auxiliary line.

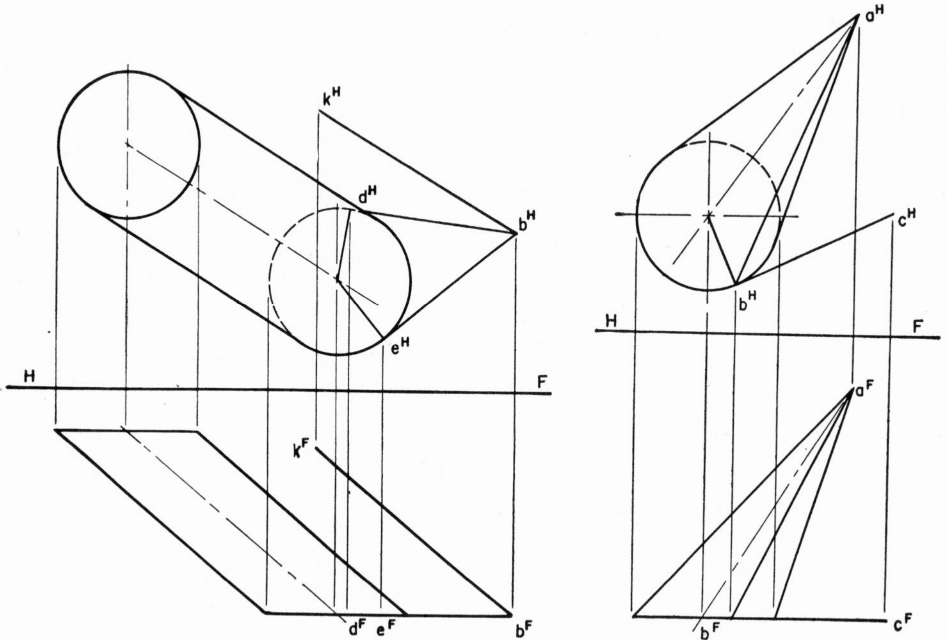

FIG. 8.2. Tangent Plane through a Given Point

FIG. 8.3. Plane Tangent to a Cone

Discussion: In Figure 8.2 the elliptical cylinder and the point K are assumed to be given. The auxiliary line KB is drawn through the point K and parallel to the axis of the cylinder. The line KB pierces the plane of the base of the cylinder at the point B. The lines BD and BE may be drawn through B and tangent to the base of the cylinder. The line KB and either of the tangents BD or BE determine a plane that contains K and is tangent to the surface.

8.6. Problem 8.3. To find the projections of a plane that is tangent to a given cone in a given element of that surface.

Given: The projections of a cone and a line of that surface.

Required: To find the projections of the plane that is tangent to the given cone in the given element.

Solution: Find two lines of the tangent plane.

Analysis:

1. Draw two projections of the cone and the given element of that surface.
2. Draw a tangent to the cone at some point of the given element.

Discussion: In Figure 8.3 it is assumed that the cone and the element BA of that surface are given by the conditions of the problem. The line BC is a tangent to the base of the cone at the point B. The intersecting lines BA and BC determine a plane that is tangent to the cone in the given line of the cone.

8.7. Problem 8.4. To draw the projections of a plane that contains a point and is tangent to a given cone.

Given: The location in space of a cone and a point.

Required: The projections of a plane that passes through a point and is tangent to a given cone.

Solution: Find two lines of the required plane.

Analysis: (*Case I. The point is in the surface.*)

1. Draw the projections of the cone and the point.
2. Draw an element of the cone through the point.
3. Draw a tangent of the cone that intersects the element.

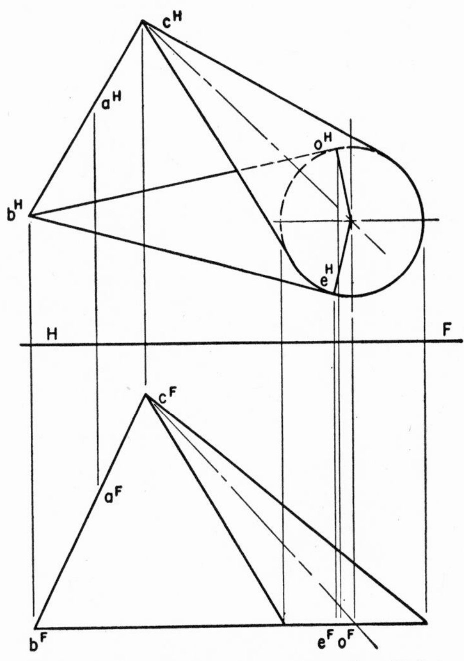

FIG. 8.4. Tangent Plane through a Point

Discussion: The solution of this problem in accordance with the analysis involves nothing new. An element of the cone may be drawn through the given point. The tangent may now be drawn to intersect the element as in Problem 8.2.

Analysis: (*Case II. The point does not lie on the given cone.*)

1. Draw two projections of the cone and point.
2. Draw an auxiliary line through the point and the apex of the cone.
3. Extend the line until it pierces the base, or other plane section, of the cone.
4. Draw a tangent of the cone through the piercing point of the auxiliary line.
5. Draw the projections of the plane that is determined by the tangent and auxiliary line.

Discussion: The elliptical cone and the point A are given in Figure 8.4. The auxiliary line through the apex C and the given point A pierces the plane of the base at B. Two lines may be drawn through B and tangent to the base of the cone. The auxiliary line BC and either of the tangents through B determine a plane that passes through point A and is tangent to the cone.

8.8. Problem 8.5. To find the projections of a plane that is tangent to a sphere and passes through a given point.

Given: The location of a point and a sphere.

Required: The projections of the plane that is tangent to the sphere and contains the given point.

Solution: Determine two lines of the plane.

Analysis: (*Case I. The point lies on the sphere.*)

1. Draw two projections of the given sphere and point.
2. Draw a line from the given point to the center of the sphere.
3. Draw the projections of the plane that is perpendicular to that line at the given point.

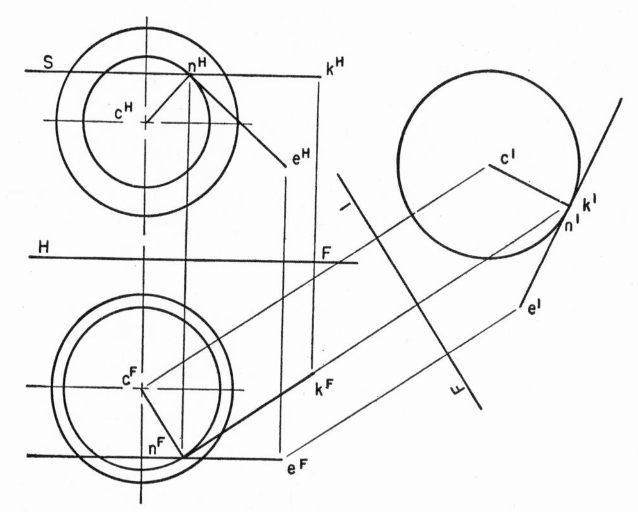

FIG. 8.5. Plane Tangent to a Sphere

Discussion: It is assumed that the conditions of the problem locate the H and F projections of the sphere and the H projection of the point N as in Figure 8.5. The F projection of the point N is located by passing an auxiliary plane S through the point and parallel to the F plane. Such a plane cuts the sphere in a circle, the F projection of which is a circle having c^F as a center. The F projection of the point N lies in the F projection of the circle at n^F. The line CN joins the point N on the surface with the point C at the center of the sphere.

The auxiliary plane *1* is parallel to the line CN, and the line c^1n^1 is the projection of CN on *1*. The required plane projects on *1* as the line $e^1k^1n^1$ which is perpendicular to c^1n^1. The H and F projections of any two lines of this plane may be used to determine its location in space.

If either of two perpendicular lines is parallel to a projection plane, their projections on that plane will be perpendicular. The plane tangent to the sphere at N may, therefore, be determined without projecting the sphere on an auxiliary plane. The line EN of Figure 8.5 is parallel to H, and the H projections of CN and EN are perpendicular. The line KN is parallel to F, and the F projections of CN and KN are perpendicular. Both EN and KN are perpendicular to a radius of the sphere and determine a plane that is tangent to the sphere at the point N.

Analysis: (*Case II. The point does not lie on the sphere.*)

An infinite number of planes may be passed through such a point and tangent to the sphere. In any definite problem the location of the plane would be governed by the conditions of that problem. Such a problem would, in general, reduce itself to that of Problem 8.6.

8.9. Problem 8.6. To find the projections of a plane that contains a given line and is tangent to a given sphere.

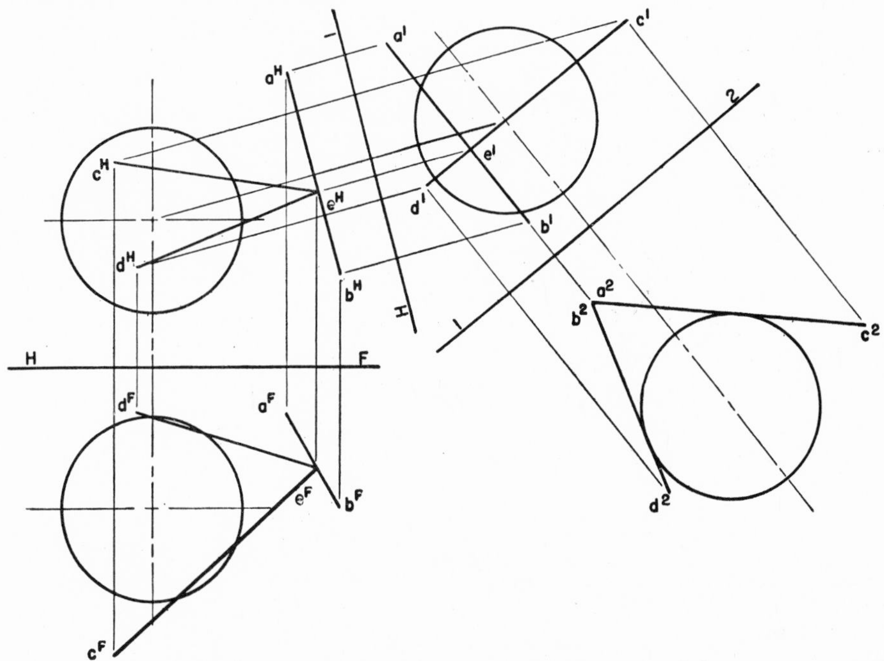

FIG. 8.6. Plane through a Line and Tangent to a Sphere

Given: The location in space of a sphere and a line.

Required: The projections of a plane that contains the line and is tangent to the given sphere.

Solution: Determine two lines of the required plane.

Analysis:

1. Draw the projections of the line and sphere.
2. Project the line and sphere on a plane that is perpendicular to the line.
3. Draw the projections of the required plane.

Discussion: Assume that the sphere and line AB of Figure 8.6 are given. The line AB projects as a point, a^2b^2, on a plane *2* that is perpendicular to AB. The lines $a^2b^2c^2$ and $a^2b^2d^2$ are the edge views of two planes passed through the line and tangent to the sphere. A plane passed through the center of the sphere and perpendicular to AB is pierced by AB at the point E. The intersecting lines AB and CE determine one plane, and AB and DE another plane, that passes through the line AB and is tangent to the sphere.

8.10. Problem 8.7. To find the projections of a plane that is tangent to a torus and passes through a given point.

Given: The projections of a torus and of a point.

Required: The projections of a plane that contains the given point and is tangent to the given torus.

Solution: Determine two lines of the plane.

Analysis: (*Case I. The point lies in the surface.*)

1. Draw the projections of the torus and the given point of that surface.
2. Assume a plane through the point and the axis about which the generating circle of the torus was revolved.
3. Project the torus on a plane that is parallel to the plane described above.
4. Draw two lines of the required plane.

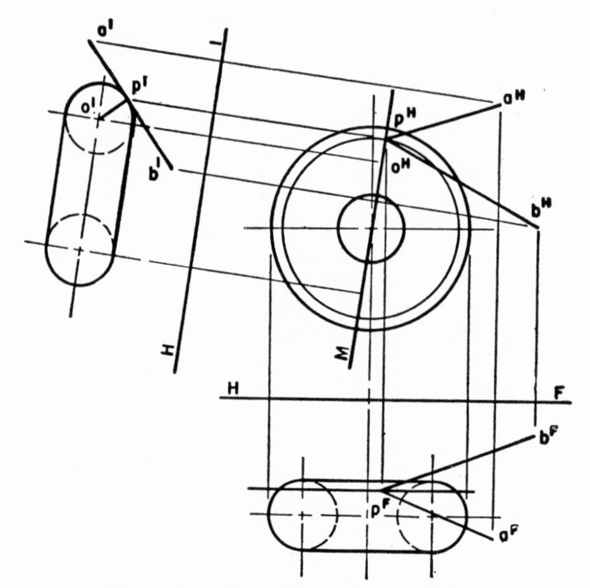

FIG. 8.7. Plane Tangent to a Torus

Discussion: In Figure 8.7 it is assumed that the H and F projections of the torus and the horizontal projection of point P on that surface are given by the conditions of the problem. An auxiliary plane that is passed through the point P, and which contains the axis of the generating circle of the torus, is shown in the figure as plane M. Plane *1* is assumed parallel to plane M. The torus projects on plane *1* with the center of the generating circle at o^1. Point P projects on *1* as p^1. The line drawn through the point P to the center of the generating circle O projects on the plane *1* as o^1p^1. The required plane projects on *1* as $a^1p^1b^1$. Any lines of that plane may be selected to determine the H and F projections of the plane.

Analysis: (*Case II. The point is not in the given surface.*)

As in the case of the sphere, the number of solutions of the problem is infinite. In any definite problem which involves passing a plane through a given point and tangent to a torus, the location of that plane will be restricted by other conditions. When so restricted, the problem may be solved, in general, by the methods that have been discussed.

8.11. Application Problems.

8.1. *Layout 1.* The HF axis is 3″ above the lower margin. The line M(8, 2½, ½), N(6, 1, 2½) is the center line of an oblique elliptical cylinder, having 1½″ circular bases parallel to H. Find two lines that determine a plane that is tangent to the cylinder in an element that passes through point K(7, 1, ?). Point K is on the upper surface of the cylinder. Project the plane and cylinder on an auxiliary plane that is perpendicular to the tangent plane.

8.2. Same as Problem 8.1 except that the point is K(7, ?, 1¼).

8.3. Same as Problem 8.1 except that the point K(7, 2½, ?) is on the lower surface.

8.4. Same as Problem 8.1 except that the point K(7, ?, 1¼) is on the front surface.

8.5. *Layout 1.* The line A(9, 1, ½), B(8, 2½, 2½) is the center line of an oblique cylinder having 1¼″ circular bases parallel to H at the points A and B. Two planes passed through the point C(7, 1½, 1½) are tangent to the cylinder. Find the dihedral angle between the planes.

8.6. *Layout 1.* The line A(9, ½, 1), B(8, 2½, 2½) is the center line of an oblique cylinder having 1¼″ circular bases parallel to F at the points A and B. Two planes that are tangent to the cylinder pass through the point C(7, 1½, 1½). Find the dihedral angle between the planes.

8.7. *Layout 1.* Assume points A(9, 2½, ½), B(7, 2½, 2), C(8, ½, ½), and D(9, 1, 1½).

A 12″ cylindrical fuel supply tank is to be mounted between the planes ABC and BCD, and in contact with both. Find the H and F projections of the lines of contact. Scale 1″ = 1′ 0″.

8.8. *Layout 1.* What is the maximum diameter of a cylindrical tank that may be mounted tangent to planes ABC and BCD of Problem 8.7, if the line of contact with BCD passes through the point D? Scale of tank 1″ = 1′ 0″. Find the H and F projections of the center line of the cylinder of indefinite length.

8.9. *Layout 1.* A line through E(8½, 1, 1½) and parallel to B(7, 2½, 2), C(8, ½, ½), is the center line of a right circular cylinder of 1¼″ diameter. Two planes through the line BC are tangent to the cylinder. Find the H and F projections of another point of each plane.

8.10. *Layout 1.* The point A(8, 2½, ½) is the apex of an oblique cone, the 1¼″ circular base of which is parallel to H with its center at B(9, 1, 2½). Two planes that are tangent to the cone pass through the point C(7½, 1, 2). Find the dihedral angle between the planes. Draw the H and F projections of the elements of the cone in which the planes are tangent to the cone.

8.11. *Layout 1.* The point A(8, ½, 2½) is the apex of an oblique cone, the 1¼″ circular base of which is parallel to F at the point B(9, 2½, 1). Two planes that are tangent to the cone pass through the point C(7½, 2, 1). Find the dihedral angle between the planes. Draw the H and F projections of the elements of the cone in which the planes are tangent to the cone.

8.12. *Layout 1.* Two planes pass through the line A(8, ½, 2½), C(7½, 2, 1), and are tangent to a 1½″ sphere whose center is at the point B(9, 1½, 1½). Find the H and F projections of another point of each plane.

CHAPTER IX

INTERSECTIONS OF SURFACES

9.1. Intersections. The drawings used by the engineer in the design of a machine or structure are, in general, line drawings. Such drawings consist to a very large extent of projections of the lines of intersection of the various surfaces of the object drawn. The intersection of the planes that form a prism are lines which are commonly called edges. The projection of these edges on the projection planes is all that is required to describe that prism graphically. Nearly all machine parts and elements of structures have some prismatic or other geometric form. The assembly of these parts into the complete structure involves the intersection of the various parts. The draftsman's problem is to find the intersection of the various surfaces of the structure and to project those intersections on the conventional projection planes.

The intersection of any two surfaces is a line. Two plane surfaces intersect in a straight line. Two curved surfaces will, in general, intersect in a curved line. Such intersections may, in special cases, have a mathematical formula and be determined analytically. All intersections can be found or closely approximated by graphic methods.

9.2. Determination of Intersection. The intersection of two surfaces is composed of all the points common to those surfaces. The intersection of two planes is determined by locating two points that are common to those planes. The intersection of two curved surfaces may be closely approximated by locating a number of points that are common to the surfaces and drawing a smooth curve through those points. The number of points to be used would depend upon the kind of surfaces and the accuracy desired.

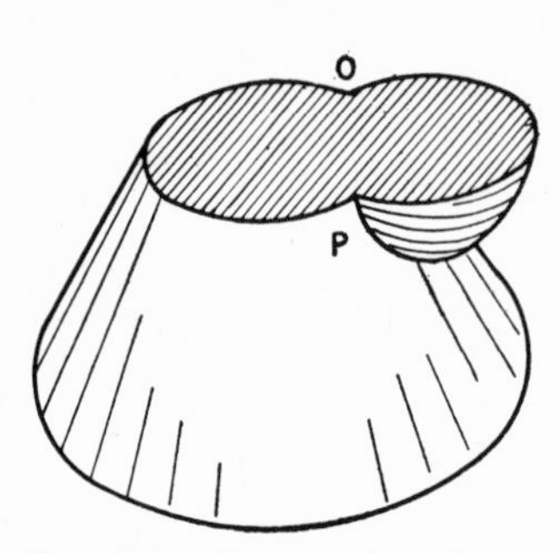

FIG. 9.1. Intersecting Cone and Sphere

Points that are common to two surfaces may be located in many different ways. A general solution is to intersect both of the given surfaces by a third surface. The latter may be a plane, a cylinder, a sphere, or other magnitude. Whatever surface is used, it should have a simple intersection with the given surfaces such as straight lines or circles. The intersections of the given surfaces with the assumed surface are lines intersecting on the latter. A point of intersection of those lines is common to both given surfaces and is one of the required points. Any number of points may be found in this way to determine the complete curve.

The foregoing discussion is more easily understood if such an intersection is illustrated by a figure. In Figure 9.1 a right circular cone is intersected by a sphere.

Points O and P in the intersection are found as described previously by assuming a plane perpendicular to the center line of the cone. The intersection of such a plane with the cone is a circle. This circle intersects another circle cut from the sphere at the points P and O. Since all points of one circle lie in the cone and all points of the other circle lie in the sphere, the points P and O lie in the intersection of the cone and sphere.

Figure 9.2 illustrates the use of a plane in finding the intersection of a cone and cylinder. The plane is assumed through the apex of the cone and parallel to the center line of the cylinder. The intersection of the elements of the surfaces determines the points M and N in their intersection.

9.3. Problem 9.1. To find the projections of the intersection of a given plane and prism.

Given: The location in space of a plane and a prism that is intersected by the plane.

Required: The projections of the lines in which the prism is intersected by the plane.

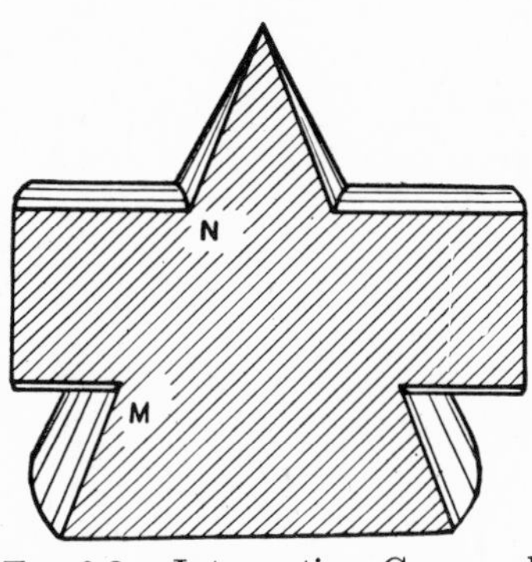

FIG. 9.2. Intersecting Cone and Cylinder

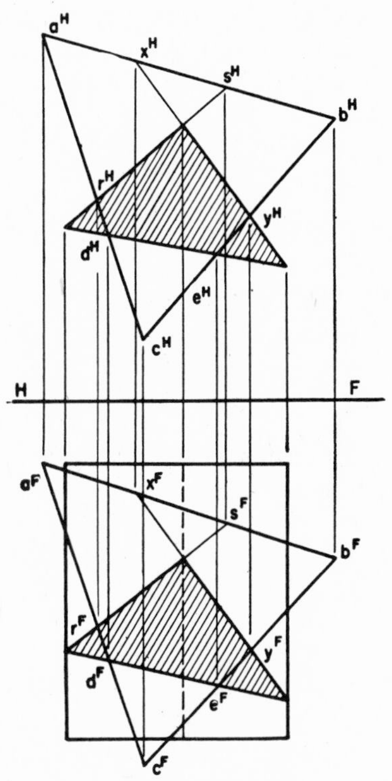

FIG. 9.3. Intersecting Plane and Prism

Solution: Determine the intersections of the planes of the prism with the given plane.

Analysis: *Method I.*

1. Draw the projections of the given plane and prism.
2. Assume auxiliary planes that are coincident with the planes of the prism.
3. Find the intersections of the auxiliary planes with the given plane.

Discussion: In Figure 9.3 the plane of ABC intersects the vertical triangular prism in the lines that bound the shaded area. The line of intersection of the plane of ABC with the right rear plane of the prism is the line XY. This intersection is found by assuming the plane of the prism to be extended so that it is pierced by the lines AB and BC of the plane ABC. The line AB pierces this plane at X, and the line BC pierces it at Y. The H projection of X is x^H at the intersection of a^Hb^H and the edge view of the extended plane. The F projection of X is in the F projection of AB at the point x^F. The H and F projections of the point Y, in which the line BC pierces the extended plane, are found at y^H and y^F. The intersection of the plane ABC with the front plane of the prism is found by a similar construction to be DE, and with the left rear plane to be RS. These lines determine the required intersection.

Analysis: *Method II.*

1. Draw the projections of the given plane and prism.
2. Project the plane and prism on an auxiliary plane that is perpendicular to the given plane.
3. Find the points in which the edges of the prism pierce the given plane.
4. Join the piercing points with the required lines of intersection.

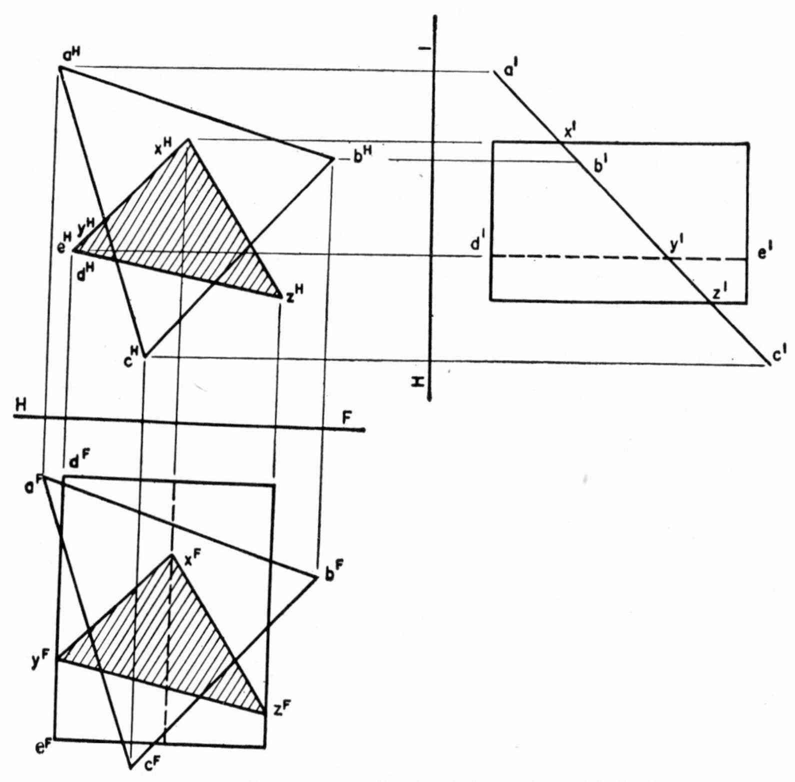

FIG. 9.4. Intersection by Auxiliary Plane Method

Discussion: Another method of finding the intersection of a plane with a prism involves the use of an auxiliary plane that is perpendicular to the given plane. The lines of intersection of the planes of the prism with the given plane are determined by the points in which the edges of the prism pierce the given plane. Figure 9.4 illustrates this method.

In Figure 9.4 the plane *1* is taken perpendicular to the plane *ABC*, and to *H*. The plane *ABC* projects on *1* as the line $a^1b^1c^1$. The edge *DE* of the prism projects on plane *1* as d^1e^1 and pierces the plane *ABC* at y^1. The piercing points of the other edges of the prism are found by the same method to complete the intersection.

9.4. Problem 9.2. To find the projections of the line of intersection of a given plane and pyramid.

Given: The location in space of a pyramid and a plane that intersects the pyramid.

Required: The projections of the lines in which the pyramid is cut by the plane.

Solution: Find the points in which the plane is pierced by the edges of the pyramid.

Analysis: *Method I.*

1. Draw the projections of the plane and pyramid.
2. Find the points in which the plane is pierced by the edges of the pyramid.
3. Join the piercing points to outline the required intersection.

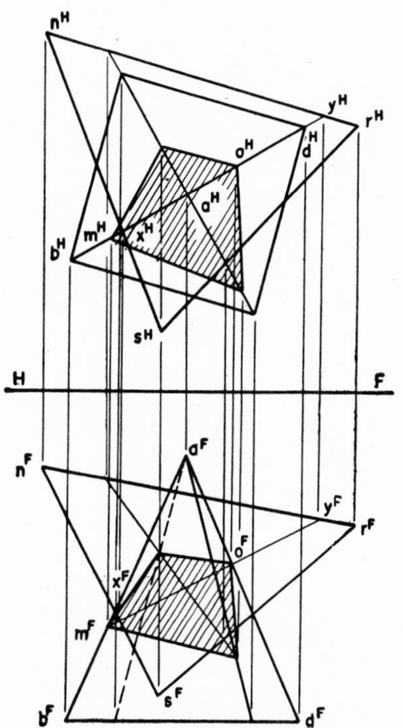

FIG. 9.5. Intersecting Plane and Pyramid

Discussion: In Figure 9.5 the plane *NRS* and the square pyramid are assumed to be given. The pyramid is intersected by the plane in the lines that bound the shaded area. These lines are determined by the piercing points of the edges of the pyramid.

The piercing points of the edges *AB* and *AD* on the plane *NRS* may be found by assuming a plane passed through them and perpendicular to *H*. The *H* projection of such a plane is the line through $a^Hb^Hd^H$. The line *XY* is the intersection of the assumed plane and the given plane. The *H* projection of *X* is x^H at the point in which the line pierces the assumed plane. The *H* projection of *Y* is y^H at the point in which *NR* pierces the assumed plane. The *F* projection of *X* is in the *F* projection of *NS* and of *Y* in the *F* projection of *NR*. The *F* projection of *XY* intersects the *F* projection of *AB* and *AD* at the points m^F and o^F. The point *M* is the point in which *AB* pierces *NRS*, and the point *O* is the point in which *AD* pierces that plane. The *H* projections of *M* and *O* are in the *H* projections of *AB* and *AD*. The *H* and *F* projections of the points in which the other edges of the pyramid pierce the plane *NRS* may be found by a similar construction.

Analysis: *Method II.*

1. Draw the projections of the given plane and pyramid.

2. Project the plane and pyramid on an auxiliary plane that is perpendicular to the given plane.
3. Find the points in which the edges of the pyramid pierce the plane.
4. Join the piercing points with the required lines of intersection.

Discussion: In Figure 9.6 a right square pyramid and a plane *NRS* are assumed to be given. Plane *1* is perpendicular to the plane *NRS* and the *H* plane. The

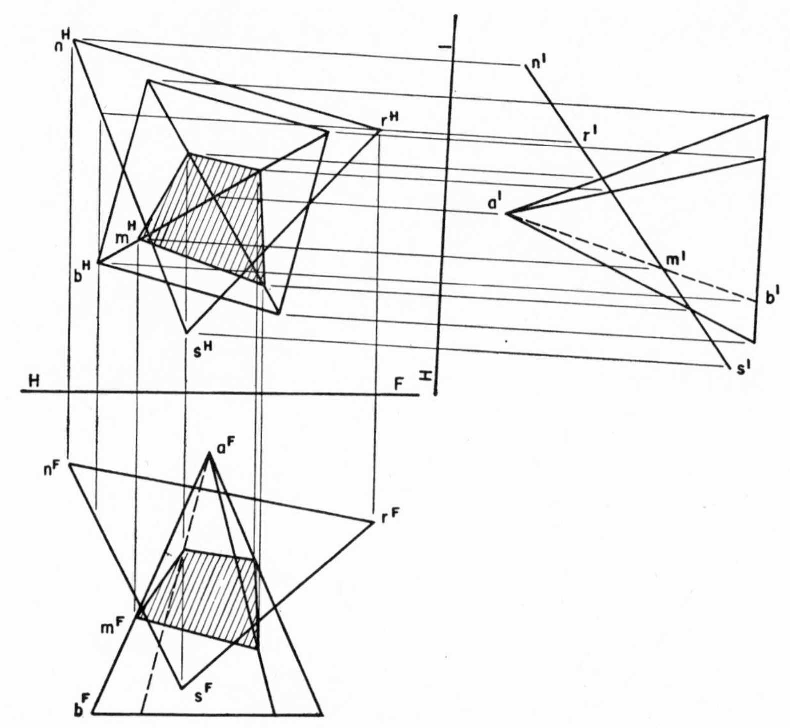

Fig. 9.6. Intersection by Auxiliary Plane Method

plane *NRS* projects on *1* as the line $n^1r^1s^1$, and the edge *AB* as a^1b^1. The edge *AB* pierces the plane *NRS* in the point *M*, and m^1 is the projection on plane *1*, m^H the *H* projection, and m^F the *F* projection. The points in which the other edges pierce *NRS* are found by the same method. The lines which join the piercing points of the edges are the lines in which the plane is intersected by the pyramid.

9.5. Problem 9.3. To find the projections of the line of intersection of a plane and cylinder.

Given: The location in space of a cylinder and a plane that intersects the cylinder.

Required: The projections of the intersection of the plane and cylinder.

Solution: Determine points that are common to the surfaces.

Analysis: (*Case I. The plane is parallel to the center line of the cylinder.*)

1. Draw the projections of the given plane and cylinder.

2. Project the plane and cylinder on a plane that is perpendicular to the given plane.
3. Determine the points in which the plane is pierced by the base of the cylinder.
4. Join the points in their proper order with straight lines.

Discussion: In Figure 9.7 the elliptical cylinder is intersected by the plane determined by the points *A*, *B*, and *C*. The cylinder and plane are projected on an

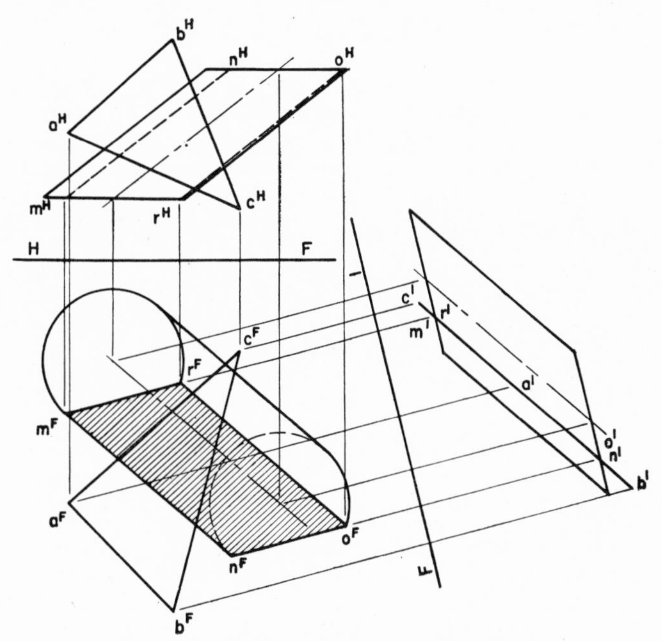

FIG. 9.7. Intersecting Plane and Cylinder

auxiliary plane *1* that is perpendicular to the given plane and to *F*. The given plane projects on plane *1* as a line. The bases of the cylinder are cut by the plane at the points *M*, *N*, *O*, and *R*. The *H* and *F* projections of these points determine the required projections of the intersection.

Analysis: (*Case II. The plane is oblique to the center line of the cylinder.*)

1. Draw the projections of the given plane and cylinder.
2. Project the given plane and cylinder on a projection plane that is perpendicular to the given plane.
3. Assume elements of the cylinder and determine their projections on the projection planes.
4. Find the points in which these elements pierce the given plane.
5. Draw the required intersection through these points.

Discussion: It is assumed in Figure 9.8 that the cylinder is a right circular cylinder perpendicular to *H* and that it is intersected by the plane *ABC*. The projection plane *1* is assumed perpendicular to *H* and to the given plane. Plane *ABC* projects on plane *1* as a line cutting the given cylinder. The points at which the elements cross the edge view of the plane *ABC* are the points in which those elements pierce *ABC*. The piercing points of the elements are points common to the plane and the cylinder. The element *ED* pierces the plane *ABC* at the point *O* which has its projection on plane *1* at o^1. The frontal projection of the point *O* is found in the *F* projection of the element *DE* at o^F. Any number of elements might be assumed and their piercing points found by similar constructions. A smooth curve may be drawn through the piercing points, which will closely approximate the required intersection.

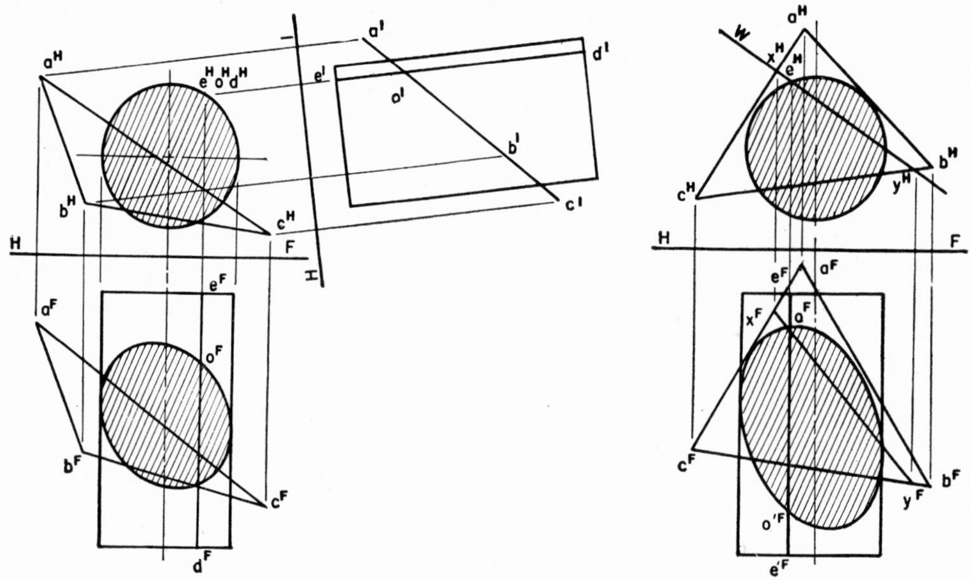

FIG. 9.8. Plane Oblique to Cylinder FIG. 9.9. Direct Method

A more direct method of finding the piercing points of elements is illustrated by Figure 9.9. A plane *W* that is parallel to the axis line of the cylinder intersects the plane *ABC* in the line *XY*. The cylinder is intersected by plane *W* in two elements. The element at *E* is intersected by the line *XY* at the point *O*. The point *O* lies in both surfaces and is one point of the intersection. Any number of planes may be assumed to complete the curve.

9.6. Problem 9.4. To find the projections of the line of intersection of a plane and cone.

Given: The location in space of a cone and a plane.

Required: The projections of the line of intersection of the plane and cone.

Solution: Find the projections of points that are common to the surfaces.

Analysis: *Method I.* (*Case I. The plane passes through the apex of the cone.*)

1. Draw the projections of the plane and cone.
2. Project the plane and cone on a projection plane that is perpendicular to the given plane.

3. Locate the points in which the curve of the base pierces the given plane.
4. Join these points of the base with the apex. These elements are the lines of intersection of the cone and plane.

Discussion: In Figure 9.10 a right circular cone with its center line perpendicular to H is cut by the given plane that passes through the apex. The projection plane *1* is assumed perpendicular to H and perpendicular to the given plane ABC. The given plane projects on plane *1* as the line intersecting the base of the cone at e^1d^1.

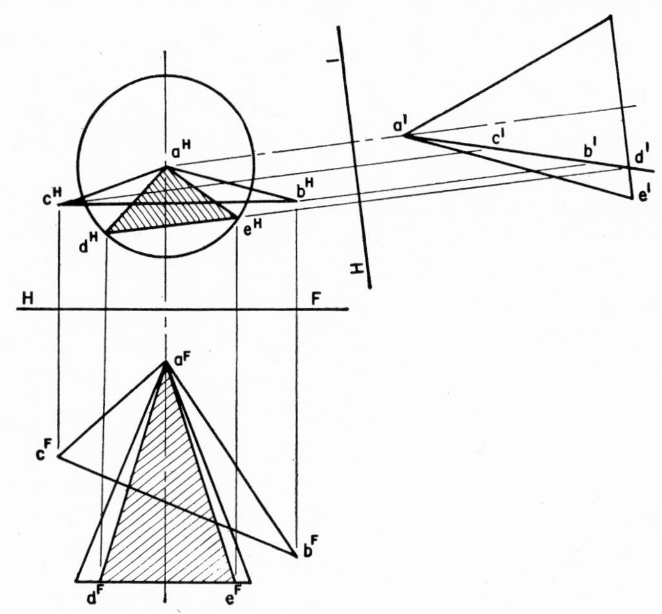

Fig. 9.10. Intersecting Plane and Cone

The H projections of E and D are found at d^He^H. The intersection of the plane and cone is in the lines AE and AD which are elements of the cone.

Analysis: *Method II.*

1. Draw the projections of the cone and the points that determine the plane.
2. Draw auxiliary lines through the apex and the given points.
3. Find the points in which the auxiliary lines pierce the plane of the base of the cone.
4. Join the piercing points to determine where the base is cut by the plane.
5. Draw the intersection of the cone and plane.

Discussion: In Figure 9.11 it is assumed that the right circular cone and the plane ABC are located as shown. The extended line AC pierces the plane of the base of the cone at Y, and the extended line AB pierces it at X. The H projection of XY crosses the base of the cone in the points d^He^H. The point A at the apex and the points D and E of the base of the cone may be joined to determine the required intersection.

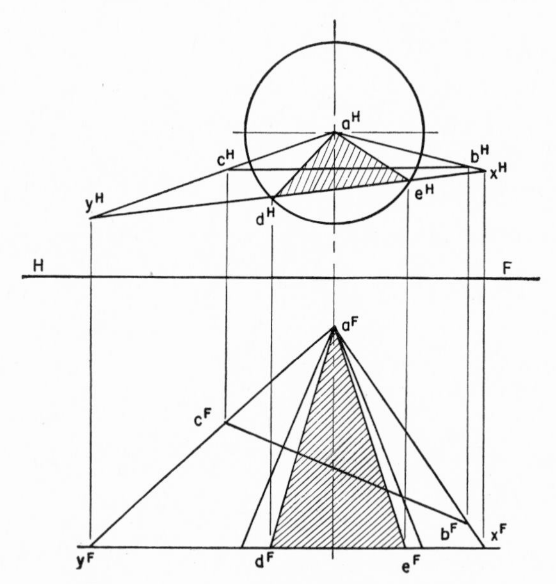

FIG. 9.11. Intersecting Plane and Cone

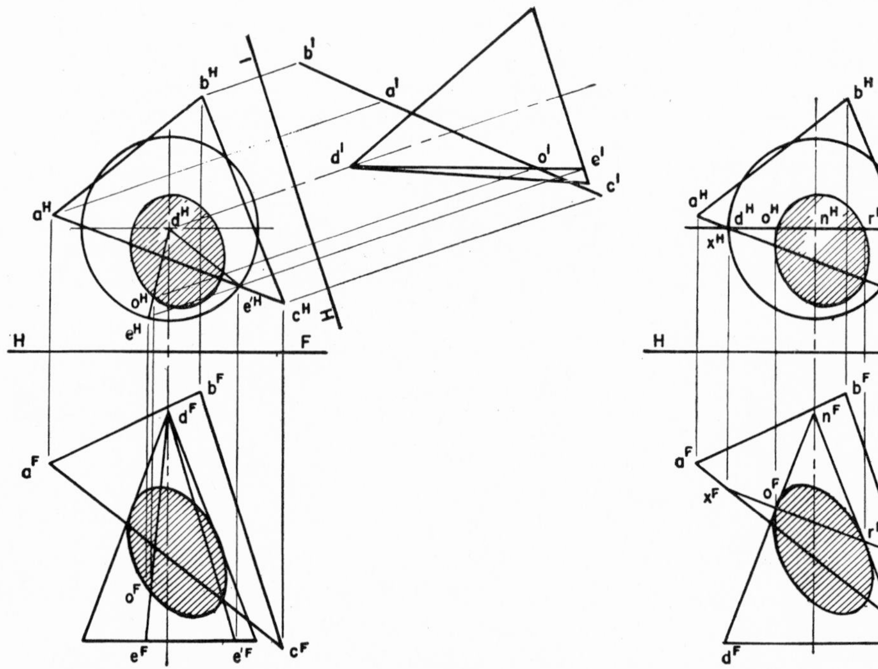

FIG. 9.12. Plane Cuts All Elements of Cone

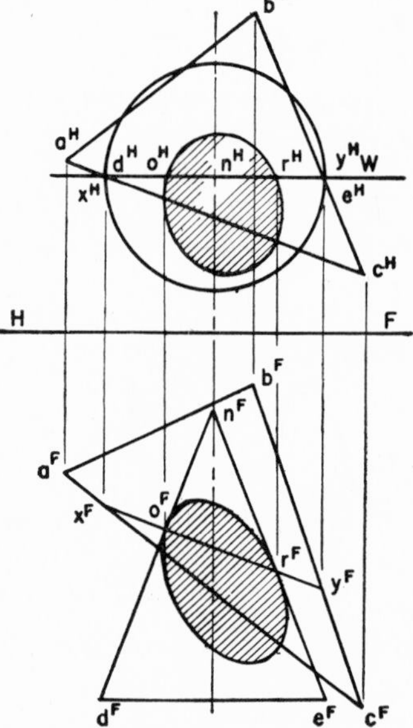

FIG. 9.13. Direct Method

Analysis: *Method I.* (*Case II. The plane is oblique to the center line of the cone.*)

1. Draw the projections of the cone and plane.
2. Project the plane and cone on a projection plane that is perpendicular to the given plane.
3. Find the piercing points of elements assumed on the cone.
4. Draw a curve through the piercing points of the elements.

Discussion: In Figure 9.12 a right circular cone is assumed, which is intersected by the plane *ABC*. The projection plane *1* is assumed perpendicular to *H* and to the given plane *ABC*. On plane *1* an element of the cone is seen to pierce the given plane at point *O*. The horizontal projection of this point is found in the horizontal projections of the element. Similarly, the frontal projection of the point is found in the frontal projection of the element. The curve of intersection may be drawn through a series of points found in this manner.

The second method of finding the piercing points of the elements is frequently convenient. In Figure 9.13 a vertical plane passed through the elements *ND* and *NE* intersects the given plane in the line *XY*. The line *XY* intersects the elements in the points *O* and *R*. Since these points are common to the cone and the plane, they must lie in the intersection of the two surfaces. Any number of points may be found in like manner to determine the required curve.

Analysis: *Method II.*

1. Draw the projections of the plane and cone.
2. Project the cone and plane on a projection plane that is perpendicular to *H* and to the given plane.
3. Assume auxiliary planes that are parallel to *H* and that cut the cone in circles and the given plane in lines.
4. Draw the curve of intersection through the points in which the circles and lines intersect.

Discussion: In Figure 9.14 a right circular cone is intersected by a given plane *ABC*. Projection plane *1* is assumed perpendicular to the given plane, and the cone and plane are projected on it. The auxiliary plane *W* is parallel to *H* and projects as a line on planes *1* and *F*. The intersection of *W* with the cone is a circle. The *H* projection of this circle has its center at n^H. The point *O* is common to the cone and plane and projects on the plane *1* at o^1. The *H* projection of *O* lies at o^H in the *H* projection of the circle. The frontal projection of *O* lies in the frontal projection of the plane *W* at o^F. By assuming additional planes enough points may be found in the line of intersection to determine that curve.

Figure 9.15 illustrates a more direct method of applying the foregoing analysis. The plane *W* intersects the cone in a circle and the given plane *ABC* in a straight line. The *H* projection of the circle has its center at n^H. The intersection of the plane *W* and the plane *ABC* is the line *XY*. Since the circle lies on the cone, and the line XY on the plane, the points O and E must lie in the required intersection. Additional points may be found in like manner to complete the curve.

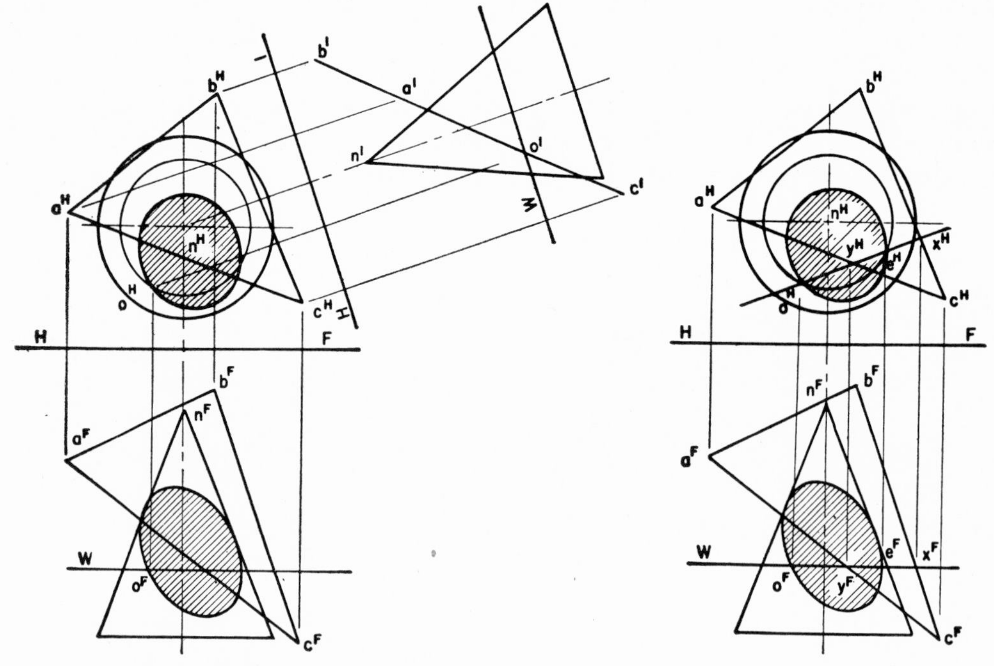

FIG. 9.14. Intersection by Horizontal Planes

FIG. 9.15. Direct Method

9.7. Problem 9.5. To find the line of intersection between a prism and a cylinder.

Given: The description of a prism and a cylinder that intersect.

Required: To find the line of intersection of the given surfaces.

Solution: Locate points that lie in both surfaces.

Analysis:

1. Draw the projections of the given prism and cylinder.
2. Find the intersections of the planes of the prism with the cylinder.

Discussion: In the H projection of Figure 9.16 the line AB is seen to pierce the cylinder at e^H and e'^H. The F projections of these points are found in the F projection of the line. Additional lines that pierce the cylinder may be found by assuming lines of the upper and lower planes of the prism. In the figure the line XY is a line of the upper plane. The line RO is also a line of that plane. Any number of lines of the planes may be taken through the lines XY or XZ and their piercing points determined. The projections of the required curve are drawn through the projections of the piercing points. The intersections of the other planes of the prism with the cylinder are found by similar methods.

It will be observed that this problem is an adaptation of Problem 9.1. In the discussion and illustration of the preceding paragraph a special case is assumed in which the center line of the cylinder is perpendicular to H. In general, the cylinder and intersecting prism may be projected on an auxiliary plane in such a manner that this method may be used for any problem. If the cylinder is so located that this method will not give a more direct solution than the method of Problem 9.3, the latter may be used. It will be seen that the two methods differ only in the assumption of elements of the plane surfaces in one case and of elements of the cylinder in the other case. The choice of methods would depend on the location of the cylinder with respect to the projection planes.

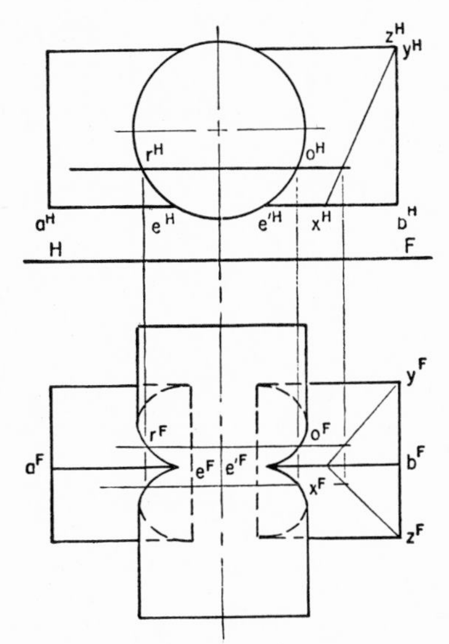

Fig. 9.16. Intersecting Prism and Cylinder

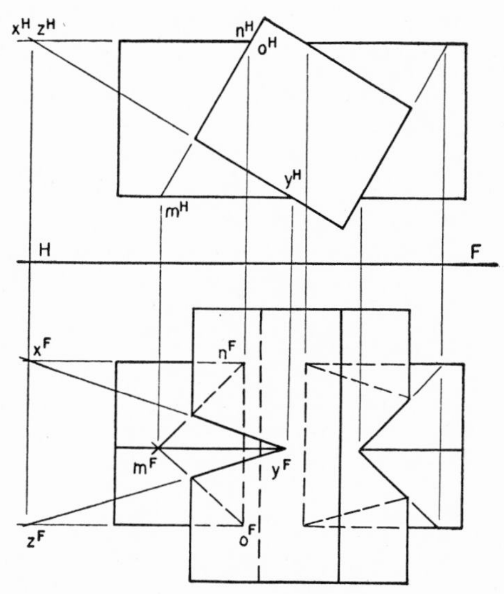

Fig. 9.17. Intersecting Prisms

9.8. Problem 9.6. To find the projections of the line of intersection of two prisms.

Given: The location in space of two intersecting prisms.

Required: The projections of the line of intersection of the prisms.

Solution: Locate points that are common to the intersecting plane surfaces.

Analysis:

1. Draw the projections of the two prisms.
2. Draw the projections of the intersections of the planes that form the prisms.

Discussion: It is assumed in Figure 9.17 that the vertical rectangular prism and the horizontal triangular prism are given. The intersection of the various planes that bound the prisms may be found by any of the methods that have been discussed. In the figure, the left front face of the vertical prism has been extended to intersect the extended upper surface of the horizontal prism in the line XY, and the lower surface of the horizontal prism in the line YZ. By similar construction the rear left surface of the vertical prism is found to intersect the horizontal prism in the lines *MN* and *MO*. The rear surface of the horizontal prism intersects the vertical surface in the line *NO*. The intersection of the surfaces on the right may be found by like construction to complete the drawing.

9.9. Problem 9.7. To find the line in which two given cylinders intersect.

Given: The location in space of two intersecting cylinders.

Required: To find the projections of the line in which they intersect.

Solution: Locate points that lie in both surfaces.

Analysis: *Method I.*

1. Draw the projections of the cylinders.
2. Project the cylinders on projection planes that are perpendicular to the center lines of the cylinders.
3. Assume auxiliary planes that are parallel to both center lines and which cut the cylinders in elements.
4. Draw the required intersection through the points where the elements of one cylinder intersect the elements of the other cylinder.

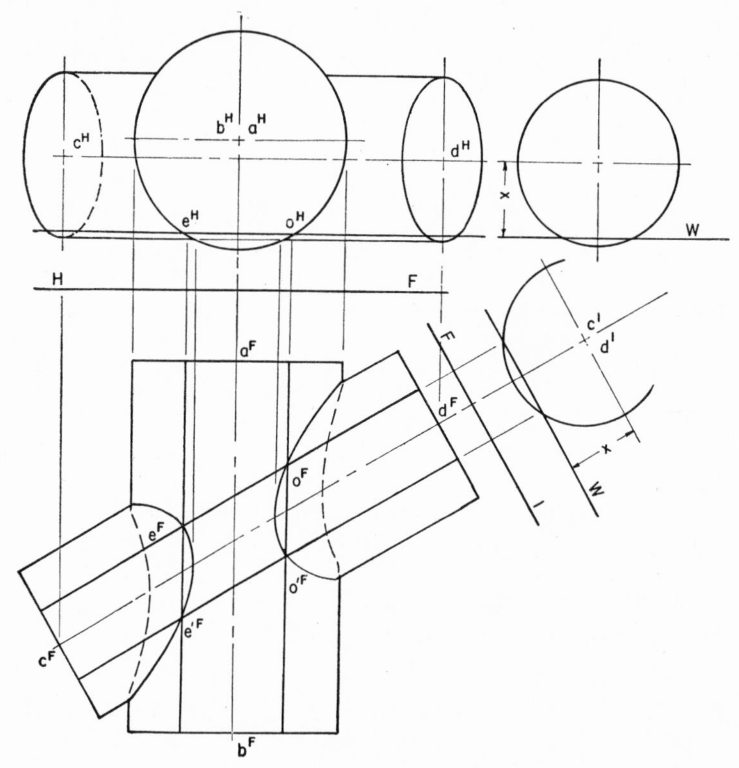

Fig. 9.18. Intersecting Cylinders

Discussion: In Figure 9.18 a special case is shown in which one of the cylinders is perpendicular to *H*. The projection plane *1* is assumed perpendicular to the center line *CD* and perpendicular to *F*. On this projection plane the line of intersection projects as a circle, with center at c^1d^1. Since the cylinder with center line AB is perpendicular to H, the H projection of the line of intersection is in the circle, with its center at a^Hb^H.

Plane W is parallel to the center lines of both cylinders and projects on H as a line. This plane cuts the vertical cylinder in two elements. The projection of plane W on the auxiliary projection plane is also a line and cuts the oblique cylinder in two elements. The elements of the oblique cylinder intersect the elements of the vertical cylinder in the points E, E', O, and O'. Additional points in the line of intersection may be determined if additional planes are assumed. By assuming a number of planes a series of points are found through which a curve may be drawn which would closely approximate the required intersection.

It is frequently convenient to draw an end view of the oblique cylinder in both projections and to locate the planes relative to the center line. In the figure the plane W is located a distance X from the center of the oblique cylinder. This method merely substitutes the projections of the center line, in place of the HF and $F1$ axis lines, as a reference line from which to take measurements.

Analysis: *Method II.*

This method is only used in the special case in which the center lines of the cylinders intersect. Instead of using planes as auxiliary surfaces as in Method I, spheres are used. The steps necessary in the solution are:

1. Draw the projections of the cylinders.
2. Assume spheres which have their centers at the point of intersection of the center lines of the cylinders.
3. Find the intersections of the sphere with both cylinders.
4. Draw the required line through the points where the intersections intersect.

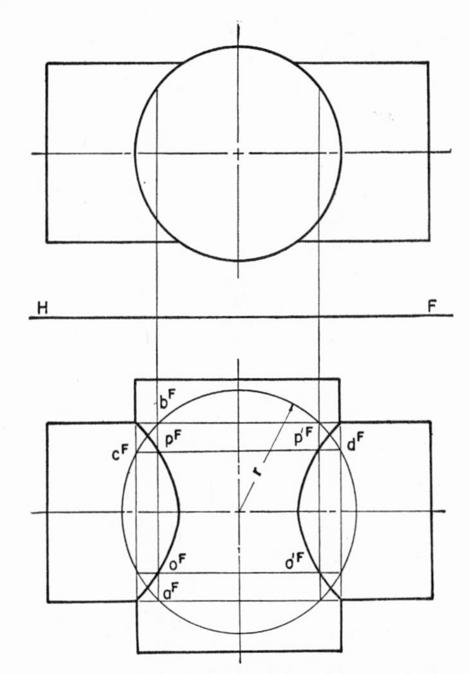

FIG. 9.19. Intersecting Cylinders, Sphere Method

Discussion: In Figure 9.19 the H and F projections of two right-circular cylinders with intersecting center lines are given. If a sphere of radius r be assumed with its center at the point of intersection of the two center lines, it will intersect the horizontal cylinder in a circle whose F projection is the line a^Fb^F. The same sphere intersects the vertical cylinder in a circle whose F projection is the line c^Fd^F. These two circles intersect at the points P and P'. The same sphere cuts two other intersecting circles that determine the points O and O'. If additional spheres be assumed, a number of points may be found through which the required intersection may be drawn.

9.10. Problem 9.8. To find the line in which two cones intersect.

Given: The location in space of two cones.

Required: The projections of the line of intersection of those cones.

Solution: Locate points that are common to the cones.

Analysis: (*Case I. The center lines of right-circular cones intersect.*)

1. Draw the projections of the cones.
2. Assume spheres with their centers at the point of intersection of the center lines of the cones.
3. Find the intersection of the sphere with each of the cones.
4. Draw the required curve through the points in which the intersections intersect.

Discussion: In Figure 9.20 two right-circular cones are given, whose center lines intersect at the point O. A sphere of radius r is assumed with its center at O. The F projection of this sphere is a circle intersecting the vertical cone in the line a^Fb^F. The sphere intersects the horizontal cone in the line c^Fd^F. Point N is found at the intersection of these lines. The H projections of the circle will have its center at o^H. Point N in the circle has its H projection at n^H in the H projection of the circle. The assumption of other spheres with centers at O gives additional points through which the required curves may be drawn.

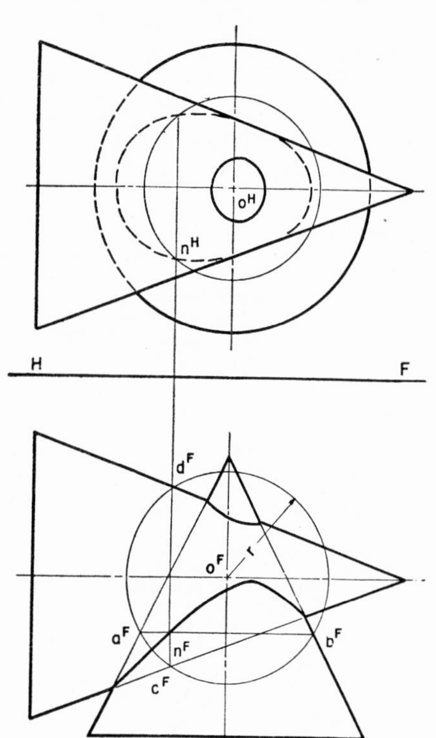

FIG. 9.20. Intersecting Cones—Special Case

Analysis: (*Case II. The center lines of the cones do not intersect.*)

The lines of intersection of a plane through the apex of a cone are straight line elements of that cone. If planes be passed through the apexes of the two cones, the lines of intersection between the planes and the cones will be straight lines intersecting in the line of intersection of the cones. Such plane intersections may be obtained as follows:

1. Join the apexes of the two cones with a straight line.
2. Assume a plane parallel to this line.
3. Assume a plane perpendicular to this line.
4. Pass planes through the apexes of the two cones to determine intersecting elements of the cones.
5. Project the points of intersection to the required projection planes to determine the required intersection.

Discussion: In Figure 9.21 the lines *OP* and *MN* are the center lines of the two right-circular cones. The line *ON* joins the apexes of the two cones. The projection plane *1* is assumed parallel to *ON* and perpendicular to *H*. The projection plane *2* is assumed perpendicular to *ON* and to plane *1*. The plane *R*, shown as a line on the projection plane *2*, is passed through the apexes of the cone and intersects the bases at points *A*, *B*, and *C*. This plane cuts the element *AO* from the

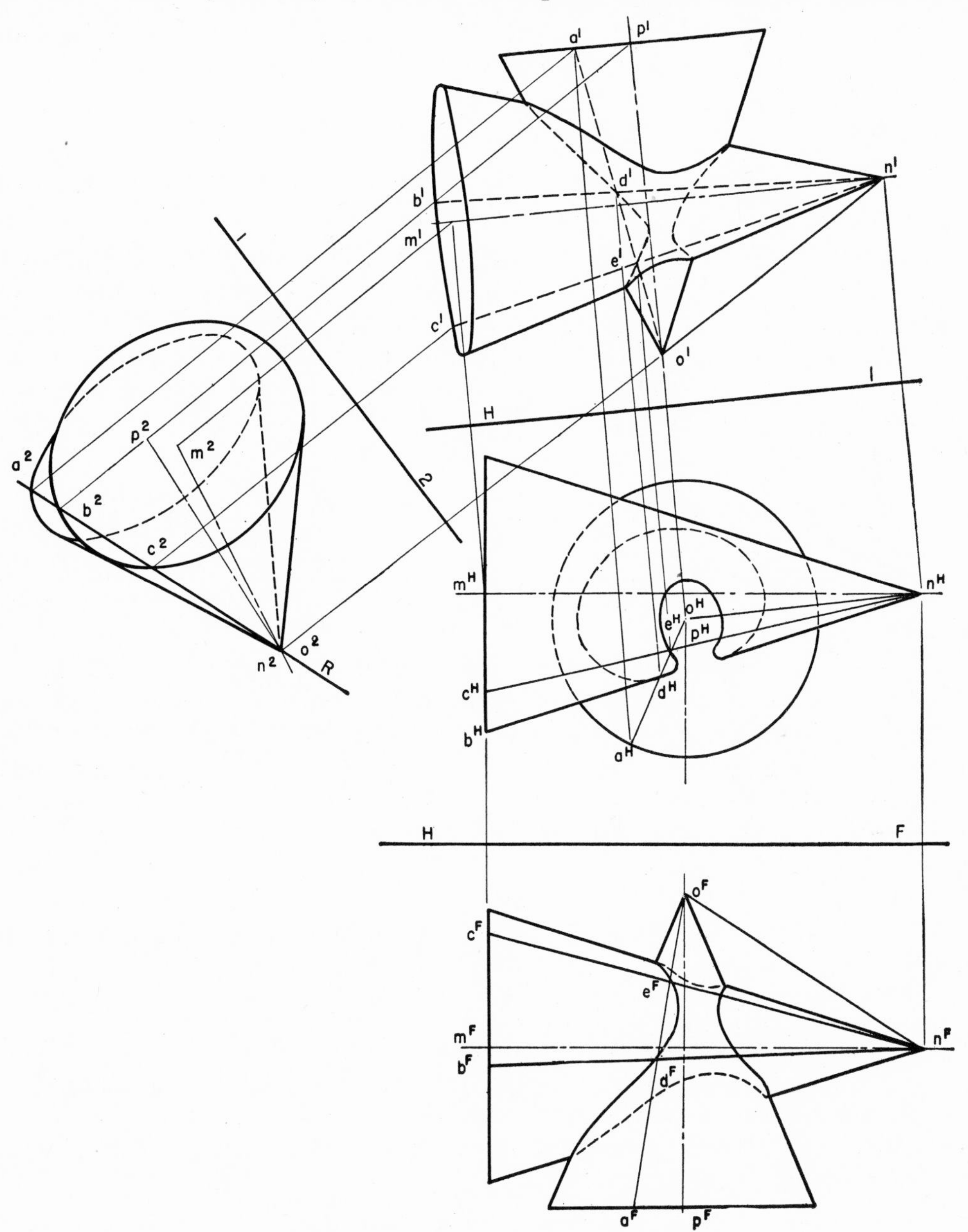

FIG. 9.21. Intersecting Cones—General Case

vertical cone and two elements, BN and CN, from the horizontal cone. The intersection of these elements locates the points D and E of the required curve. Any number of points may be determined by assuming additional planes that pass through the apexes of the cones. In the construction of Figure 9.21 only, plane R is shown in order to make the drawing more easily read.

9.11. Application Problems.

9.1. *Layout 1.* Find the intersection of the plane ABC with the given prism. Imagine that the part of the prism that is above the plane has been removed.

(a) The line ED is the center line of a hexagonal prism of 1½″ maximum diameter. One diagonal of each base is parallel to F. Use Method II. Plane ABC: A(10, 3, ¼), B(9¼, ¼, 2¾), C(7, 1¾, 1¾). Line ED: E(8½, 1¼, 2¾), D(8½, 1¼, ¼).

(b) Same as Problem 9.1 (a) except use Method I. Plane ABC: A(3½, 3, ¼), B(2¾, ¼, 2¾), C(½, 1¾, 1¾). Line ED: E(2, 1¼, 2¾), D(2, 1¼, ¼).

9.2. Same as Problem 9.1 except that the prism is octagonal.

9.3. Same as Problem 9.1 except that the line ED is the center line of a right hexagonal pyramid with its 1½″ base at the point E.

9.4. Same as Problem 9.1 except that the line ED is the center line of a cylinder of 1½″ diameter.

9.5. Same as Problem 9.1 except that ED is the center line of a right cone whose base is a circle of 1½″ diameter at the point E.

9.6. *Layout 1.* Find the intersection of the surfaces that are specified.

(a) The right-circular cone having the center line AB, with its 3″ circular base at B, is intersected by a sphere of 2″ diameter. The center of the sphere is at the mid-point of an element of the cone. Line AB: A(8, 2, ¼), B(8, 2, 2¾).

(b) The right-circular cone having the center line CD, and its 3″ circular base at D, is intersected by a 1½″ circular cylinder whose center line is EO. Line CD: C(3, 2, ¼), D(3, 2, 3). Line EO: E(2¼, 2, ¼), O(2¼, 2, 3).

9.7. *Layout 1.* A vertical right prism of 1½″ square base has the center line AB. Two of the vertical faces of the prism make angles of 30 degrees with F. The mid-point of the center line CD of a second right square prism is at the point E on line AB. The line CD is 4″ long, is parallel to F, and makes an angle of 30 degrees with H. One diagonal of the 1″ square base at C is parallel to F. Line AB: A(6, 2, ¼), B(6, 2, 3¼). Point E: E(6, 2, 1½). Find the intersection of the prisms.

9.8. *Layout 1.* A right vertical pyramid of 2″ square base has the center line AB. Two edges of the square base make angles of 30 degrees with F. The mid-point of the center line CD of a right square prism is at the point E on the line AB. The line CD is 4″ long, is parallel to F, and makes an angle of 30 degrees with H. One diagonal of the 1″ square base at C is parallel to F. A(6, 2, ¼), B(6, 2, 3¼), E(6, 2, 1½). Find the intersection of the surfaces.

9.9. *Layout 1.* A right vertical pyramid of 2″ square base has the center line AB. Two edges of the base at B make angles of 30 degrees with F. A right horizontal pyramid of 2″ square base has the center line CD and intersects AB at the mid-point of AB and CD. The line CD is 4″ long and parallel to both H and F. One diagonal of the base at C is parallel to H. A(6, 2, ¼), B(6, 2, 3¼). Find the intersection of the pyramids.

9.10. Same as Problem 9.9 except that the vertical surface is a 2″ square prism with two faces making angles of 30 degrees with F.

9.11. *Layout 1.* Find the intersection of the surfaces described below.

A vertical right circular cylinder of 2″ base has the center line AB. The line CD is the center line of a horizontal right square prism of 1″ base. Two of the planes of the prism make angles of 30 degrees with H. The line CD is parallel to F, 4″ long, and intersects AB at the mid-point of AB and CD. A(6, 2, ¼), B(6, 2, 3¼).

9.12. Same as Problem 9.11 except that CD is the center line of a right square pyramid of 2″ base. Two edges of the base make angles of 30 degrees with H. A(6½, 2, ½), B(6½, 2, 3¼).

9.13. *Layout 1.* Find the intersection of the right circular cone, whose center line is AB, with the right square prism having CD as its center line. The line CD is 4″ long, is horizontal, and intersects the line AB at the mid-point of AB and CD. The diameter of the base of the cone at B is 3″. The right section of the prism is a 1″ square, one diagonal of which is parallel to H. $A(7, 1\frac{3}{4}, \frac{1}{4})$, $B(7, 1\frac{3}{4}, 3\frac{1}{4})$.

9.14. Same as Problem 9.13 except that two faces of the prism make angles of 30 degrees with H.

9.15. Same as Problem 9.13 except that the line CD is the center line of a right pyramid having a 2″ square base, one diagonal of which is parallel to H.

9.16. *Layout 1.* Find the intersection of the two right circular cylinders having the center lines AB and CD. The vertical cylinder is 2″ in diameter and the cylinder of which CD is the center line is $1\frac{1}{4}$″ in diameter. $A(7\frac{1}{2}, 1\frac{3}{4}, \frac{1}{4})$, $B(7\frac{1}{2}, 1\frac{3}{4}, 3\frac{1}{4})$, $C(9\frac{1}{2}, 1\frac{1}{2}, 1\frac{3}{4})$, $D(5\frac{1}{2}, 1\frac{1}{2}, 1\frac{3}{4})$.

9.17. Same as Problem 9.16 except that the line CD makes an angle of 30 degrees with H, is parallel to F, with its center at the point $E(7\frac{1}{2}, 1\frac{1}{2}, 1\frac{3}{4})$.

9.18. *Layout 1.* The right circular cone of center line AB is intersected by the horizontal cylinder having the center line CD. The line CD intersects AB at the mid-point of both AB and CD. The diameter of the base at B is 3″. The diameter of the horizontal cylinder is $1\frac{1}{2}$″. Find the line of intersection by one method and check one point by a second method. $A(7\frac{1}{2}, 1\frac{3}{4}, \frac{1}{4})$, $B(7\frac{1}{2}, 1\frac{3}{4}, 3\frac{1}{4})$.

9.19. Same as Problem 9.18 except that the center line CD makes an angle of 15 degrees with H.

9.20. *Layout 1.* The lines AB and CD intersect at the mid-point of both. Line AB is the center line of a right circular cone having a circular base $3\frac{1}{2}$″ in diameter at the point B. Line CD is horizontal, parallel to F, 4″ long, and the center line of a right circular cone with 3″ base at C. $A(6, 2, \frac{1}{4})$, $B(6, 2, 3\frac{1}{4})$. Find the intersection of the cones.

CHAPTER X

APPLICATIONS TO SHADES AND SHADOWS

10.1. Introductory. The appearance of a three-dimensioned object cannot be satisfactorily described by orthographic projection without rendering shades and shadows on the drawing. An elevation shows the lengths and heights of an object, as well as the location relative to each other of the details of the object, if they lie in a plane that is parallel to the plane of projection. The plan shows lengths and widths, but not the height. A person who is experienced in reading orthographic drawings can get a mental concept of the appearance of a structure from a study of its plan and elevation. To the inexperienced, the plan and elevation of an object are two unrelated and expressionless drawings.

A well-rendered perspective drawing gives the best graphic description of the appearance of an object but requires a considerable amount of time and effort to produce. In a perspective, the distances that are perpendicular to the picture plane are so expressed that they may be visualized by the observer. This effect of depth is added to that of length and breadth in the perspective drawing by means of foreshortening and vanishing certain lines. When rendered shades and shadows are added to a perspective, the effect is that of a photograph of the object.

The distances perpendicular to the projection plane can be expressed, to a limited extent, on an orthographic drawing. Projections from a plane surface cast shadows on that surface, and recessions from a plane usually receive shadows from some source. If a source of light is assumed, and the shades and shadows on the object due to that light be accurately located on the drawing, the effect will approximate that of a perspective. A rendered elevation loses some of its flatness and presents somewhat the same appearance as the structure or object when viewed from a distance.

It is not within the scope of this chapter to discuss the art of rendering, nor to give instruction and practice in the many short-cut methods employed by the draftsman in locating shadows. The location of a shadow is a descriptive geometry problem, and the "rules" and "methods" that are employed by the draftsman have their foundation in the principles that are discussed in the following paragraphs. The intent of this chapter is to discuss the geometric principles in such a manner that the student may cast simple shadows on his drawings; also, to give the geometric foundation upon which a student may base a more complete course of study.

10.2. Shade. If an object receives light from any source, the side of the object that is toward the source will be illuminated and the side away from the source will be in shade. The line that separates the illuminated from the shaded area is called the shade line.

10.3. Shadow. If an opaque object be placed between a source of light and a surface, the object will cast its shadow on that surface. The line that separates the illuminated and shadowed area of the surface is called the line of shadow.

10.4. Source of Light. Theoretically, the source of light used in casting shadows may be located anywhere. In the design of interiors of buildings the source is sometimes assumed to be that of artificial light or that from a window. It is customary, in architectural work, to assume that the source is an infinite distance away. If this assumption is made, the rays of light will be parallel to each other and will have parallel projections on the projection planes. The location of the shadows on the planes that receive them can be found more readily when this source is assumed.

10.5. Conventional Light. The assumption of parallel rays of light in the direction of the diagonal of the cube of Figure 10.1 is so general that such rays may be

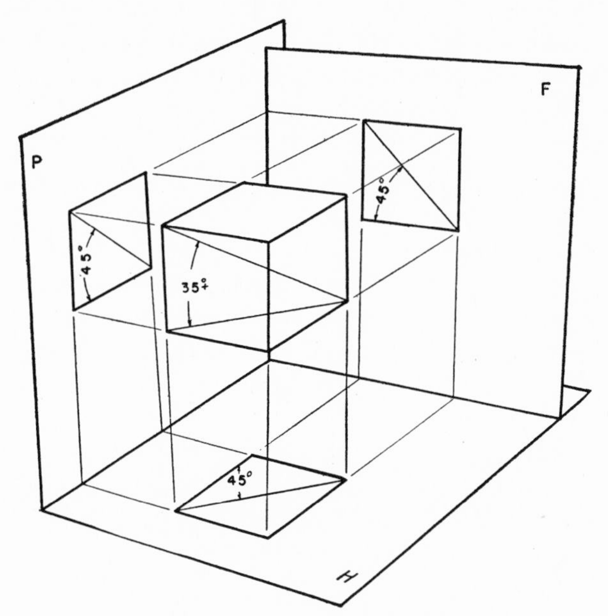

FIG. 10.1. Conventional Light Ray

called conventional light. It may be seen that the diagonal of the cube makes an angle somewhat in excess of 35 degrees with each of the principal projection planes. The projection of this ray on *H*, *F*, or *P* is 45 degrees with the axis lines. Although this assumption has become almost universal in casting shadows, any other direction might be used if so desired. In the problems of this chapter conventional light will be used unless another source is specified and located.

10.6. First Quadrant Projections. Perspective, shades and shadows, and many architectural design problems are handled more readily in the First Quadrant, and almost all literature relative to such work assumes that location in space. Since the direction of the light rays is downward and backward, they would be intercepted by the projection planes before reaching the object if the object was in the

Third Quadrant. Also, the projection planes could receive no shadows if they are above and in front, as in Third Quadrant projection. In rendering shades and shadows it is convenient to visualize a floor or the surface of the ground as the horizontal projection plane that receives a shadow. Also, a wall or a vertical surface of the object may be visualized as the frontal projection plane. Such a visualization of the projection planes places the object in the First Quadrant if the planes are to receive shadows.

The student will soon overcome his natural tendency to visualize the problem in the Third Quadrant if he constructs a model or a pictorial drawing of the First Quadrant and imagines the points of his problem to be located in his model.

10.7. Problem 10.1. To find the shadows of a given point on the *H* and *F* projection planes.

Given: The location in space of a point and of a source of light.

Required: The shadows of the point on the principal projection planes.

Solution: Find the points in which the planes are pierced by the ray of light that passes through the given source and point.

Analysis:

1. Draw the *H* and *F* projections of the given point and source.
2. Draw the projections of a ray that passes through the source and point.
3. Find the points in which the planes are pierced by the ray.

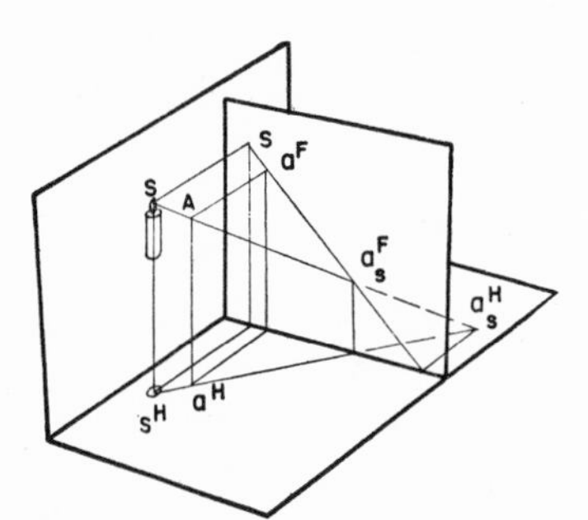

Fig. 10.2. The Shadows of a Point

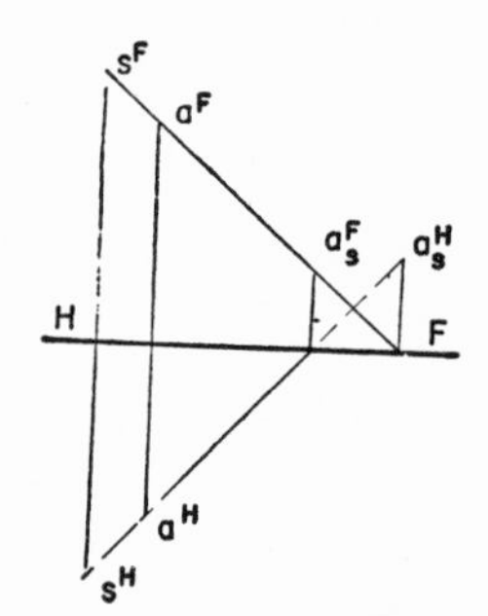

Fig. 10.3. The Shadows of a Point

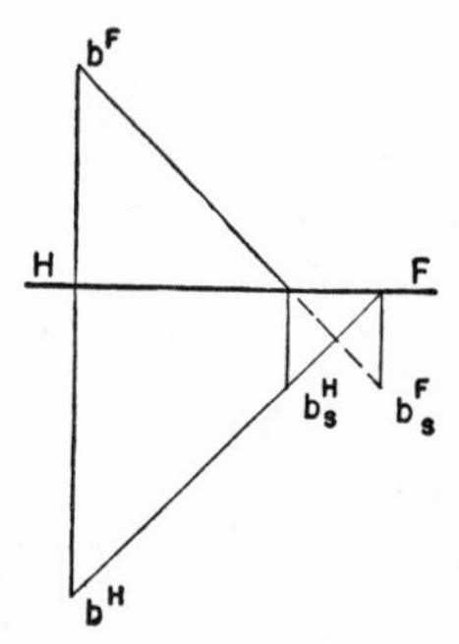

Fig. 10.4. The Shadows of a Point

Discussion: In Figure 10.2 the source of light *S* and the point *A* are assumed to be given. A ray of light from *S* through the point *A* pierces the frontal plane at $a_s{}^F$, which is the shadow of the point *A* on the frontal plane. The shadow of the point *A* on the *H* plane is $a_s{}^H$, which is the point in which the ray pierces the *H* plane. Since the *F* plane is between the point and its shadow on *H*, no actual shadow can exist on *H*. The use of this imaginary point is convenient in locating other shadows.

In Figure 10.3 the horizontal plane of Figure 10.2 has been revolved into the plane of the page. It is important that the draftsman visualize the problem as in Figure 10.2 and that he express his concept as in Figure 10.3.

In Figure 10.4 a similar problem and conventional light are assumed. The shadow of the point B on the H plane is $b_s{}^H$ and on the F plane is $b_s{}^F$. In this problem the H plane is between the point and its shadow on the F plane; hence, that shadow is a theoretical location only.

10.8. Problem 10.2. To find the shadow of a line on the H and F projection planes.

Given: The location in space of a line.

Required: The shadow on H and F of the given line.

Solution: Find the shadows of chosen points of the lines.

Analysis:

1. Draw the H and F projections of the line.
2. Find the shadows on H and F of several points of the line.
3. Join the shadows of the points.

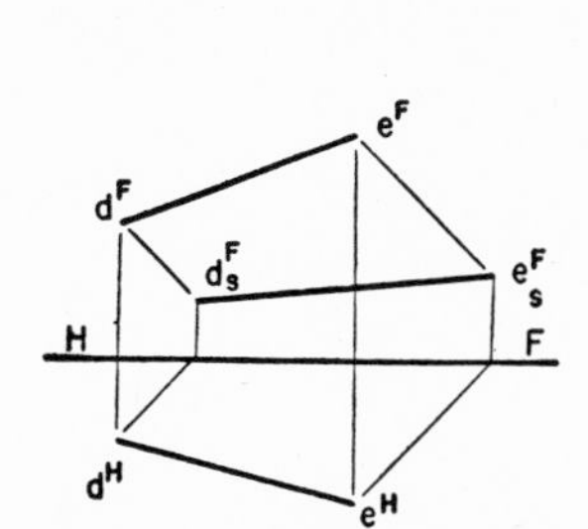

FIG. 10.5. The Shadows of a Line

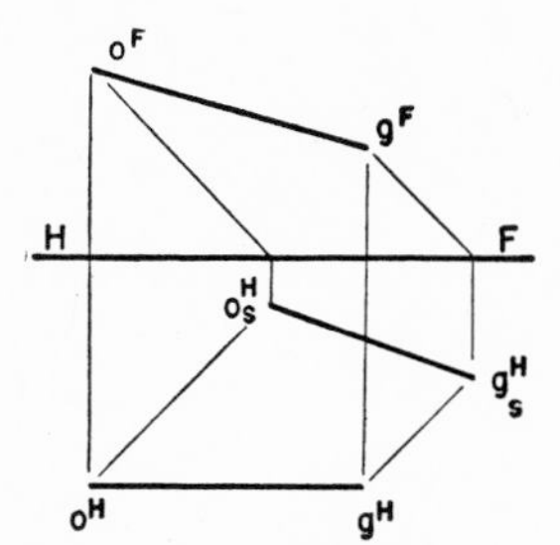

FIG. 10.6. The Shadows of a Line

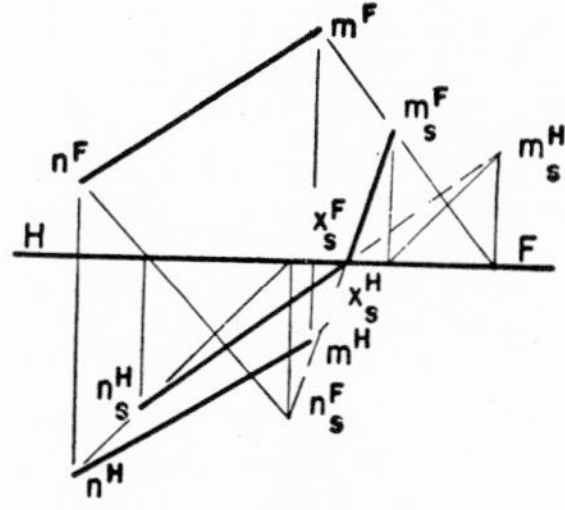

FIG. 10.7. The Shadows of a Line

Discussion: In Figure 10.5 the line DE is so located that its shadow is received by the frontal plane as the line $d_s{}^F e_s{}^F$. The points $d_s{}^F$ and $e_s{}^F$ are piercing points of the conventional rays through the points D and E.

In Figure 10.6 the line OG casts its shadow on H as $o_s{}^H g_s{}^H$. These points are the H piercing points of the conventional rays through O and G.

In Figure 10.7 the line MN is so located that a portion of its shadow falls on F and a portion on H. The shadow of M on F is $m_s{}^F$. The shadow of N on F would be at $n_s{}^F$ if the H plane did not interfere. The complete shadow of MN on F intersects the HF axis line at X. The shadow of MN on H intersects the axis line at the point X. The line $m_s{}^F x_s{}^F$ is the visible portion of the shadow on F and the line $n_s{}^H x_s{}^H$ is the visible portion of the shadow on H. The imaginary shadows are used to determine the actual shadows.

In the case of a curved line it would be necessary to find the shadows of a number of the points of that line and to draw a smooth curve through the shadows. The number of points that would be required would depend on the character of the curve and the accuracy desired.

10.9. Shadows of Special Case Lines. A very large number of the lines that are used in drafting practice fall in one of the three following groups: (a) lines that are parallel to both H and F; (b) lines that are perpendicular to H; and (c) lines that are perpendicular to F. The direction of the shadows of these lines may be memorized, so that it is not necessary to locate more than one point in any shadow.

In Figure 10.8 the line AB is parallel to both H and F. The rays of light through A and B pierce the F plane at $a_s{}^F$ and $b_s{}^F$. The line $a_s{}^F b_s{}^F$ is the shadow of AB on F and is parallel to the HF axis line. This is a characteristic of the shadows of all lines that are parallel to both H and F. *If a line be parallel to both H and F, its shadows on H and F will be parallel to the HF axis line.*

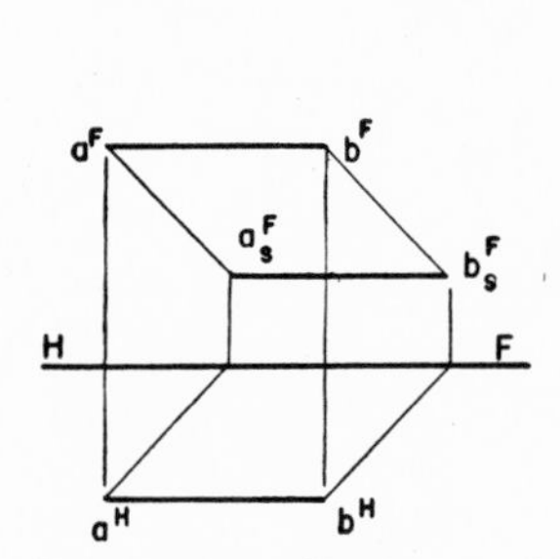

Fig. 10.8. Shadows of Special Case Lines

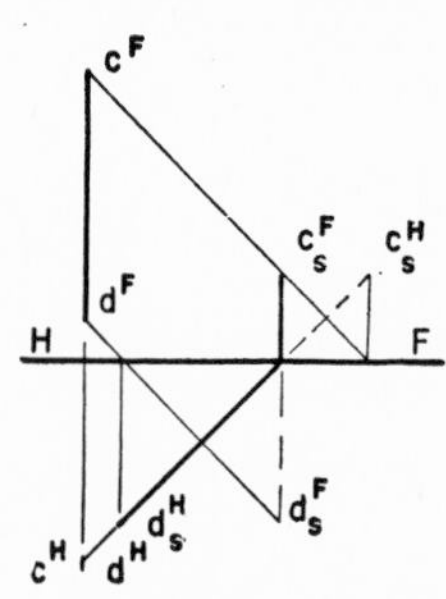

Fig. 10.9. Shadows of Special Case Lines

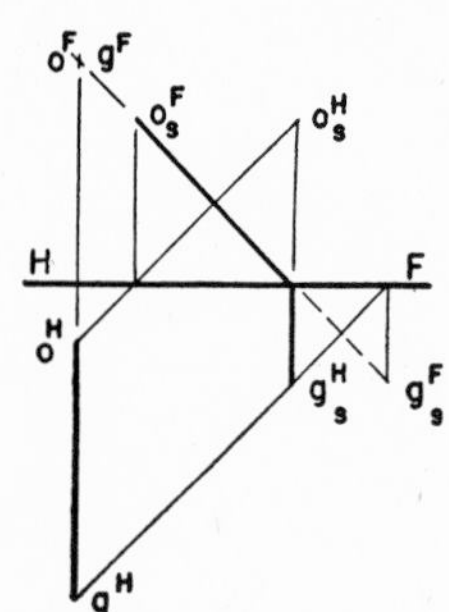

Fig. 10.10. Shadows of Special Case Lines

In Figure 10.9 the line CD is perpendicular to H. The shadow of CD on H is the line $d_s{}^H c_s{}^H$. The shadow of CD on F is $c_s{}^F d_s{}^F$. It may be seen that the shadow on H is necessarily a 45-degree line and that the shadow on F is a vertical line. *If a line be perpendicular to H, its shadow on H will be a line at 45 degrees with the HF axis line, and its shadow on F will be a vertical line.*

In Figure 10.10 the line OG is perpendicular to F. The shadow of OG on F is the line $o_s{}^F g_s{}^F$, which makes an angle of 45 degrees with the HF axis line. The shadow of OG on H is the line $o_s{}^H g_s{}^H$, which is perpendicular to the HF axis line. *If a line be perpendicular to F, its shadow on F will be a line that makes an angle of 45 degrees with the HF axis line, and its shadow on H will be a line that is perpendicular to the HF axis line.*

It may be seen by an inspection of Figures 10.7, 10.9, and 10.10 that *the shadows of a line on H and F will intersect the HF axis line at the same point.*

10.10. Problem 10.3. To find the shadow of a plane figure on the H and F projection planes.

Given: The location in space of a plane figure.

Required: The shadow of the plane figure on the H and F planes.

Solution: Find the shadows of points that will determine the required shadow.

Analysis:

1. Draw the H and F projections of the given plane figure.
2. Draw the H and F projections of rays that pass through points of the figure.
3. Find the H and F piercing points of the rays.
4. Join the piercing points.

Discussion: In Figure 10.11 the plane triangle *ABC* is assumed. The shadows of *A*, *B*, and *C* on *F* are found at a_s^F, b_s^F, and c_s^F. When joined by straight lines these points determine the outline of the shadow on the *F* plane. The portion of the shadow that is received by *F* is indicated in the figure by vertical shade lines. The shadow of the point *C* on *H* is the point c_s^H. Since the shadows on *H* of the lines *AC* and *AB* must cross the *HF* axis line at the points in which their shadows on *F* cross that line, the outline of the shadow on *H* is determined. This area is indicated in the figure by horizontal shade lines.

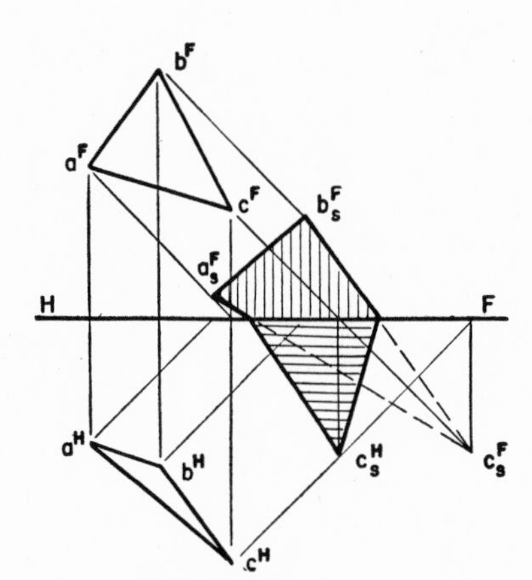

FIG. 10.11. The Shadows of Plane Figures

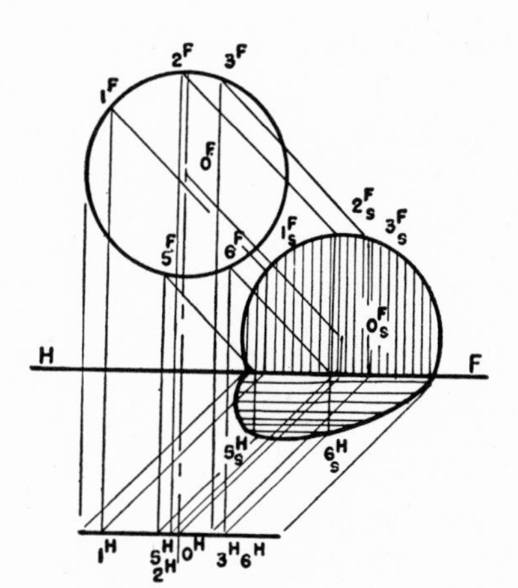

FIG. 10.12. The Shadows of Plane Figures

In Figure 10.12 a plane figure bounded by a curved line is assumed. The shadow of the figure on *F* is determined by the shadows of points of the curve. The visible portion of this shadow on *F* is indicated by vertical shade lines. The shadow on *H* is determined by the shadows of several points of the curve on that plane. This shadow is indicated by horizontal shade lines.

10.11. The Shadows of Special Case Figures. The plane surfaces with which the draftsman is concerned are to a large extent either parallel or perpendicular to the plane on which the shadow is cast. In general, the outlines of such figures may be found by shorter methods than by the use of points, as in the preceding article.

In Figure 10.13 the plane figure *BCDE* casts its shadow on *F*. The lines of this figure are special case lines, and these shadows may be determined as in Article 10.9. The shadow of the point *B* on *F* is b_s^F and of *D* is d_s^F. Since *BC* and *DE* are parallel to both *H* and *F*, their shadows will be drawn through b_s^F and d_s^F parallel to the *HF* axis line. The lines *DC* and *BE* are perpendicular to *H*, and their shadows on *F* are perpendicular to the *HF* axis line. When these lines are drawn, a plane figure of the exact size and form of *BCDE* is found to be the required shadow.

In Figure 10.14 a circular plane figure that is parallel to *F* is assumed. It will be seen by inspection that this figure is similar to 10.13, in which the shadow is the exact size and form of the plane surface. It is possible, therefore, to locate the shadow of the center of the circle and to draw the circular shadow using a radius of the same size as that of the plane figure.

In Figure 10.15 a plane figure *KLMN* that is perpendicular to both *H* and *F* is assumed. The lines that bound the figure are special case lines. The shadow is readily found by the methods of Article 10.9.

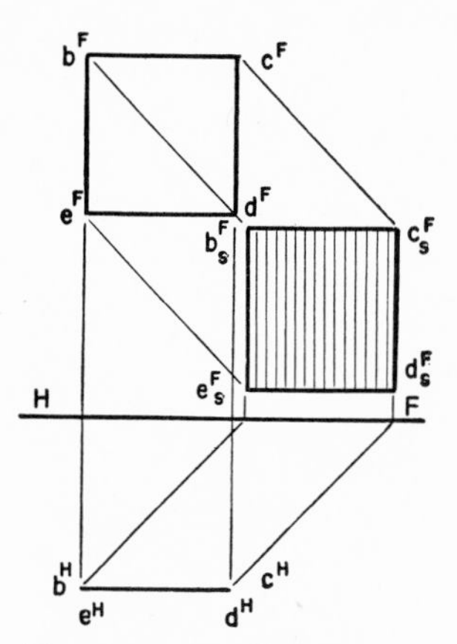

Fig. 10.13. Shadows of Special Case Figures

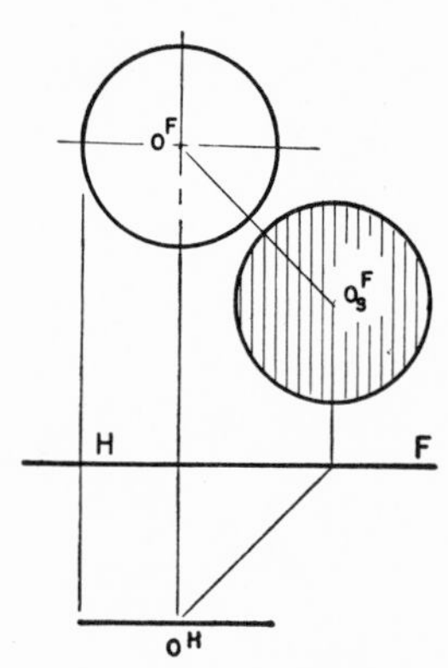

Fig. 10.14. Shadows of Special Case Figures

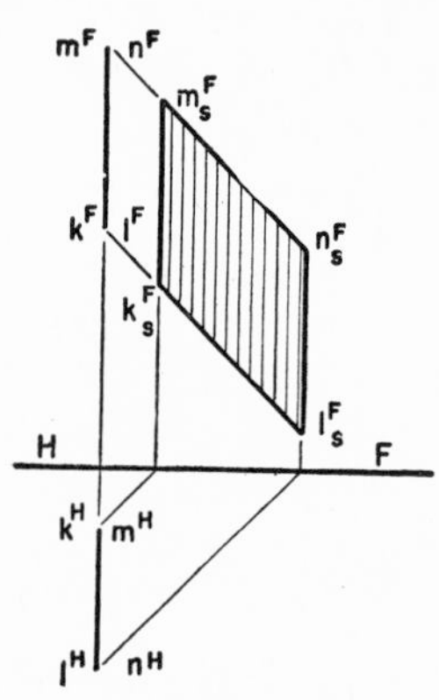

Fig. 10.15. Shadows of Special Case Figures

10.12. Problem 10.4. To find the shadow of a solid on the *H* and *F* projection planes.

Given: The location in space of a solid.

Required: The shadow of the solid on the *H* and *F* projection planes.

Solution: Find the shadows of the surfaces that bound the solid.

Analysis:

1. Draw the *H* and *F* projections of the solid.
2. Find the shadows of the surfaces that bound the solid.
3. Draw the envelope of the shadows of all the planes.

Discussion: In Figure 10.16 the shadow of a cube is shown on the *F* plane. The shadows of the lines that form the edges of the cube are indicated by letters that correspond with those of the edges. The envelope of the shadow is $a_s{}^F e_s{}^F g_s{}^F h_s{}^F d_s{}^F b_s{}^F$. The shadows of the other edges fall within this envelope and would need no consideration.

It should be noted that the lines whose shadows form the envelope of the shadow are the edges that separate the illuminated from the shaded surfaces of the solid. Thus, in Figure 10.16 the lines *AE* and *EG* of the top plane are lines that separate illuminated surfaces from shaded surfaces, and their shadows form a portion of the envelope. The lines *GH*, *HD*, *DB*, and *BA* are similar lines. The edges *AC*, *CD*, and *CG* separate surfaces which are illuminated, and the edges *BF*, *FG*, and *FE* separate surfaces which are in shade. Both latter groups cast their shadows within the envelope and need not be considered.

By definition, the lines that separate illuminated from shaded areas are shade lines. In the case of the cube or other solid bounded by plane surfaces, the shade line is a definite line. In the case of a curved surface the shade line is a line in the theoretical sense only. The blending of shaded into illuminated surfaces does not result in a definite line. For the purpose of instruction in the location of shades and shadows they may be considered as definite lines.

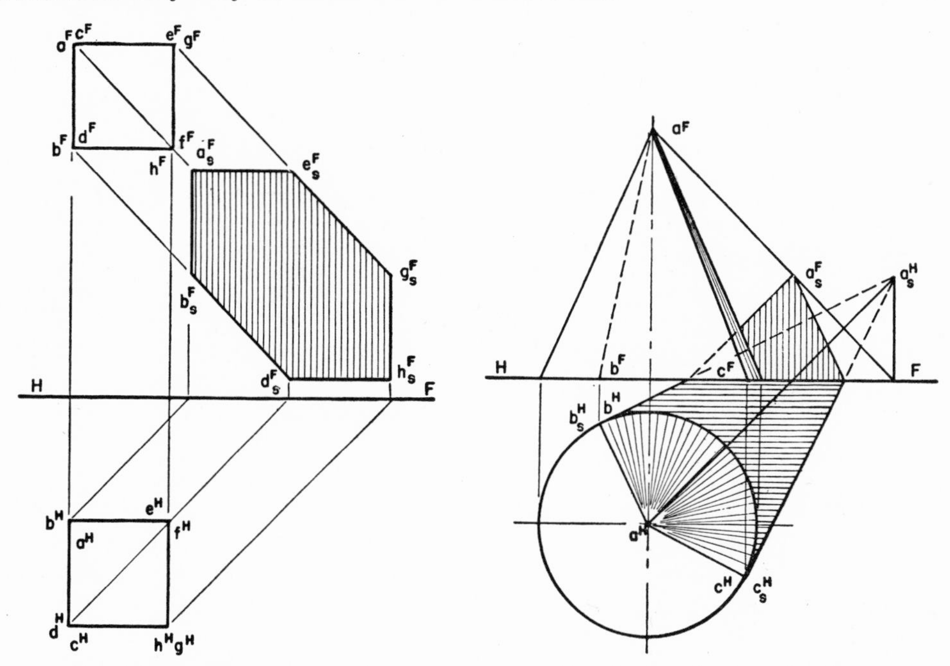

FIG. 10.16. Shadow of a Cube

FIG. 10.17. Shadow of a Cone

Figure 10.17 shows the shade lines and shaded areas of a cone and the shadow of that cone on H and F. It is obvious that the shadow on H will be tangent to the base of the cone if the base rests on H. The apex A casts its shadow on H at $a^H{}_s$. The shadow of the cone on H is the area $a_s{}^H b_s{}^H c_s{}^H$, and the shade lines of the cone are the elements AB and AC. The shadow of the point A on F is $a_s{}^F$. The shadows of AB and AC on F must cross the HF axis line at the same point that their H shadows cross that line. The shadow of the cone on F is, therefore, the area shaded in vertical shade lines.

10.13. Problem 10.5. To find the shadow of a line on any vertical surface.

Given: The location in space of a line and a vertical surface.

Required: The shadow of the line on the given surface.

Solution: Find the points in which the surface is pierced by rays of light that pass through points of the line.

Analysis:

1. Draw the H and F projections of the given line and surface.
2. Draw the projections of rays of light through chosen points of the line.

3. Find the points in which the surface is pierced by the rays.
4. Draw the shadow of the line through the piercing points of the rays.

Discussion: In Figure 10.18 the lines AB, BC, CE, and AD of the cap are edges that separate illuminated from shaded areas; hence, they will cast shadows. The shadow of the line AB on the vertical face of the pilaster is a horizontal line through a_s. The shadow of this line on the wall is a horizontal line drawn through b_s. The shadow of BC on the wall is the vertical line b_sc_s. The shadow of AD on the wall and pilaster face is the continuous straight line through d_s and a_s. The shadow of CE on the wall is a 45-degree line through c_s. The shadow of OG on the wall is a vertical line through g_s.

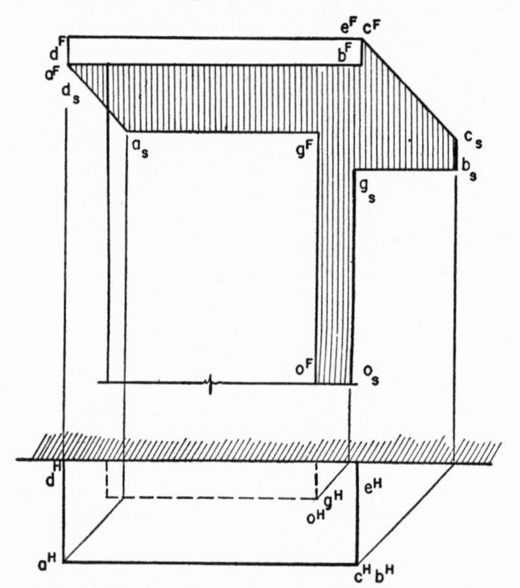

FIG. 10.18. Architectural Applications

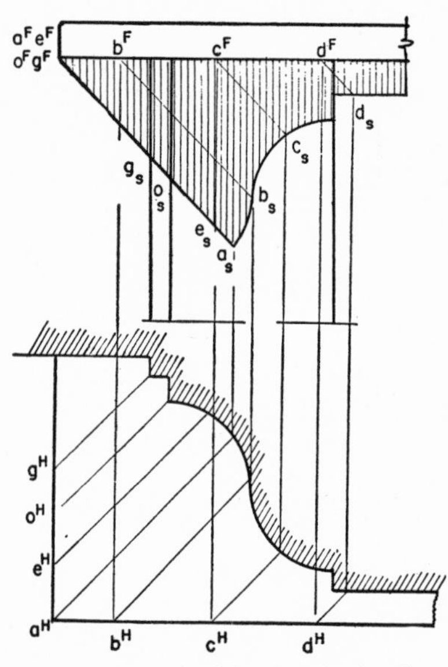

FIG. 10.19. Architectural Applications

In Figure 10.19 the lines $ABCD$ and $AEOG$ cast their shadows on the vertical moulding. The rays of light passed through A, E, O, and G have F projections that are coincident. The shadow of the line $AEOG$ is, therefore, a 45-degree line through a_s, e_s, o_s, and g_s. The shadow of A, B, and C on the curved surface is a curve drawn through a_s, b_s, and c_s. The shadow of this line on the vertical plane of the moulding is a horizontal line through d_s.

10.14. Problem 10.6. To find the shadow of any line on a surface of revolution.

Given: The location in space of a line and a surface of revolution.

Required: The shadow of the given line on the given surface.

Solution: Find the shadows of several points of the line.

Analysis:

1. Draw two projections of the line and surface.
2. Assume rays of light passed through chosen points of the line.

3. Find the points in which the rays pierce the surface.
4. Draw a smooth curve through the piercing points.

Discussion: The problem is given a practical significance in Figure 10.20 by the choice of a familiar architectural form. The circle at the top of the scotia casts its shadow on the curved surface below it. The location of the shadow line is determined by the points a_s, b_s, c_s, etc., which are the shadows on the scotia of the points A, B, C, etc.

The shadows of A, B, C, etc., may be found by the slicing method. In this method vertical planes are imagined to be passed through the light rays and to

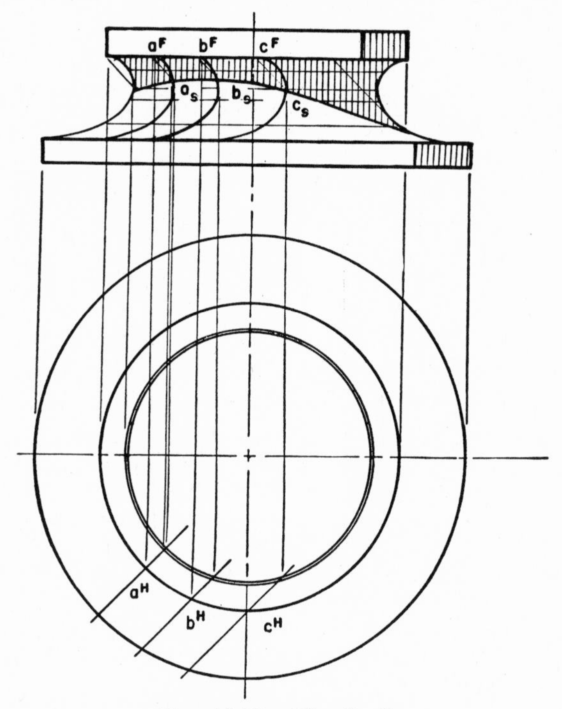

FIG. 10.20. The Scotia

intersect the given surface. In Figure 10.20 a vertical plane that contains the ray of light through A is seen to intersect the curved surface in the curve cut from the surface by that plane. The curve intersects the F projection of the light ray at the point a_s, which is the F projection of the shadow of A on the surface. Enough points may be found in this manner to determine the shadow.

10.15. Problem 10.7. To find the shadow in a spherical headed niche.

Given: The front view of a spherical headed niche.

Required: To find the shadow in the niche.

Solution: Find the shadows on auxiliary planes that intersect the niche.

Analysis:

1. Draw the H and F projections of the niche.

2. Assume auxiliary planes parallel to the face of the niche.
3. Find the intersections of the spherical head with the auxiliary planes.
4. Find the shadows of the edge of the spherical head on the auxiliary planes.
5. Find the points in which the shadows cut the intersections of the planes and niche.

Discussion: The plane M is assumed in Figure 10.21 and it intersects the spherical head in the circle drawn through m. The shadow of the edge of the head

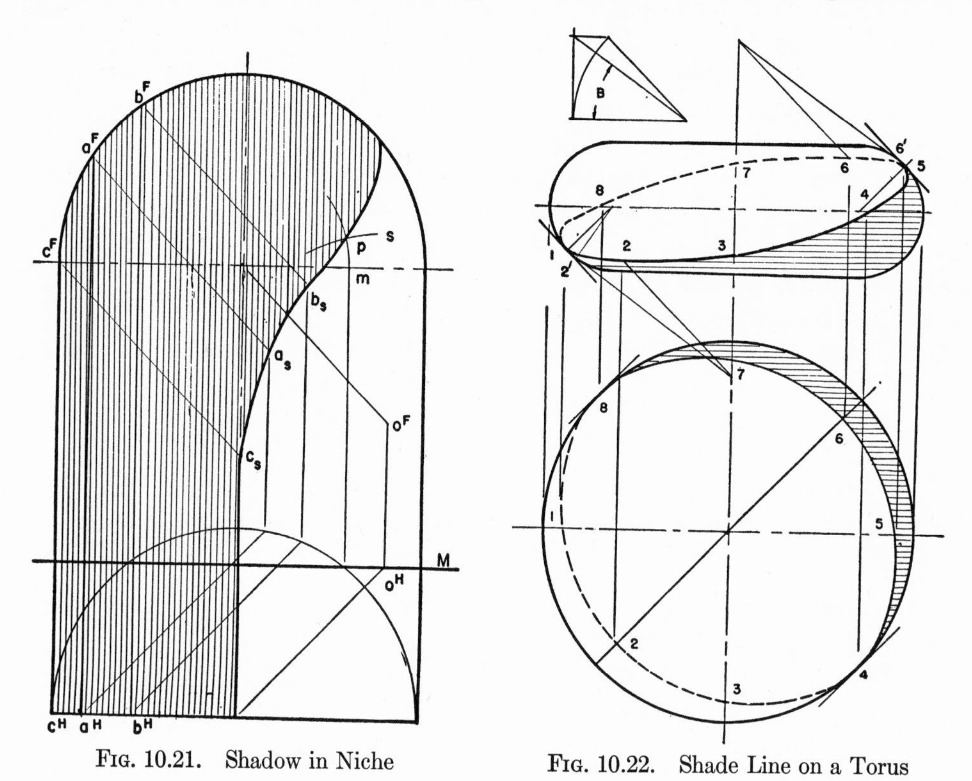

FIG. 10.21. Shadow in Niche

FIG. 10.22. Shade Line on a Torus

on the plane M is the circle through point s and whose center is o^F. The circles through s and m lie on the plane M and intersect at p. Since the circle through m lies on the surface of the head the point p is also in the head and is a point of the required line. Any number of additional points may be found by assuming planes parallel to plane M.

The shadow on the cylindrical surface may be found by assuming light rays through points such as A and B of the figure and finding where these rays pierce the surface.

10.16. Problem 10.8. To find the shade line on a torus.

Given: The H and F projections of a torus.

Required: The shade line on the torus.

Solution: Locate points in which light rays are tangent to the surface.

Analysis: See Figure 10.22.

1. Find points in which light rays are tangent to the surface of the torus.
2. Draw the curve through the points of tangency.

Discussion: Points *1* and *5* of the figure are determined by drawing 45-degree tangents to the contours of the frontal projection. A vertical light plane passed through the axis of the torus cuts that surface in halves on which the shade line will be similar in form and symmetrically located with respect to the plane. Since the curves on the two halves are similar, the points *3* and *7* may be located symmetrically with *1* and *5*. Points *4* and *8* are located by drawing 45-degree tangents to the torus in the plan view. Points *2* and *6* lie in a vertical plane passed through the axis of the torus. Such a plane contains the rays of light that are tangent to the surface at points *2* and *6*. The angle between H and the rays is found to be B as shown in the figure. Since this angle lies in a plane that is inclined to F, it must be revolved parallel to F to determine the points of tangency. In the figure the lines are tangent to the surface in the points *2'* and *6'*. When revolved to their original position in the 45-degree plane, their projections on F will be at points *2* and *6*.

If the shadow on F, or any vertical plane, is required, it may be found by finding the shadows of the points of the shade line and drawing a curve through them. The shadow of the great circle is often used as an approximation of this shadow.

10.17. Application Problems.

10.1. *Layout 4.* Assume conventional light. Find the shadows on H and F of the lines located as follows:

(a) Line AB: $A(2\frac{1}{2}, -\frac{1}{4}, -1\frac{1}{2})$, $B(1\frac{1}{4}, -\frac{3}{4}, -1\frac{3}{4})$.
(b) Line CD: $C(2\frac{3}{4}, -1\frac{1}{4}, -\frac{1}{2})$, $D(1\frac{3}{4}, -1\frac{1}{2}, -1\frac{1}{4})$.
(c) Line EG: $E(2\frac{3}{4}, -1\frac{1}{2}, -1)$, $G(1\frac{1}{2}, -\frac{3}{4}, -1\frac{1}{4})$.
(d) Line KM: $K(2\frac{3}{4}, -1\frac{1}{2}, -\frac{1}{2})$, $M(1\frac{1}{2}, -\frac{1}{2}, -1\frac{1}{4})$.
(e) Line NO: $N(2\frac{1}{2}, -1\frac{1}{2}, -1)$, $O(2\frac{1}{2}, -0, -1)$.
(f) Line RS: $R(2, -\frac{3}{4}, -0)$, $S(2, -\frac{3}{4}, -1\frac{3}{4})$.

10.2. *Layout 4.* Assume conventional light. Find the shadows on H and F of the lines located as follows:

(a) Line AB: $A(2\frac{3}{4}, -\frac{1}{2}, -1\frac{1}{2})$, $B(1\frac{1}{2}, -1\frac{1}{4}, -\frac{1}{2})$.
(b) Line CD: $C(2\frac{1}{2}, -1, -1\frac{1}{2})$, $D(2\frac{1}{2}, -1, -0)$.
(c) Line EG: $E(2, -0, -1)$, $G(2, -1\frac{3}{4}, -1)$.
(d) Line KM: $K(2\frac{1}{2}, -1, -\frac{1}{4})$, $M(1\frac{1}{4}, -1\frac{1}{2}, -\frac{3}{4})$.
(e) Line NO: $N(2\frac{3}{4}, -\frac{1}{2}, -1\frac{1}{4})$, $O(1\frac{3}{4}, -1\frac{1}{4}, -1\frac{1}{2})$.
(f) Line RS: $R(2\frac{3}{4}, -\frac{3}{4}, -1\frac{1}{2})$, $S(1\frac{1}{2}, -1, -\frac{3}{4})$.

10.3. *Layout 4.* Assume conventional light. Find the shadows on F of the plane figures described and located as follows:

(a) A $\frac{1}{2}''$ square having its center at $A(2\frac{1}{4}, -\frac{3}{4}, -1\frac{1}{4})$ is parallel to F and two of its edges are parallel to H.
(b) A $\frac{1}{2}''$ square having its center at $B(2\frac{1}{4}, -\frac{3}{4}, -1\frac{1}{4})$ is parallel to H and two of its edges are parallel to F.
(c) A $\frac{1}{2}''$ square with its center at $C(2\frac{1}{4}, -\frac{3}{4}, -1\frac{1}{4})$ is perpendicular to both H and F. Two edges are perpendicular to H.

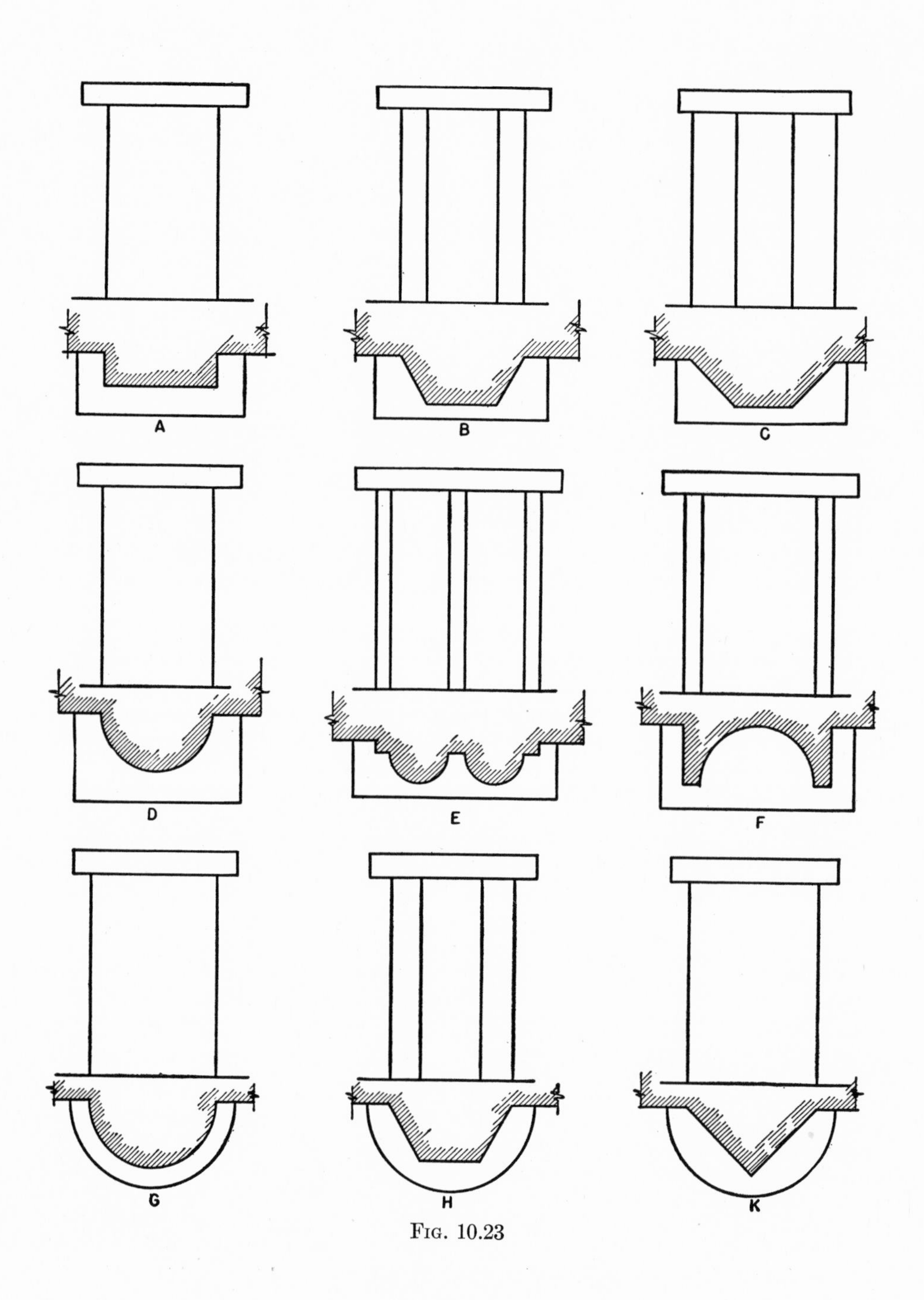

Fig. 10.23

(d) A ½″ circle with its center at $D(2\frac{1}{4}, -\frac{3}{4}, -1\frac{1}{4})$ is parallel to F.
(e) A ½″ circle with its center at $E(2\frac{1}{4}, -\frac{3}{4}, -1\frac{1}{4})$ is parallel to H.
(f) A ½″ circle with its center at $D(2\frac{1}{4}, -\frac{3}{4}, -1\frac{1}{4})$ is perpendicular to both H and F.

10.4. *Layout 3.* Assume conventional light. Find the shadows on H and F of the plane figures described and located as follows:

(a) A 1″ square is parallel to F with its center at $A(3\frac{1}{2}, -1\frac{1}{4}, -1\frac{1}{4})$. Two edges of the square are parallel to H.
(b) A 1″ circle is parallel to F with its center at $B(3\frac{1}{2}, -1, -1\frac{1}{4})$.
(c) A hexagon 1″ in minimum diameter is parallel to F with its center at $C(3\frac{1}{2}, -1\frac{1}{4}, -1\frac{1}{4})$. Two edges are parallel to H.
(d) An octagon 1″ in minimum diameter is parallel to F with its center at $D(3\frac{1}{2}, -1, -1\frac{1}{4})$.

10.5. Same as Problem 10.4 except that in each location the plane figure is perpendicular to both H and F.

10.6. *Layout 2.* Assume conventional light. Find the shadows on H and F of the surfaces described and located as follows:

(a) The center line of a vertical right hexagonal pyramid is 3½″ to the left of P and 1½″ in front of F. The base is 2″ in maximum diameter and lies on H with two edges parallel to F. The altitude of the pyramid is 3¼″.
(b) Same as (a) except that the surface is a cone. Find the shade lines and the shadow of the cone.

10.7. *Layout 2.* Assume conventional light. Find the shadows on F of the solids described and located as follows:

(a) The center of a cube is located at $A(3\frac{1}{2}, -1\frac{3}{4}, -3)$. Two faces of the cube are perpendicular to both H and F.
(b) The center of a sphere is located at the point $B(3\frac{1}{2}, -1\frac{3}{4}, -3)$. (The shadow of a sphere is the envelope of the shadows of the circles cut from the sphere by planes taken parallel to the F plane.)

10.8. *Layout 1.* Assume conventional light. Draw the pilaster forms of Figure 10.23—*A*, *B*, and *C*—making them double size with their center lines 8½″, 5½″, and 2¼″ to the left of P. Find the shadows on the pilasters and on the wall indicated in the figure.

10.9. Same as Problem 10.8 except that the pilaster forms indicated in Figure 10.23—*D*, *E*, and *F*—are to be drawn.

10.10. Same as Problem 10.8 except that the pilaster forms of Figure 10.23—*G*, *H*, and *K*—are to be drawn.

10.11. *Layout 1.* Omit HF axis lines.

(a) The vertical center line of a 3″ spherical headed niche is 7½″ to the left of P. Draw the plan and elevation similar to Figure 10.21 and find the shadow in the niche.
(b) The vertical axis of a scotia is 2¾″ from P. The base of the scotia is 3″ in diameter and the cap 2″ in diameter. The nappe is ¾″ in height and of a form similar to Figure 10.20. The base and cap are ¼″ in height. Find the shadows on the surfaces of the scotia.

10.12. *Layout 1.*

(a) The line $A(9\frac{1}{2}, -3, -3)$, $B(6\frac{1}{2}, -3, -3)$ casts its shadow on the 2½″ sphere whose center is the point $C(7\frac{1}{2}, -1\frac{1}{2}, -1\frac{1}{2})$. Find the shadow of the line on the sphere using the slicing method discussed in Article 10.14.
(b) Assume the HF axis 4½″ above the lower margin. The line $C(4, -3\frac{1}{2}, 0)$, $D(4, -3\frac{1}{2}, -3)$ casts its shadow on a torus. The axis of revolution of the torus is a vertical line through $D(3, -2, -1)$. The generatrix of the torus is a 1″ circle, and the radius of revolution is 1″. The plane of the great circle passes through the point D. Find the shadow of the line CD on the surface of the torus. Find the shade line on the torus.

CHAPTER XI

GLOSSARY

Adjacent Planes: Any two mutually perpendicular and intersecting projection planes.

Adjacent Planes, Set of: A set of adjacent planes consists of three projection planes, two of which are perpendicular to the third.

Auxiliary Projection Plane: *See* Projection Plane.

Auxiliary Projection: *See* Projection.

Axis: The center line of a symmetric object. A line about which a magnitude is revolved. The line of intersection of two projection planes about which those planes are assumed to be revolved.

_FP_ Axis: The Frontal-Profile intersection is designated as the *FP* axis. On a drawing, a letter *F* is placed near one end and a letter *P* near the other end of the line representing the intersection.

_HF_ Axis: The Horizontal-Frontal intersection is designated as the *HF* axis. On a drawing, the letter *H* is placed near one end and the letter *F* near the other end of the line representing the intersection.

_HP_ Axis: The Horizontal-Profile intersection is designated as the *HP* axis. On a drawing, a letter *H* is placed near one end and the letter *P* near the other end of the line used to represent the intersection.

_1–2_ Axis: The intersections of Auxiliary Planes are indicated on a drawing by placing the numbers of the planes close to the ends of the lines that represent their intersections. The intersection of an auxiliary plane with one of the principal planes is indicated by placing the letter designating the principal plane at one end, and the number designating the auxiliary plane at the other end of the line segment representing that intersection.

Bearing: Direction of the *H* projection, or plan view, with respect to some specified reference line. Example: The line bears north 60 degrees east.

Co-ordinate Plane: *See* Reference Plane.

Dip: The dihedral angle that a plane makes with the horizontal reference plane.

Flush: Unbroken or even surface; on a level with the adjacent surface.

Frontal Plane: *See* Projection Plane.

Frontal Projection: *See* Projection.

Graphics: Art or science of drawing, especially according to mathematical rules.

Horizontal Plane: *See* Projection Plane.

Horizontal Projection: *See* Projection.

Line: The path of a moving point. Lines are infinite in length.

Location of a Line: The location of a line in space is specified by locating two points that lie on that line, or by locating one point of the line and stating its direction relative to two of the principal planes. A line is considered unlimited in length.

Projection of a Line: The projection of a line is designated by the projections of two points of the line. For example, the horizontal projection of the line segment AB is a^Hb^H.

Trace of a Line: A trace of a line is the point in which a line intersects or pierces one of the principal planes. The H trace of a line is designated by the letter H, and the projections of the point H are lettered as in the case of any other point. Similar notation is used for the F trace and the P trace of a line.

Loci: Plural of Locus.

Locus: An element that contains every point that satisfies a given condition.

Magnitude: A geometric quantity such as a point, line, plane, cone, etc.

Oblique: Neither perpendicular nor parallel with.

Oblique Line: A line that is not parallel with or perpendicular to either of the principal projection planes.

Oblique Plane: A plane that is not parallel with or perpendicular to either of the principal projection planes.

Outcrop: The intersection of a stratum with a specified plane.

Plane: A surface on which any two points may be joined with a straight line that lies on the surface.

Location of a Plane: The location of a plane in space is specified by locating three points that lie on the plane, or by locating the intersection of the plane with two of the principal projection planes. These intersections are called traces. The intersection of a plane with other than a principal plane is not called a trace.

Projection of a Plane: The projection of a plane is designated by the projection of three or more points that lie on the plane. If traces are used to locate the plane in space, the plane is called by some letter such as R, S, or T. On a drawing, the projection of the trace on the plane on which the trace lies is marked with the lower case designating letter, with proper superscript, placed near each end. The other projection of the trace lies in the intersection of the principal planes and is not marked.

Piercing Point: A piercing point of a line is the point in which a line pierces any plane other than one of the principal planes. Piercing points are lettered as any other points.

Point: A position in space.

Designation of a Point: A point in space is designated by a capital letter and its location is specified by stating distances from the principal planes. For example, the point A is 2 inches to the left of P, 1 inch behind F, and 3 inches below H.

Projection of a Point: The projection of a point is marked on a drawing by the use of a lower case letter and a capital letter superscript that indicates on which of the planes the projection lies. For example, the projection of the point A on the frontal plane is marked a^F, on the horizontal plane a^H, and on an auxiliary plane as a^1, a^2, etc.

Projection: A projection is a representation of a magnitude on a plane of projection. If an object is placed between a source of light and a plane, a shadow of the object will be projected on the plane. In drawing a projection of a point on a plane, a line called a projector is drawn from the point to the plane. The point in which the projector pierces the plane is the projection of the point on that plane. A projection is frequently called a view, an image, or a picture.

Auxiliary Projection: An auxiliary projection is a view projected on an auxiliary plane and may be called an auxiliary view. On a drawing, the projection of the point A on the auxiliary plane numbered *1* is marked a^1, on plane *2* it is marked a^2, etc.

Frontal Projection: A frontal projection is a view projected on the frontal plane and is frequently called the front elevation, front view, or vertical projection.

Horizontal Projection: A horizontal projection is a view projected on the horizontal plane and is frequently called a plan or top view in engineering or architectural work.

Orthographic Projection: An orthographic projection is a projection in which the projectors are perpendicular to the projection plane. If the projection plane is perpendicular to the sun's rays, an object placed between the sun and the plane will cast a shadow which is an orthographic projection of the object on that plane. In drawing, the projectors drawn from a magnitude are perpendicular to the plane of projection. A projection on a frontal plane may be called an F projection, or an elevation. A projection on a horizontal plane may be referred to as the plan, a map, or a top view.

Profile Projection: A profile projection is a view projected on the profile plane and may be called a profile view or a right or left side view.

Projection Plane: A projection plane is a plane of unlimited extent upon which a particular view of a magnitude may be projected. An object in three-dimensional space can be completely represented by views drawn upon three mutually perpendicular planes of projection. Additional planes are frequently used to clarify the drawing of the object.

Auxiliary Projection Plane: An auxiliary projection plane is any projection plane other than one of the principal projection planes. Auxiliary projection planes are designated by numbers in the order in which the planes are used on a drawing. For example, if three auxiliary planes are used, the first one is called plane *1*; the second, plane *2*; and the third, plane *3*.

Frontal Projection Plane: A frontal projection plane is a vertical reference plane from which distance to the front or rear may be measured. A magnitude may be on, in front of, or to the rear of the frontal plane. The frontal plane is designated by the capital letter F.

Horizontal Projection Plane: A horizontal projection plane is a reference plane from which a distance above or below may be measured. A magnitude, such as a point, line, etc., may be on, above, or below a horizontal plane. The horizontal plane is designated by the capital letter *H*.

Principal Projection Plane: The principal projection planes are the horizontal, frontal, and profile planes. The horizontal and frontal planes divide space into four quadrants. The three principal planes divide space into eight octants.

Profile Projection Plane: A profile projection plane is a vertical reference plane that is perpendicular to both *H* and *F* from which distances to the right or left may be measured. A magnitude may be located on, to the right, or to the left of, a profile plane, which is designated by the capital letter *P*.

Projector: A projector is a line drawn from a point in space to a projection plane. Also, the projecting line drawn between two projections of a point.

Quadrants: The four sections into which space is divided by the horizontal and vertical projection planes.

Quadrant I: The First Quadrant is that portion of space that is above *H* and in front of *F*.

Quadrant II: The Second Quadrant is that portion of space that is above *H* and to the rear of *F*.

Quadrant III: The Third Quadrant is that portion of space that is below *H* and to the rear of *F*. In engineering drawing, an object is assumed to be in the third quadrant.

Quadrant IV: The Fourth Quadrant is that portion of space that is below *H* and in front of *F*.

Reference Plane: A reference plane or co-ordinate plane is a plane of unlimited extent to which a magnitude (point, line, plane, etc.) is referred in order to specify exactly its location in space. In three-dimensional space, an object can be specifically located, if its position with reference to three mutually perpendicular planes is stated.

Revolution: Revolution is the operation of rotating a magnitude about an axis into a new position. The new position is indicated by the subscript 1 on a drawing. If successive revolutions are made, successive numbers are used as subscripts to indicate the order.

Right Section: A right section is a section cut from a symmetric object by a plane taken at right angles with its axis line.

Stratum: A stratum is a sheetlike layer of ore, rock, or earth between beds of a different kind of material.

Strike: Strike is the direction, or bearing, of a horizontal line that lies on a plane surface.

INDEX